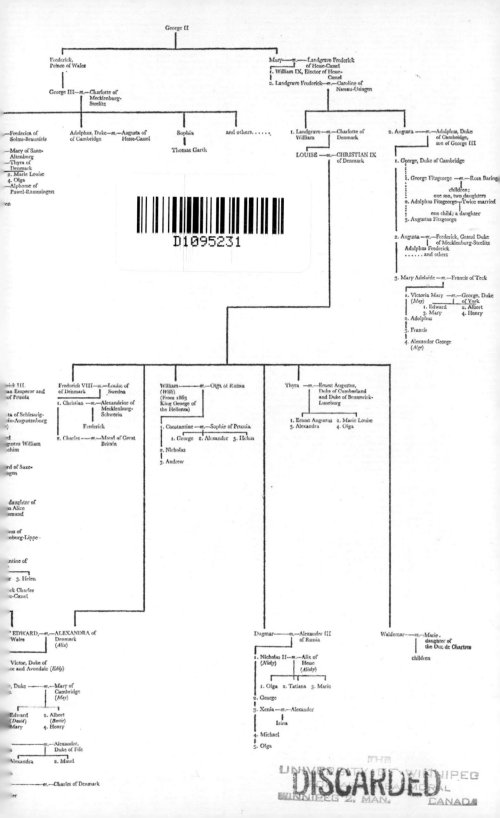

Bertie

BERTIE

Albert Edward, Prince of Wales
A NOVEL

Tyler Whittle

HEINEMANN ; LONDON

William Heinemann Ltd
15 Queen Street, Mayfair, London W1X 8BE

LONDON MELBOURNE TORONTO
JOHANNESBURG AUCKLAND

First published 1974
© Michael Tyler-Whittle 1974
SBN 434 86489 7

Printed in Great Britain by
Cox & Wyman Ltd
London, Fakenham and Reading

to

Arthur Plant

AUTHOR'S NOTE

Though a fictional treatment, *Bertie* is entirely faithful to the known facts. No character has been invented and nothing has been deliberately distorted or omitted simply to make the writing easier or to suit a preconceived idea. The few small liberties taken to bridge gaps in the documentary evidence lie always within the seemliness of historical probability.

T. W.

PART ONE

1

Albert Edward, Prince of Wales, gazed in admiration at his father, who had upturned a large terracotta rhubarb-forcer, propped it in position with bricks and stakes, and suspended a mothing-lamp inside. This, Prince Albert explained, scientifically reduced the area of search – and there was less likelihood of breaking the lamp with the collecting net.

'Now, Bertie,' said his father quietly. 'Swing your net horizontally over the rhubarb-forcer.'

The boy did as he was told and a largish moth fluttered in a corner of the fine mesh.

Carefully he transferred it to a big pill box fitted at one end with glass. The moth, hoping to escape that way, moved immediately towards the glass, and thus could be examined at leisure. A new species or a different variety of an old one was put in the killing-bottle. Other, valueless captives were put in a special container to be released when the mothing was finished and the lamp dowsed.

The moth which had just been captured was ordinary enough. Bertie shook it gently into the special container. Then he grasped the net and watched and waited with his father.

He enjoyed mothing with Papa; more, in fact, than with anyone else, though Mr Anson, Papa's secretary, politely pretended to be enthusiastic whenever he went mothing.

On two unforgettable occasions, Mama had actually gone mothing with him, but either she was remote and silent – worried, he supposed, about state matters or family troubles – or talking about the beauties of the evening air, or the prospect at half-dark, or some romantic association with Scotland's past, for she was for ever quoting poems and asking if he knew who had written them. And, simply by being there, she took Bertie's mind off the

3

business in hand. Queens, he concluded, didn't make good moth-hunters. At least Queen Victoria didn't.

Bertie's brothers and sisters were equally disappointing.

Vicky, his elder sister, wanted to use moth hunting as an excuse for being out later than the proper hour, but Miss Hildyard the governess refused to co-operate. One experience had been enough. Miss Hildyard, whom they all called Tilla, had seen bats ghosting through the dark to gobble up the moths encircling the lamp and she had screeched, covered her cap with both arms, and run off as fast as an engine. Silly Tilla. Mortified at this check to her plans, Vicky had said rude things about her governess – that she had barely enough hair to trap the tiniest bat, most of what she wore being a manufactured wig. For this ill-mannered, though strictly accurate remark, Vicky had earned a rebuke from the official royal governess who had supervision of all the royal nurseries and school-rooms, the widowed Lady Lyttelton, dearest 'Laddle' to her charges; and the rebuke had so scared her that she had been put off moth-hunting for ever.

Alice, Bertie's favourite sister, was really too young for mothing, and besides that, far, far too fat. Tilla had the greatest difficulty in getting her out of doors. Like Bertie himself, Alice loved eating – gourmandizing Tilla said it was – and she absorbed anything from filched sugared violets to the stodgiest of nursery puddings. Why, on her fourth birthday in April last year down at Osborne, she had been given a frisky lamb, bedecked with bells and ribbons and answering to the name of Milly, and all Alice had wanted to do was eat it. Alice would never make a moth-hunter.

The rest of Bertie's brothers and sisters were far too little.

MacKay the piper and Grant the gillie were sometimes sent out with him; but MacKay didn't pretend to show any interest, and Grant had a habit of teasing the boy because – although born with a string of grand Scotch titles – he still considered the Prince a Sassenach and not entitled to wear the Highlander's kilt.

Very, very rarely Laddle was persuaded to go with him. Then it was different. At her feet he had learnt his prayers, alphabet, sums, and how to enjoy fun and he loved her very dearly. As a moth-hunter, Laddle compared to Tilla with all her squawks was like the sun to a burnt-out star. Or he ought to say the moon. Papa was the best of all. He was the sun of moth-catchers. No one really matched Papa at anything. . . .

4

A repeater chimed from Prince Albert's pocket. He took it out, regarded it, and, though both knew it was time for Bertie to go to bed, nothing was said and the watch was returned to its place. Such latitude was unusual. The Prince was an exact man. But Bertie was not unduly surprised. In this year of 1848 things had been happening which had upset a score of royal routines.

Rebellions had erupted in more than a dozen European states. Part of the Prussian royal family were temporary refugees in England. The King of the French had been chased out of his country disguised in goggles and was now living at Claremont. And, at a threat to the Queen and his children by some sort of English revolutionaries called Chartists, Papa had swept the family away from the centre of things to Osborne on the Isle of Wight. The defence of London and the kingdom had been left in the hands of the old Duke of Wellington. He, of course, had settled everything; but it had been an upsetting summer, sometimes frightening, and everyone had become accustomed to abrupt changes in the daily programme.

Now, at their new home beside the river Dee, there was even less strictness of routine. Possibly it was on account of the smallness of Balmoral House. Compared with Windsor and Buckingham Palace and Osborne and even Brighton and Claremont, it was so small that the Ladies and Gentlemen of the Household were in some discomfort, and the family were all on top of one another. Papa had plans, of course, to build a larger house and lay out a park and gardens. He had told Bertie all about his ideas, as was his habit, and Bertie had half-listened, as was his, his mouth open at Papa's cleverness. But all this was to come. At the present they were living modestly in a little Scotch castle like ordinary gentlefolk, not protected by detachments of the Brigade of Guards but by a single policeman who marched regularly round the grounds defending his sovereign and keeping off peepers with a truncheon and a bullseye. And the great difference, the feeling of being on holiday, had nibbled holes in the normal daily programme.

Nevertheless even Bertie was astonished when Papa's repeater chimed the next quarter and they were still out moth-hunting. Before it had struck again, and by this time they had packed up his equipment and were leaving the kitchen garden, he discovered

5

why. Papa wanted to say something important, and always – unless he was in a passion – he took his time and was very deliberate before he said anything important.

At the gate to the kitchen garden he laid a hand on Bertie's shoulder. 'My boy,' he said, 'this seems a good opportunity for a word.'

'Yes, Papa.'

They sat on a bench against the wall, the mothing-lamp on the ground between Bertie's legs, shining on his scarlet stockings.

'You are seven, or almost so, and too grown-up now to be in the care of ladies.'

'Yes, Papa, though . . .'

'The Baron', interrupted Prince Albert, 'has been very specially attentive to the matter.'

Bertie shivered.

Baron Stockmar had been Papa's tutor, physician to great uncle Leopold, King of the Belgians, and he was confidential adviser to half the royal families of Europe. But he considered it his special destiny to look after the English royal family, and he had left his own family and his home in Germany and taken apartments in Windsor Castle. There he led an isolated, odd existence; indifferent to Court protocol, when not shuffling down the corridors in green slippers and a dressing-gown, he was for ever writing memoranda.

The Prince of Wales stood in great awe of him. He dreaded his pronouncements.

Prince Albert saw the happiness drain from his son's face, and saw him shiver. It concerned him because he considered Bertie's dislike of Stockmar quite irrational and he knew that it could not be reasoned away. He could not share Victoria's view that growing up was merely something to be faced and got through, not unlike swallowing a daily draught of nasty medicine. Having had a cut-off, endlessly dull childhood herself, the Queen believed that being sent supperless to bed or a sharp slapping far more wholesome than scoldings, and indeed she had once beaten the Prince of Wales before her own Ladies in Waiting. His father would never have done that but all the same it saddened him that the heir to the throne should be an unreasonable boy with unreasonable fears.

Quietly he told him that as early as could be conveniently arranged he was to be given apartments of his own in Buckingham

Palace, and then begin a Stockmar-designed regimen of study under the supervision of a tutor.

'Yes, Papa,' said Bertie when he felt that he ought to.

Prince Albert regarded him steadily in the light from the moth-lamp. 'Princes, my boy, do not go to school, and I am certain you would not prefer to go to Eton.'

'No, thank you, Papa,' said Bertie fervently. He had been there once for a Fourth of June and the speeches had been incomprehensible, the noise alarming, and the proffered food, though tempting, forbidden him. He had also suffered the shame of hearing his mother repeat to the Provost of Eton, his latest blunder, that he had asked her if a pink were not the female of a carnation. She had not meant to be unkind but being exposed to such ridicule had not made Bertie like Eton any more. He repeated with great firmness that he would much prefer a tutor.

'And there will be other gentlemen to instruct you in special subjects,' added the Prince.

'Yes, Papa.'

'And I know you would like it if we could arrange sometimes for boys of your own age to be present at your play time.'

This struck an instant response from the Prince of Wales. He played happily for hours with fat Alice and even sometimes – when she was not feeling too Princess Royal-ish – with Vicky, but he could never have enough company and loathed solitude. His one friend, tough little William Henry, who was son to a statesman named Gladstone and one of dearest Laddle's relations as well, had been to Osborne; but he keenly felt the need of people to play with.

'Carefully chosen friends,' added his father quickly, who believed with Stockmar that the associates of a Prince of Wales should not be of ordinary clay.

'Very well, Papa.'

'Now we will go into the house. Our little talk is over and you will do your best for your Mama's sake and for mine to be manly and industrious and obedient to your new tutor.'

'Yes, of course, Papa.' Bertie picked up his mothing-lamp. As they went through the garden door a thought occurred to him. 'What is my tutor like?' he asked.

Prince Albert was candid and admitted that he and the Baron had not yet made a final decision as to the choice of a suitable

7

tutor. 'But one I believe has special claims. He is a master at Eton named Henry Birch.'

Bertie made no remark, but it struck him that the name seemed an unhappy one.

'Mama,' confided Bertie as the royal train trundled southwards. 'I am to have a tutor.'

'Yes,' said the Queen briefly.

On the way north they had travelled in a royal yacht and very ill it had made her too. But the return journey by train was almost as uncomfortable. Moreover, though the thudding was regular, the shaking took a good deal out of her. What with revolution spreading like the pest all over the continent, and never-ending worries caused by her odious Prime Minister, Lord John Russell, and her even more odious Foreign Secretary, Lord Palmerston – upon neither of whom could she have any reliance at all – and what with baby Louise being such a difficult feeder, and dear Aunt Gloucester going out of her mind, Victoria's nerves had been over-stretched for months. The six weeks in Scotland had done something to ease the strain, yet she was still in the wrong frame of mind to chitter-chatter with Bertie. Where, she wondered in vexation, was Laddle? Where was Tilla? Where was Albert? The boy ought to be kept occupied.

Unconscious of his mother's irritation, Bertie continued: 'And I am to have my own apartments in Buckingham Palace . . .'

'Did you think', she asked sharply, 'that I could be unaware of it? Nothing, nothing at all, not a single thing is done without my knowledge.'

Crestfallen Bertie looked away, and immediately his mother regretted her severity. Already she had discovered there was some truth in the Brunswick tradition that there was generally discord between sovereigns and their heirs, and she saw in Bertie too many of her own failings of intellect and temperament to care for him a great deal; but she was, after all, the child's mother, and she knew how sarcasm affected him.

'There, dear,' she said, laying a finger on his shoulder. 'I make no doubt you will do very well. Very well indeed.' Then abruptly she changed the subject. As the next day was a Sunday and the sabbatarians were exceedingly watchful she told Bertie they would

8

have to leave Crewe very early in the morning to escape detection. It was a positive nuisance, an infringement of her rights as monarch, and she found religious bigotry particularly odious.

Bertie hurriedly agreed. Personally he would not care to have been a sabbatarian at the wrong end of his Mama's tongue at that particular moment.

At a suitable opportunity, he slipped back to the royal children's carriage. Victoria pretended not to see him go. She watched him leave out of the corner of her eye with some relief.

2

During the next few months, while the Baron and the Prince and the Queen pondered and planned and interviewed tutors, Bertie made something of a nuisance of himself in the family.

Vicky was the only one who refused to let him get away with it. 'Very well, so you are going to have a tutor,' she would say scornfully. 'Bragging now won't help when you muddle your irregular verbs, and can't loop your pot-hooks, and forget the Kings of Israel and Judah and the highest mountains and longest rivers —' Vicky herself was precocious — 'It won't help then,' she would continue, and add vindictively, 'and you'll get a beating, a *beating*, probably with a scratchy, knobbly, stinging *birch*.'

'Now, Princess Vicky,' murmured Miss Hildyard, 'that will do.' And she came out with what her charges called a regular Tilla phrase: 'unkindness sells very cheap but buys very dear, you know.'

Highly strung like his mother, Vicky's awful prophecy made Bertie very apprehensive. He ceased bragging.

When he was shown the chosen apartments his heart sank. They were part of a set of inferior rooms with high windows which overlooked roofs and grimy tree tops. And they had nothing of the freshness and the light colours of the royal nurseries and the schoolrooms, and were mostly painted in a bilious shade of yellow with a dark green dado. The decorations were instructive, the furnishings lacking in any form of comfort. All had been chosen by

9

the Baron. He had also carefully scrutinized a set of brain-developing diet sheets prepared at his request by an expert. And he had selected all the Prince's instructors.

Bertie's heart sank lower and lower as they were presented – specialists in Scripture, Hand-writing, Drawing, Music, French and German – but when his Tutor was finally presented, and he turned out to be the Eton Master with the sinister name of Birch, Bertie felt that things might not be as bad as he had come to fear.

To begin with they watched each other warily.

Henry Mildred Birch was a clergyman and the son of a clergyman and a considerable scholar. But he had the special advantages of being young and patient and he lacked the rust of the little Prince's other instructors. Nevertheless he had been selected by the Baron, which at first made Bertie very suspicious and, when he wished, Bertie could be exceedingly obstinate. Mr Birch guessed this. Further, being aware that the boy had been endowed with a great sense of his own importance and that it was frequently nourished by toadying courtiers and servants, he sensed that he was likely to resent discipline and be disobedient. It was natural that, to begin with, they should spar a little, but neither was over-aggressive, and they quickly settled into a friendly relationship. In fact, of course, Bertie needed his Tutor's kindness more than he realized, and he rapidly discovered that Mr Birch was the only bearable part of the Baron's schedule for the training and education of the heir to the English throne.

Stockmar's schedule was formidable – and, being based on the principle that Bertie should only be surrounded by 'those who are good and pure', it eliminated Prince Albert's idea of inviting children in to share his play. The Baron saw nothing wholesome in the natural mischievousness of schoolboys. He drew up a plan which accounted for every minute of the day, and except on rare occasions such as Christmas or birthdays, it was never relaxed. It meant that Bertie had fewer holidays than any schoolboy in the kingdom. As for recreation, a minimum of riding and rowing was permitted as necessary exercise, otherwise his supervised play was restricted to afternoon walks, recitations in three languages, and theatricals.

After a time Bertie's younger brother Affie joined him but neither sparked easily from the other. Had it not been for Mr

10

Birch their life would have been unbelievably monotonous. As it was he injected a sense of fun into some of their most dreary enterprises and he risked Baron Stockmar's displeasure by allowing them to see Lady Lyttelton and Miss Hildyard from time to time. The day would come when they would have to be separated entirely from their former environment but Birch doubted the wisdom of hurrying the process. They had all the time in the world to make the parting as painless as possible. Then he expressed warm approval, amounting to enthusiasm, when Prince Albert – without reference to the Baron – proposed extra natural history expeditions, or took his sons sailing and bathing. Most of all Birch liked Prince Albert's plan to teach his sons the realities of life by having them instructed in bricklaying and gardening and putting them to work with labourers under a foreman. The foreman checked their work, sent in a wage sheet once a week, and the Prince then gave them their wages. The young Prince of Wales especially benefited from this. One day, when he had lifted a row of early potatoes at Osborne, he told his Tutor that his very earliest memory was of the Irish potato famine in the late summer of 1845. He had been almost four then, and the stories he heard in the schoolroom and from the servants had appalled him. Being able to garden, to sow and nurture and harvest food, did something to remove the scar of that memory.

Prince Albert and the Tutor did fall out on occasion. One of Stockmar's dicta was that the boys' Tutors' reports should be read and commented on before luncheon. The children dined when their parents had luncheon as a family meal, but while praise peppered the appetite, scoldings for bad work did not. The Prince of Wales frequently began and ended the meal in tears and ate next to nothing in between. It could not be good for him, said Birch, and begged Prince Albert to modify the plan, but the Prince considered such criticism beyond the competence or work of a tutor, and he said so.

On occasion Birch felt he had to be severe. When he caught the boys boasting he deflated them immediately. When he found the Prince of Wales bullying his younger brothers or sisters, or in any way insulting the servants, he was particularly strict. And he beat the boys when they were lacking in respect.

One day he overheard Bertie laughing at the Queen because she had lost an important bunch of keys in the Park and had half the

11

Court and soldiers in London searching for them. It served Mama right he said, for being so critical about his own carelessness, and suddenly found himself being soundly whipped for impertinence both to his sovereign and to his mother.

But after a first, heated, vengeful storm, the Prince admitted his fault. He admired Birch. He grew to respect him. Birch mattered.

3

On rare occasions the Queen took her children with her when out driving.

None of them cared for it. Sitting beside Mama or facing her, bolt upright, every button buttoned, every lace laced, everything exactly so; and trying to maintain a balance between the strict silence and stillness required by custom and the need to be gracious to the lower orders who shouted and waved and raised their hats and shook pocket handkerchiefs, was a considerable strain. Vicky, who had a smart way of putting things, said she would sooner run to the top of Loch-na-Gar by Balmoral in her heaviest, stuffiest pelisse, than ride for thirty minutes in the Park with Mama. Bertie naturally disagreed. He always did out loud with Vicky. But secretly he thought she might be right.

He was certain of it as, on 27 June, 1850, they rumbled along to St James's where Mama was to call on her uncle, the Duke of Cambridge. It was a stifling day, and his clothes were thick, prickly, and hard when he would wish them to have been thin, smooth and soft. The birds in the park were silent; the dusty plane leaves, which could have done with a breeze and a splash to clean them up, hung like heavy bits of sugar paper. The people cheered, yes; but in a lifeless sort of fashion. Moreover they didn't have an escort, something which would have been pleasant to look at because Bertie liked the colour and glitter of uniforms, and not even Papa was there riding, as he so often did, with his Gentlemen, beside the carriage. This was a special and mournful ride because his godfather, Mama's Uncle Cambridge, was very ill and lay dying in his apartments in St James's. And, as if all this wasn't bad enough, Bertie had quarrelled that morning with Mr Birch, impulsively losing his temper because he had been rebuked, and now – equally impulsively – he regretted it and felt very miserable indeed. Then, on top of everything, Mama wore her blank, grey look and while she waved politely and nodded to the listless cheerers, her eyes, normally so blue and beautiful, were like well-washed glass and she was thunderous with her Maid-of-Honour and with Bertie and Alice and Affie who sat before her.

Ordinarily Victoria took a certain degree of pleasure in showing off her children. She recognized it, moreover, as a duty. From time to time her subjects needed to see she had a well-stocked nursery and was providing England with heirs. Only eight weeks before she had presented them with another prince. Because he shared the same birthday as the Duke of Wellington he had been named Arthur and the Duke had stood sponsor at his Christening. That had been a happy day, almost the only one, thought Victoria gloomily, in a long series of disasters.

Calamity, lately, had chased calamity. Her dear Lord Melbourne had died, then Mr Anson, Albert's loyal secretary, then good Aunt Adelaide who had been William IV's queen, then Bertie had been close to getting himself shot at a badly run partridge shoot, and now Uncle Cambridge was dying – so they said – and without his discreet direction goodness knew what Aunt Cambridge would get up to. . . .

The royal carriage went through the gates of St James's and drew up at that part of the palace called Cambridge House. Footmen placed steps and opened the doors and the royal party went inside.

The Queen's cousins Mary and George met the Queen. Princess Mary, poor girl, was huge. Prince George, on the other hand, was not at all bad looking, though to Victoria's dismay had taken up an actress and produced three strapping Fitzgeorges. He called it a 'marriage' and would not hear of marrying anyone else.

Cousin George stayed with the children and the Queen's Maid of Honour while Princess Mary took the Queen to the sickroom.

Alice politely said she was sorry – they were all sorry – that great-uncle Adolphus was so ill. She called George Cambridge, 'Uncle George'. He was pleased. 'There's always hope,' he muttered. 'And religion, of course.'

'And physicians?' suggested Bertie; and instantly blushed crimson, believing he had committed an unfortunate gaffe. According to his tutors, it was his habit.

But Uncle George did not seem to mind in the least. 'You're right, my boy,' he gruffed. 'Furthermore, there's Steinberger.' Seeing a look of astonishment on the children's faces he explained. Apparently when he himself had been very young he had caught scarlet fever and his life had been despaired of. 'My papa was at dinner when the physicians sent a message to say I was about to die and, such was his state that he seized some Steinberger and made me drink a glass. Or two perhaps, I never discovered. And, d'you know, from that moment the fever sank, the crisis passed, and here I am.'

'Steinberger,' repeated Bertie in wonder.

'An excellent Rhine wine,' said his cousin. 'We always have it on my birthday to record the miracle of long ago. I'd recommend it.'

'But great-uncle Adolphus . . .' suggested Bertie, and stopped.

'Beyond it, I fear, my boy.' Tears started to his eyes. 'Even Steinberger is no use now.'

The children remained silent after that.

Bertie hardly knew his godfather the old Duke, and remembered him only as very large, even gruffer than his son George, extremely deaf and loud-voiced, and an expert on the violoncello.

Mama was touching her cheeks with a handkerchief when she returned downstairs. Refreshments were offered and refused. There were more words of sympathy. Steps were set to the carriage again and they climbed inside. Princess Mary curtsied and Prince George bowed, standing a little out beyond the portico, as the carriage swung in a half-circle and turned to go out through the gates. There the Queen's equerry was forced back both by the narrowness of the gateway and by the crowd of people which surged forward to greet the Queen, and it was at that moment that a gentleman put his hand on the carriage side, his foot on the step, and began to belabour the Queen with his cane.

Once before Alice and Affie had seen someone make an attempt on their mother, but he had been a witless Irish boy armed with a harmless pistol and somehow it had been beyond their comprehension. But this was different. Bertie, who had never

14

seen anyone defy his mother in any shape or form, was appalled. The Queen of England, his Mama, was being struck with a cane.

It was over in a second. The man was swallowed up in the crowd who began to give him a taste of his own medicine. Bertie gazed horror-struck at Mama who was lying back unconscious. Her Maid of Honour raised her and she fell forward to the floor of the carriage.

White as wax, Bertie clutched Alice's hand. It was thrust off. 'Help,' ordered his sister frantically. But Mama recovered herself. With her Lady's aid she struggled to her feet and called to the crowd: 'Wait! Wait! Good people. I am not hurt. I am not hurt.'

The crowd gave way. At a word from the equerry the postilion whipped up his cream horses. The carriage swung away towards Buckingham Palace. The Queen, her bonnet a little awry, her lips bloodless, let her head loll a little forwards. Her Maid of Honour found smelling salts, a cambric handkerchief scented with orange water.

The three children, hand in hand, sat opposite.

Mr Birch explained carefully to the frightened Prince exactly what had happened. The gentleman who had attacked the Queen was a retired officer of the 10th Hussars. He had had no particular aim in mind except perhaps that he had never risen beyond the low rank of lieutenant and was an embittered pensioner. Fortunately, and the Tutor repeated it twice, fortunately the deep rim of the Queen's bonnet had taken the brunt of the caning, yet still she had a bruised forehead and was likely to have black eyes on the following day. 'She has been shaken and is naturally nervous,' he concluded. 'But she is in no real danger.'

The Queen, at Prince Albert's suggestion, proved this to her children by going to see them and showing them her forehead. After she had been to the schoolroom she appeared in Bertie's apartments.

He kissed her hand, and then, lightly, her cheek. His face was very close to her forehead. 'He did that with his cane?' he said aghast.

'Dear boy,' said the Queen calmly. 'It had a brass top, and was

15

rather heavy. But I am not really harmed, as Mr Birch has told you, and Papa and I plan to go to the opera after dining.' She kissed her son. 'Now should we go to the opera if I was seriously hurt?'

'No,' admitted Bertie. Then unintentionally he amused everyone by exclaiming indignantly, 'But the tip ought not to have been of brass. It should at least have been of gold.'

Afterwards, when the Queen and the Prince had left, he did something he had never done before. He threw himself into his Tutor's arms and burst into a passion of tears. When his sobs subsided, he tried to say how terrible, how truly terrible it had been to see his Mama struck and caned. . . . And he talked of his dying great-uncle who was deaf and yet had played the violoncello. . . . And he talked of Steinberger, a Rhine wine with great properties as well as an exquisite taste. . . . And he told Birch that he loved him . . . that he could never, never, never do without him. They had to stay together always.

4

The royal children were of the firm opinion that 1851 would always be remembered because of Papa's Great Exhibition. It was supposed to be a Feast of Peace and Plenty, but it caused no end of trouble and the fuss penetrated easily to the nurseries and schoolrooms and to the Prince of Wales's apartments.

Luncheons became less hectic in one sense because Papa was generally too preoccupied to conduct a formal investigation into his children's scholastic progress; but in another sense the meals were worse than before. Mama said frequently and forcefully that Papa was not to be disturbed on any account. She spoke mysteriously but with exceeding bitterness of Papa not being appreciated, of his foreignness being a loathsome bar amongst the English, of his extraordinary difficulties and problems. And the more she cared for and protected Papa, the sharper she was with her children. It seemed unfair. Long silences at luncheon, salted here and there with sighs and snaps, did not make the meals happy. The

16

Exhibition seemed to be the one topic of conversation. It posed endless problems amongst the royal children.

The opening day was Arthur's first birthday, and Bertie envied him because he was too little to go. For some reason an order came that he was to be dressed in his Highland things which were all right for stalking and mothing and being out of doors in the cold and wet of Scotland, but they were intensely uncomfortable on a sunny day trapped with thousands of people in a huge construction of glass. During the ceremony his mother held his hand and squeezed it when he gazed spellbound at a huge crystal fountain in front of him. The squeeze told him not to gape and keep alive and attend. Choirs sang, trumpets blared, organs – not one but several – played the National Anthem and the noisiest of Handel's compositions. Clergymen prayed prayers, Papa and others made speeches, a band played marches, and the royal party tramped up and down corridors looking at endless exhibits. There was too much to see and when Bertie showed a special interest in a stand which illustrated in wax the activities of the Indian Thuggees, he was told by Papa to hurry, and told, too, that a Christian Prince ought not to concern himself with a pagan sect. Vicky and the others seemed to manage better. They cried when the Exhibition was declared open. They actually found time to eat and drink the things they were offered. They were praised for looking at the right things. Apparently they were enjoying it. All Bertie wanted to do was to go home, get out of his Highland things, and be sick. . . .

That was the first memory of 1851 for Albert Edward, Prince of Wales. But the second, which came later in the year, was much stronger. He was hardly aware of its beginning; sensing something harmful just as rabbits will when a stoat is in the area – out of sight and smell and hearing – but detectable all the same. Was it in July, when the French Princess had to cut short a visit to Buckingham Palace because her son's tutor had gone off his head? Did Mama's reaction – barely perceptible as it was – tell him something? 'Tutors!' she exclaimed, looking upwards as though for heavenly support. 'Tutors!'

Dearest Laddle had left the court, saying she was now too old to look after the royal children, and Bertie could consult no one. Not Mr Birch, who was the subject of his secret fear. Certainly not Mama who was unapproachable when it was hot, which it

17

was, or anything was problematical, which this was. Nor could he go to Papa while Papa's head was crammed with his festival of Peace and Commerce.

The feeling that something was wrong grew. Though Mr Birch appeared the same as ever, Bertie sensed that he was not happy. The Church Catechism, which had always been an important part of their week's work together, was suddenly, and for no reason, dropped. Then at Balmoral that autumn neither of his parents seemed the same. Their behaviour was out of character, at one moment complaining of the heat, which Mama said was tropical, and at the next of the cold; and keeping away from their children, especially Bertie, by spending much of their time at a cottage away from the castle. While they were away both Vicky and Affie had small accidents. Vicky was knocked off her pony, but not seriously hurt. And Affie fell downstairs giving himself the most extraordinary swollen, black, green and yellow face. Mama's attitude was unusual. Instead of flying into a passion she looked again to heaven as though, if she waited patiently, all her children's problems would be solved. How solved? Bertie puzzled. He was anxious. Very anxious.

On his tenth birthday that November he overcame some of his uneasiness. There were presents and a special cake and a small party – or, at least, the imitation of one. Mr Birch did his best to make it a different day in every sense. There were no lessons. Bertie chose what he would like to have for breakfast. He was allowed an hour, a whole hour, in which to do absolutely nothing. He entertained both his parents who called on him in his apartments. And he rode in the park without Affie – a very special treat.

Two days later his father sent for him.

'Bertie,' he said, 'Mama and I have been talking to the Baron.'

The boy's heart sank. He knew that it had really been the other way round. The Baron had been talking to his parents.

Suddenly he knew what was going to happen. There was ice along his spine. 'Yes, Papa,' he said, but so huskily that his father barely caught the words.

'The Baron,' continued Prince Albert, 'has been giving his closest attention to your Tutor's reports. And he is perturbed.' He hesitated, seeing the anxiety in Bertie's face, and he tried to explain. 'For instance he does not altogether approve of the Catechism which Mr Birch has taught you so thoroughly. In the

18

Baron's opinion it includes certain non-Protestant beliefs. It is not Lutheran in the least.'

'But I am not Lutheran,' said the boy. 'Nor is Mama.'

'But the Baron is,' said Prince Albert, as though writing Q.E.D. at the end of a theorem. 'And so, in a sense, am I.'

Tears gathered in Bertie's eyes. He was well aware that this talk about the Church's Catechism was beside the point. The Baron had decided Mr Birch must go. It was as simple as that.

'And so,' his father hurried on, 'the Baron considers that a change in tutors, from one who is a clergyman ordained in the Established Church to someone of different intellectual calibre, might be to your advantage. . . .'

'Oh, no,' cried the boy. 'Oh, no, please, please, Papa. Oh, no.'

In a sense this was not only an appeal for himself and for Mr Birch. It was an appeal, too, for the love he had for his father. If Papa permitted this to happen, he could never love him in the same way again, never.

'Calm yourself,' said his father. He was distressed by such an emotional exhibition. 'Control yourself, Bertie. Be a man. Be a prince.'

'*Please*, Papa.'

Prince Albert looked away. He pretended to adjust the student's lamp on the desk before him. For the boy's sake he had to be firm. 'That will do, Bertie,' he warned. 'Your Mama and I have discussed the matter carefully and thoroughly. The Earl of Wilton has kindly agreed to present Mr Birch with a valuable living in Lancashire, and Mama will make him one of her Chaplains in Ordinary. After Christmas Mr Frederick Gibbs will be here to look after you and Affie.'

Birch, as he said his prayers that night, prayed hard that Albert Edward, Prince of Wales, would accept their painful separation in a proper spirit of obedience and humility. But he knew in his heart that he would not.

5

Frederick Weymouth Gibbs was a young barrister with high recommendations. He had been interviewed the previous June by the Queen and Baron Stockmar, and they had decided that the children would be more firmly handled and more wisely treated by such a man. Mr Birch had done wonders, of course, with the poor material at his disposal but the Baron suspected that his reports had not been adequately detailed, that he erred towards being over-gentle with his charges, and that, though a clergyman of impeccable character, he had not been quite zealous enough in his pursuit of the devil in the Princes Albert Edward and Alfred.

Prince Albert had slightly alarmed the Queen by wondering if it was in the boys' interests to commit them to the care of a lawyer whose father had been a bankrupt and his mother insane, but the Baron had calmed her fears. Through his youthful career Mr Gibbs had been brilliantly successful and he had a gratifying distaste for childish faults. He would correct weaknesses of character, chasten any deviations from the laid down regimen, check any tendency to depravity, strengthen the princes' moral sinews.

Mr Gibbs arrived on 15 January and spent four days with the two princes and Mr Birch, observing their routine and noting in his mind what alterations might be desirable. He spoke privately with the Baron, who agreed to the changes and suggested other improvements. He walked privately with the Queen, who gave a frank appraisal of the faults of both her elder sons, hiding absolutely nothing. Amongst his many other failings, she said, the Prince of Wales had a nervous, unmanageable temper and a hangdog look which needed correcting; and Prince Alfred was heedless and indifferent to all punishment. Mr Gibbs also had a talk with Prince Albert who was more interested in why the Prince of Wales had defects than the defects themselves. Finally, he spoke with his predecessor, who was much out of spirits and who begged him to handle his charges with as much gentleness as dexterity.

When Mr Birch left for the north country the boys were in tears. The Queen thanked him for all he had been able to do and noted that he was quite overcome at the parting. Prince Albert shook him warmly by the hand. Gibbs bowed.

On that first day Bertie tried his utmost. He begged the new Tutor to forgive their glumness but pointed out that it was quite natural under the circumstances. Mr Birch had been with them a long time. He had promised to write and no doubt he would, but they did miss him.

Mr Gibbs was as taciturn as he was humourless. He merely nodded his great head and said that, were platitudes not tasteless and unbecoming, he would remark that time was a great healer. But as platitudes of all kinds were to be avoided, it would be simpler to say nothing about personal attachments and get on with their arithmetic.

Both boys reacted to this. Affie, never very much a favourite of Mr Birch and jealous of his closeness to Bertie, showed he was quite prepared to accept the new Tutor. Bertie, on the other hand, promised himself to use platitudes and worn-out phrases as much as he could – a promise he kept with great determination in his speech, private journal, and letters to the end of his long life. It was the preliminary declaration of war and, deciding that Affie had gone over to the enemy, Bertie was prepared to treat him as such.

The progress of the initial stages of the war between the Prince of Wales and Mr Gibbs was coldly recorded in the latter's private diary:

January 27th: The P. of W. was still in an excited state. In the morning it was difficult to fix his attention . . . The music with Miss Anderson was not a good lesson. In the afternoon he quarrelled with Prince Alfred in the Conservatory . . .

January 28th: Began better – we finished the sums left unfinished yesterday – but walking, he was excited and disobedient – trying to make Prince Alfred disobedient also – going where I wished not to go – threatening to go even when he did not go – and breaking and plucking the trees in the Copse. I played with them, but it only partially succeeded. On the

21

*Terrace he quarrelled with, and struck, P. Alfred, and I had to
hasten home. We met the Queen while this was occurring . . .*

*January 29th: Mr. Leitch the drawing Master came. P. of W.
very angry with P. Alfred, and pulled his hair, brandishing a
paper-knife. I forbade the lesson – he was at first very angry,
remained so some time, but cooled.*

That Gibbs tried, there can be no doubt. He was fixed with an
absolute determination to overcome these princely tantrums. But
however brilliant he had been at the Bar, he found difficulty in
being explicit in the schoolroom. One of his first failures was in
explaining to Bertie exactly who and what he was, and how that
one day he would be King of England.

Oddly, no one had ever done this before. The boy had always
known that and his brothers and sisters were special, otherwise
people would hardly have troubled themselves so particularly over
every minute of their waking lives, but at the age of ten he still
did not realize his own position. Mama being Queen, and so
exceedingly dominant a woman, had made him think that
Vicky, naturally, would succeed her. Matriarchy was at the centre
of his world. The tutor's explanation merely fogged his mind; so
much so that he actually asked for an explanation from Mama
herself.

In her own journal on February 12th that year Queen Victoria
wrote:

*Walked out with Bertie. . . . He said that he had always believed
Vicky would succeed. . . . I explained to him the different
successions. . . . He took it all in. . . .*

Heir to the throne or not, Bertie did not let up in his war with the
new Tutor. Gibbs' private diary recorded further attacks, of
increasing ferocity:

*February 28th: . . . I had to do some arithmetic with the P. of
W. Immediately he became passionate, the pencil was flung to
the end of the room, the stool was kicked away. . . . I wanted
some Latin done. He flung things about – made grimaces –
called me names, and would not do anything for a long time.*

22

March 8th: A very bad day. The P. of W. has been like a person half silly. I could not gain his attention. He was very rude, particularly in the afternoon, throwing stones in my face.

It was a war which upset everyone a great deal. The Queen looked at the daily reports and was dismayed. Prince Albert tried to be kind to his son, and found himself repulsed, absolutely pushed away. The Baron hoped there would soon be signs of improvement. Mr Gibbs, calm in the face of disobedience, abuse and stone-throwing, was grimly determined to succeed. Each night Bertie cried himself to sleep, to wake in starts with tears on his cheeks again, hot tears, and to dream of Mr Birch who had gone away, and his Papa whom he had loved and who had let him down, and of Mama – remote, a hand to be kissed, and of Gibbs, the odious Frederick Weymouth Gibbs, Barrister at Law, and of the ogre Baron Stockmar whom he hated, loathed, detested. . . .

6

Prince Albert was by no means stupid. Indeed he was one of the most enlightened men of his age, and with it, he had a sensitivity which made him feel things very deeply. Often, since he had arrived in England, he had been hurt, but hardly anything hurt or baffled him so much as his eldest son's war against his Tutor. He dearly loved Bertie and, led the right way, he was sure the boy might make one day a great sovereign. For this reason he was being given the most brilliant opportunities to improve his mind and enjoy the best which art and science could offer. Yet he totally lacked concentration. He hardly learnt a thing. He was positively vapid.

Prince Albert accepted the sad change in their personal relationship as the sacrifice which some men were obliged to make in order to improve their sons, but he was inexpressively worried. In fact he was so worried that he did a very rare thing and actually confided his anxieties to the Baron. It was as good as doubting a Stockmar dictum. The Baron reassured him. The dear boy was

23

going through a firing but Gibbs would be the making of him. The Baron had every confidence in Gibbs. Nevertheless, on reflection, perhaps one concession would be permitted. It would involve a risk in some degree – for princes, to Stockmar's mind, were better segregated, like prime beef cattle, from ordinary herds – but certain Eton boys might, perhaps, be invited over on set days to talk and play and drink tea. . . .

Prince Albert arranged everything with care. He included in the list of boys William Henry Gladstone, who had played with Bertie at Osborne. The rest were selected like bloodstock. But the tea parties were not a success after all.

Being constantly on the defensive had made the Prince thoroughly self-centred. He could be exceedingly boorish to servants and his brothers and sisters and, by now, only his favourite sister Alice was safe from his bullying. He was therefore both unpleasant and overbearing with his guests sent over from Eton; so much so that, on Gibbs' prompting, Prince Albert took it on himself to attend the tea parties from time to time. This stopped the bullying, but it stopped everything else too. Only William Henry spoke. The others were overawed by Prince Albert and had their tongues in a vice.

The Prince spoke to the Queen. What could they do about their eldest boy?

Victoria already saw so much of her own worst failings in Bertie, and so many of those of her Hanoverian relations whom she always called 'the wicked uncles', that the sight of him gave her a heavy sense of guilt. She wanted to do her best for him. Sensibly she suggested that as scholarship was not his *forte*, he should be trained as a soldier. Affie had decided to enter the Navy. Cousin George, now the Duke of Cambridge, had made the Army his career. It would teach the boy discipline and pander to his liking for uniforms and ceremonial.

The Prince exclaimed at this. Bertie was behaving disgracefully and it was ludicrous to consider pandering to his likings. Anyway, the Baron insisted that, as heir to the Crown, the boy had to have some knowledge, however slight, of constitutional history, and, in order to be a fulfilled person, he had to learn an appreciation of science, literature, archaeology and art. Moreover the company of subalterns was likely to be contaminating.

The Queen sighed, and shrugged, said she prayed daily that

24

Bertie would soon grow up and become dependable again, and she forgot the business in her present welter of awful anxieties – because her latest baby, little Leopold, had the dreaded bleeding disease and the future was black for them all on his account; and because MacKay her piper was undoubtedly going out of his mind; and because unless something was soon done, that odious Lord Palmerston would push the country into a war with Russia.

The Prince did not give up easily. He had long and profitable conversations with the Reverend Mr Turner who had recently been appointed the Prince of Wales' classical tutor and Chaplain, and that autumn he took the trouble to try and interest Bertie in the laying of the foundation stone of the new Balmoral Castle. He even repented of his decision not to give the boy any sort of treat until he came to his senses and arranged for Phelps and his company of actors to play *Henry V* at Windsor on Bertie's birthday. The boy would enjoy the stirring Harfleur and Agincourt speeches. . . .

Then suddenly and – it appeared to him – quite madly, he found himself involved in an affair in which his own personal integrity was impugned. Palmerston was pushing England to war and, considering it his duty, Prince Albert tried to intervene. Within a month he was the most unpopular man in Great Britain. There were rumours he was to be impeached. Ballad-sellers peddled songs which reported he had already been found guilty of treason and committed to the Tower.

The Queen was so indignant that she insisted on her husband's honour being vindicated by speeches in Parliament, and Palmerston, having won his point and coerced England to join with France in a war against Russia, was willing to accommodate her. But the English were not easily convinced and Prince Albert, in struggling to preserve his reputation, momentarily forgot his anxieties about Bertie. Yet somehow, in his educational isolation, Bertie heard of his father's troubles. Nervously, after a time, he mentioned them. By then things had settled down; Palmerston was the country's hero, England was at war with Russia, and there was no more wild talk of the Queen's consort being committed to the Tower; but Bertie wanted his father to know he thought his detractors were scoundrels. It brought the two together again, not as before, of course; their relationship could never be quite the same after Birch's dismissal; but Prince Albert was touched.

For the first time he began to take a line independent of the Stockmar system and treated his son less as a child. He persuaded the Queen that Bertie, as heir to the Crown, had a duty and a right to be present when departing troops were reviewed and given royal farewells. And so, as a proud twelve-year-old – although once more in his heavy Highland things – the Prince of Wales accompanied his mother on board a royal yacht as she led out her Baltic Fleet from Portsmouth and then stood to while the great battleships, dressed overall, passed the little yacht one by one, saluting their sovereign with gunfire and the shrilling of bosuns' pipes and the National Anthem played by Royal Marine bands, as they sailed off for the war.

Quite deliberately Prince Albert fostered his elder sons' martial spirit by constructing miniature forts beside the Swiss Chalet at Osborne, where, to Gibbs' strong disapproval, he interrupted the daily timetable to explain to Bertie and Affie what redoubts were and gabions and fascines and parallels and merlons, and the distinct important difference between muskets and rifles, and, in the newly introduced high explosion shells, what were carcass shells, and what were heavy bouquets.

Finally he interested Bertie in his own work of examining the working, or rather, the malfunctioning of the British Army Commissariat. This task had been laid on him by Lord Palmerston, who had a high respect for his methodical, analytical capabilities and who wanted to know where the faults lay. Prince Albert found out. And, believing that an exact regard for the truth was essential to the boy's development of character, and that circumspection had to be learnt early by an heir to the Crown, he took a risk and confided in Bertie a good many of the facts about the war. His son respected the confidences and kept the facts mostly to himself, though, as they contradicted what Mama was often saying, he found them absolutely amazing. He learnt that many of the generals in commands were too old and too odd. The cavalry commander, the Earl of Lucan, was a maniac and a martinet. Doddery Lord de Ros, the Chief of Staff and Supplies, had no experience at all and spent most of his time on the Crimea sunbathing. Lord Rokeby, who could face any sort of military calamity, nearly went out of his mind and sulked for days when French troops stole his patent water-closet. Lord Raglan, the Commander-in-Chief, though a brave man and deeply loved, found it all a bit too much

26

for him. When his blunders were censured by the government, Bertie heard of it. When 'Uncle George' of Cambridge made a fool of himself at Inkerman and returned home with nervous exhaustion, Bertie heard of that too. He knew about the lack of discipline, the breakdown in the commissariat, the unreasonable amount of looting, the stupidity of those who arranged comforts to be sent out to the troops which resulted in the men being given boots, topcoats, galoshes by the ton in blazing weather, and being inundated on occasion by a quaint conglomeration of combs, beer, pepper, Bibles, hassocks, velvet smoking-caps, curried venison and maraschino. There were military triumphs, of course, and he thrilled with all England to hear of the gallantry of the troops in the Crimean campaign, especially of the folly and the glory of the Charge of the Light Brigade.

Mr Gibbs watched in anger and frustration. The Prince of Wales, who could keep nothing useful in his head, now easily assimilated facts and figures and miscellaneous information which could be of no use to him at all. He struggled without success to memorize dates and facts in history. He knew nothing of ablative absolutes and the *Idylls of the King* – but he absorbed details of the Crimean War with the eagerness and success of a military cadet. He even knew exactly how and why Miss Nightingale was failing as well as succeeding in her astonishing work.

The Crimean War was one of the most disastrous and shameful in the history of British arms, but it was of enormous consequence to the Prince of Wales. Though at a remote distance he was at last involved with the people he would one day rule. Moreover, being able to succeed in something, his self-confidence was partially restored and he behaved more rationally and quietly. Then, for the first time he was given the opportunity of visiting a foreign court.

The alliance with France obliged the Emperor and Empress to pay a State Visit to England, and Bertie went with his mother and father and elder sister on a return visit to France.

He was quick to notice the difference between the Courts of Versailles and St James's, and he at once fell in love with Paris – a love he was never to abandon.

For ten days he was able to enjoy himself as he never had before. Not only was he free from the spectre of Gibbs in the background but he adored sightseeing, going to a meet of the Imperial Hunt

27

at St-Germain, and – best of all – attending a ball in the Galerie des Glaces at Versailles where thousands of candle lights twinkled and reflected on the crystal chandeliers.

At supper he sat next to the Empress and he charmed her. With careful deliberation, which was later to become one of his chief characteristics, he had taken the trouble to find out something about his hostess. He knew her long name and he repeated it to her as though it were verse: 'Marie-Eugénie Ignace Augustine de Montijo'. Tall, elegant, and beautiful, the Empress had once been called 'all fire and flame'. To Bertie she was simply lovely. In as many words he told her so. He told her how much he was enjoying France, how he and the Princess Royal would like to stay longer at the Palace of St-Cloud. The Empress Eugénie was touched; and said that she, too, regretted their imminent departure. But he and his sister could not be spared at home. The Queen and Prince Albert could not do without them.

'Not do without us, Ma'am? Not do without us?' Bertie frowned. 'There are six more of us at home. They don't want us.'

Nervous that his candour might have been overheard, the Empress hastily changed the subject.

To her husband, who was twenty years older than she, Bertie was even franker. The Emperor was not an especially attractive man, having an oversize head, a goatee beard and needle-point moustaches, but Bertie liked his jolliness. Apparently, in his English exile he had enrolled as a special constable to maintain order at the time of the Chartist riots. He made such fun of the story. He made such fun of everything, whereas his own Papa was as solemn as Stockmar had taught him to be, and Mama was simply Mama. Bertie had reached that critical stage of adolescence when a boy can be so easily ashamed of his parents. Beside the beautiful Empress, Mama was a fright; and while the Emperor talked so excitingly of his time in London, all Mama could say was that she recalled meeting him at a charitable function in aid of wash houses in the Fulham Road.

Snuggling against the short and portly Emperor, nephew to the Great Corsican, Bertie gave him the final accolade of his affection: 'I wish,' he said shyly, 'I wish that I were *your* son.'

And so Napoleon III, as an ally in the Crimean War, was added to Bertie's private list of heroes.

Oddly enough, Lord Palmerston, who had pushed the war along, was also on the list. The Prime Minister was short-sighted, deaf, rheumaticky, dyed his hair and whiskers, and had false teeth which were in permanent danger of shooting out of his mouth, but Bertie knew that Lord Palmerston strongly disapproved of Baron Stockmar, and his vitality and endurance, his great age, and his capacity for making Mama hysterical and Papa speechless put him high amongst Bertie's heroes.

When the royal visit to France ended and Bertie once more faced the regimen which so deadened his spirits, he wished with all his soul that he had the bouncy French Emperor and the equally bouncy English Prime Minister to deal with Gibbs and Stockmar.

They'd be able to do it. Sure enough.

7

In 1856, when the Crimean War ended, the Prince of Wales received a locket from the French Imperial family. It contained a scrap of the Empress's hair, a single hair of the Emperor's (could it have been from the needle-point moustache?) and a wisp of the baby hair of a newly born Prince Imperial. Bertie was delighted with the gift, treasuring it as something very special, and frequently during the next two years he touched it as a talisman of good luck because in that time he was so often miserable.

He lost battle after battle with the implacable Gibbs, suffered in sullen silence regular rebukes from his parents, and made no secret of his joy when the Baron made another delphic utterance that it was time for him to leave his Windsor apartments, return home to Germany and at last rejoin his deserted wife and family. But, whether in Windsor or in Coburg, the Baron's influence was ineradicable. His regimen for the upbringing of the Prince of Wales was already accepted as sacred.

Had it not been for Alice, who could bring out the best in him, and had it not been for an irrepressible energy which was part of his Hanoverian inheritance, Bertie might have pined and simply gone under beneath the strain of trying to live up to the strict standards set by Gibbs. He was certainly tempted to lose his faith in goodness.

Sometimes he witnessed or overhead or he sensed quarrels between his parents, when Papa invariably seemed to get the worst of it but Mama seemed to suffer more. To please him or herself she had given him the special title of Prince Consort and Bertie discovered from a royal page that everyone seemed to think this funny. From the same page he also learnt that at Court and in Society as a whole his parents were known as Joseph and Eliza. It was embarrassing to learn that people laughed at his parents. He was even more embarrassed when his mother had another child: a spherical little girl, christened Beatrice, but known to everyone as Baby.

Inadvertently a new loneliness was thrust on Bertie. Affie was removed to begin his naval training, leaving him entirely alone to face Gibbs and the other tutors, and Vicky married Prince Fritz of Prussia whose uncle, the reigning king, had gone completely out of his mind. Then to his amazement he found that his own marriage prospects had become a topic of consequence, important enough, anyway, for Stockmar to poke his finger into it, and he and Uncle Leopold of Belgium and Papa were busy drawing up a list of possible brides. Six, apparently were German – and already busy applying themselves to the English language. A seventh was Danish. And no one else was considered suitable.

He only heard by chance about the eligible seven, though when he asked to see their portraits Papa quickly told him matters had not gone that far. In fact he came to the glum conclusion that, cocooned as he was from contact with the real world, it was a wonder he heard anything at all. Major events were fed to him by Gibbs: amongst them that the French alliance which he personally valued so highly was gradually crumbling to pieces and that an assassin had made an attempt to blow up his dear friends, the French Imperial family, and that the sepoys in India had mutinied, massacring hundreds of Europeans, and Papa had suggested the English Crown take over from the Company and Mama be called the Great Mogul. . . . Everything he heard seemed to be distressing or ridiculous.

Bertie consistently refused to be agreeable to Gibbs although, to bribe his co-operation, Gibbs took him on a series of walking tours as 'special treats'. The first was with Gibbs alone. The second was to the Lake District and included with four of the seven Etonians who had attended those awful tea parties. The third to Europe was far more exciting. He and the ubiquitous Gibbs and the Etonians went abroad and the boys managed to enjoy themselves – though there was a fearful outcry, and Papa preached a Stockmar sermon which went on for hours, because his son had kissed a pretty girl in Bonn.

Bertie simply hung his head and half listened. He was sixteen but virtual isolation from companions of his own age had not kept him ignorant or innocent. Like many another boy he had long before learnt what was what, and a good deal more, from servants, and particularly from prurient footmen and grooms. He knew all about his two grandfathers, both of whom had kept women. He knew about Papa's brother, Uncle Ernest, who still led a rip-roaring life in Coburg. He knew and he liked the Fitz-george children, and to his amusement had discovered that his erstwhile heroes, both Napoleon III and Lord Palmerston, were well-known roués. As for Mama's uncles, of whom she was so ashamed, their colourful wickedness excited his warmest admiration – especially George IV who had liked elderly ladies, gin and laudanum, and William IV who, like Uncle George, had adored an actress and peppered the aristocracy with nine delightful Fitz-clarences. Then there had been Uncle Sussex, as learned as he was lusty; and depraved, ugly Uncle Ernest, now King of Hanover, who, they said, was capable of anything, but was every inch a king. Bertie had even discovered that Mama had had a 'wicked aunt', his own godmother old Princess Sophia who had succumbed to the charms of an elderly general and had given him a bastard son. . . . What did Papa expect of him? That girl in Bonn had been round and pretty, worth more than a kiss, and had Gibbs not been so detestably ever-present, he would have risked more, and probably got it, too. He was past the stage when passionate desires filled him with dread as well as with longings. Immature in so many other ways, physically he was already as sensual as his Hanoverian forebears.

A certain degree of remorse set in when his chaplain began to prepare him for Confirmation. Offences against purity, he was told, were so exceedingly dreadful, and Confirmation was so exceedingly important. In royal circles at that time this was particularly true, for the ceremony not only had a deep

31

religious significance, but it was also important socially. Before Confirmation one could neither receive the Sacrament nor be counted as an official part of the Queen's Court. It followed that the Confirmation of a Prince of Wales was a momentous affair.

A little time before the event Bertie was photographed modestly from the rear, kneeling at a Gothic altar-rail against grey drapes, and copies were circulated through the kingdom. The picture had a faint atmosphere of the mediaeval squire's vigil before knighthood and was exceedingly popular.

On the day preceding the ceremony, the Dean of Windsor and the Archbishop of Canterbury gave the boy a full hour's oral examination in the presence of his parents. He was pleased to prove to be so knowledgeable in the Catechism, which had been the lever, or reason for the loss of beloved Mr Birch. As for the rest, he managed – just. And on the following day, dressed magnificently, and in an elaborate setting of members of the Royal Family, the Household, peers and political leaders, Bertie took upon himself the promises made on his behalf sixteen years before by three members of the Saxe-Coburg family, 'wicked' Aunt Sophia and the Duke of Cambridge, both now dead, and the King of Prussia, now off his head.

' "Defend, O Lord, this thy child," prayed Archbishop Sumner in a reedy voice, "with thy heavenly grace, that he may continue thine for ever, and daily increase in thy Holy Spirit, more and more, until he come unto thy everlasting kingdom".'

Bertie was moved. He received his First Communion the next day, and, three months later, he tried to arrange with his chaplain to receive the Sacrament for a second time. But Gibbs stepped in. He believed that official sanction had to be obtained for such a departure from schedule, and, though he saw no positive harm in it himself, he felt obliged to consult the Prince's parents without delay.

The Prince Consort's reply was immediate, short and forceful. Although receiving Communion three times a year was enjoined on members of the Church of England, he and the Queen had made it their practice to do so twice and it would be difficult for his son to justify divergence from that custom. He was not prepared to quarrel with Papa. Not over that. Not yet.

Nevertheless Confirmation gave him a measure of independence

32

which he had never known before. After the doubtful pleasure of a walking tour with Gibbs in Ireland, where he found the food plain to the point of dullness in Killarney, Bantry and Skibbereen, he was established in a grace-and-favour house of his own called White Lodge in Richmond Park. The ubiquitous Gibbs was to be in overall command and Mr Turner the Chaplain was also to continue in the household, but three equerries were chosen to serve him in monthly rotation, equerries selected by the finest of fine Stockmar combs. One, Lord Valletort, was good with a pencil and at the pianoforte, the two others had both won the V.C. in the Crimean War and were also linguists. All three equerries were issued with general orders outlining the disciplinary values governing the life of the Prince of Wales. 'Lounging ways' were to be prevented, such as 'lolling in armchairs or sofas' or 'a slouching gait with hands in the pockets'. The Prince was to be taught 'the frivolity and foolish vanity of dandyism', 'the most scrupulous civility', and 'a *practical* joke should never be permitted'. Accompanying this deadening outline were more diet sheets which greatly tantalized the ever-hungry boy: cocoa and an egg for breakfast; a light luncheon – with pudding best avoided – and seltzer water to drink; dinner equally light, with claret and seltzer in hot weather, sherry and seltzer in cold.

'How necessary it all is,' wrote the Prince Consort to Stockmar in distant Coburg, hearing that his son had thrown things at his valet and been reduced to screaming rages.

8

Two valuable advantages came out of the move to White Lodge.

Despite outward appearances the Cambridge family had never got on well with either the Queen or the Prince Consort and in the past there had been explosive scenes. These had varied in degree from the Duchess's staunch refusal to stand when Albert's health was toasted and her self-exile for years from Court, to her publicly expressed scorn for the new-fangled fashion of afternoon tea which the Queen herself thought most acceptable. It had made Victoria seethe to hear her aunt declare the one-legged old Marquis of Anglesea had been quite right to describe it as a meal only fit for the heathen, his abhorrence going so far that the ladies of his household had to hide tea trays under high sofas whenever they heard him coming.

The struggle had gone backwards and forwards over small things and large until, with the death of the Duke of Cambridge, and then that of Aunt Gloucester and Princess Sophia, the Duchess found herself the only member of the old royal family left in England, and she had made peace with Victoria. Thereafter this haughty, stately and stout duchess, with shiny black pomatum on her hair, spent her time between her rooms in St James's and her house at Kew, worrying mainly about two of her children.

Princess Augusta, the elder girl, had been successfully married off to the Mecklenburg–Strelitz family long ago; but her son George, now Duke of Cambridge, and by Victoria's appointment, Commander-in-Chief of her army, had a fancy actress in Queen Street, Mayfair, and nothing she could do or say would make him renounce her and take a respectable wife. He loved his Louisa or Mrs Fitzgeorge as she was called, and that was that. The Duchess' Lady-in-Waiting, Lady Geraldine Somerset, most heartily agreed with her – for she herself doted on 'poor George' and she wished to be Duchess of Cambridge herself. The remaining Cambridge princess, Mary Adelaide, had the good fortune to be well-liked by everyone, and the centre of much attention season after season, but she also had the great misfortune to be colossal. With republican directness the American Minister to the Court of St James's described her as a 'very fat, very thick-set, and very proud young lady of at least two hundred and fifty pounds'. Marrying her off was something of a problem, though good offers had been made, and refused on account of the fact that the proposers were Roman Catholics. Princess Mary Adelaide might be stout but she was devout and would not consider changing her religion. For the moment the search was still going on, though Mary Adelaide herself was in no sort of hurry. By far the most popular member of the British royal family, the masses loved her, and cheered and waved their hats whenever they saw her bowl by in a carriage noticeably low on its springs. It was Lord Clarendon who had wittily nick-named the Prince and the Queen Joseph and Eliza, and he it was who called the Duchess of Cambridge and her daughter 'the stout parties from Kew' but he was very well disposed towards the Princess and when he was Foreign Secretary wanted to help her find a husband, regretting that 'no German Prince will venture on *so vast an undertaking*'.

The Prince of Wales, with the natural cruelty of a small boy, had always laughed at fat Cousin Mary, and his upbringing had done nothing so far to fine out his coarser qualities. Therefore he was prepared to laugh behind his hand when, because Kew was so close to White Lodge, he was invited there for his first formal dinner party. He knew all the tales about Princess Mary Adelaide; how she was called at Court 'our domestic Embonpoint'; how she danced nimbly but essentially like a hippopotamus and that at one great affair when dancing with the Comte de Paris she had collided with another girl and knocked her flat; how she worried his Mama who, like many little people found her huge cousin formidable, positively oppressive; and how, as if in defiance of a fate which demanded that she should dress unostentatiously to hide her shape, she revelled in rich and unbecoming stuffs, over-trimmed bonnets, loads of jewellery, and extravagant hair arrangements of artificial doves and grapes, real butterflies, hyacinths and paeonies.

But Bertie had never before been in such close proximity to Mary Adelaide's charms. He found her delightful. He found he could even confide in her and after dinner he did so. They avoided 'Uncle George' who was dining that evening and escaped from Aunt Cambridge and Lady Geraldine into the grounds.

Mary Adelaide already knew something of the Prince's circumstances and knew that he was regimented from morning until night, and she begged him to make himself a frequent visitor at Kew. 'Use us, Bertie, as a window to look out at the world.'

He did.

Not so often that it would be remarked and criticized, but sufficiently often to make him better acquainted with the Cambridges, he would row up-river with an equerry from Richmond or Mortlake and, mooring his craft alongside the Brentford Ferry landing-stage, go ashore and visit his great-aunt and Mary Adelaide. Sometimes he sent her letters, including in one 'parts of a pheasant' which he had shot, and which she might like for trimming a hat.

She did. The bright colours delighted her. And he would occasionally propose himself for dinner or luncheon.

On one of those visits he saw amongst the plethora of photographs on Mary Adelaide's pianoforte, the portrait of a good-looking girl and asked who it might be. It was a young friend, explained his cousin, what they called in the family 'a Rumpenheim relative'.

She told him about Schloss Rumpenheim, willed by a grandson of George II to all six of his children equally, on the understanding that it was to be used for family reunions. Thus, once in every two years, the elegant eighteenth-century house was packed with his descendants for several weeks, and amongst them were always the Cambridges, Rumpenheimers through their mother, and this girl, who was a Rumpenheimer through her father, Prince Christian of Schleswig-Holstein-Sonderburg-Glücksburg.

'When she was little,' said Mary Adelaide, 'I used to push her in a pram under the elm trees at Rumpenheim. And since we have become warm friends. Her name is Alexandra, but in the family she is always Alix.'

Bertie's memory was only retentive when something mattered to him. He recalled, suddenly, as he looked at the portrait, the list of potential brides drawn up by Stockmar, Uncle Leopold and Papa. It included this girl, Alexandra; and despite her father's name the one non-German of them all. She looked very pretty. Very pretty.

Of the three equerries given to him on taking up residence at White Lodge, Bertie had a preference for Major Robert Lindsay of the Scots Fusilier Guards. Princess Mary Adelaide observed this. She also observed that the Major did not regard his duties simply as a bore, but also had a genuine interest in the welfare of the Prince of Wales. On an afternoon when Bertie and he had dined at Kew, the Princess arranged it so that she had a moment's private talk with the Equerry. She was brief and to the point. No one, she said, could fail to notice the Prince of Wales' defects of character, but she was convinced he would not and could not improve as long as he was held in the vice of Frederick Weymouth Gibbs. Did the Major agree? Not at all put out by her frankness – for people expected it of Princess Mary Adelaide – he agreed very warmly

36

indeed. Very well, then, she demanded, what was the Major going to do about it?

At that he spread his hands in a regretful gesture. An equerry could help to make the Prince's life easier, perhaps more interesting. But there were limits. Dislodging Mr Gibbs lay far beyond them.

'I know, dear Major,' urged the Princess, 'that you will do all that is possible.'

She laid her hand on his arm. They walked to catch up with the Prince of Wales, who was walking with Lady Geraldine. Despite her bulk Mary Adelaide moved daintily and there was no doubting her extraordinary poise. Nor her benevolence. Who else in all his family bothered about the disagreeable Prince of Wales? That evening she was wearing light blue and had a wreath of diamonds and cornflowers round her wavy hair. Her scent was light, not the heavy smell of Parma violets but the sweeter scent of the English wild plant. For one extraordinary, dazzling moment, Robert Lindsay forgot that he was a mere Major in the Scots Fusilier Guards and that the lady beside him was a Princess of the Blood more than twice his own weight. . . . Later he was to become Lord Wantage and marry an heiress and have children, but he never forgot that improbably romantic moment at Kew in the early summer of 1858.

An opportunity to do as she had asked arose more quickly than either could have expected.

The Prince of Wales was summoned to accompany his parents on a state visit to Cherbourg. It was to be a single day's visit only, but was of great importance as the two nations sat more and more uneasily as allies, and it had been noted that, for some strange reason, the Prince of Wales seemed to get on especially well with the French Imperial family. He might be useful. And so his cloistered life was temporarily broken into and he and an equerry went with the Duke of Cambridge down to Osborne and accompanied his parents on the royal yacht *Victoria and Albert* over to Cherbourg.

Major Lindsay was the equerry because he happened to be trilingual, and he sympathized with the Prince who again had been ordered to don his Highland things. Apparently the French thought the costume fetching. Nevertheless, though sweltering in the heat, Bertie was happy to be in France again. He eyed the

37

Emperor with amazement. It seemed impossible that he should be the satyr which rumour said he was. At dinner he sat on one side of the enchanting Empress. His father sat on the other side, but it was Bertie who had most of her attention. He could still remember her long Spanish name, and he still thought her lovely. He did not know that the visit was of supreme diplomatic importance; that Europe waited to hear what the Emperor and Prince Albert, prompted by their foreign ministers, would say in their public speeches. All he recalled was a stupendous luncheon, a stupendous dinner, the Empress archly giving him a flower wrapped round with maidenhair fern, and afterwards, a stupendous display of fireworks.

The Prince Consort was a poor sailor and delighted that the return crossing was so calm. He was delighted, too, that their political mission had gone so well. Certainly no more could have been done at present. And he was delighted with Bertie's undoubtedly valuable contribution to the happy buoyancy of the visit. His *savoir faire* had been marked, his charm appreciated. Where the poor boy got it from only Heaven knew, but he had that rich gift of princes, the ability to please, even entrance, with a modest charm. Therefore the Prince Consort was disposed to listen and pay careful attention when Victoria's cousin, George of Cambridge, accompanied by Major Lindsay, Bertie's equerry, came to his cabin on board the *Victoria and Albert* and made their statement. In fact the statement was Lindsay's. George of Cambridge was there simply as a sympathetic observer. 'Yes, sympathetic,' he emphasized, when the Prince Consort showed his astonishment. 'The boy's next to the throne, and we can't have him perpetually in low spirits, or, damn it, he'll get like his great-grandfather.'

The Prince Consort was even more startled. Victoria's grandfather, George the Third, had been a lunatic for the last few years of his reign. Was it possible that being too strict with Bertie was affecting his nerves?

'It seemed essential that he should be given the very best education,' he began.

His cousin-by-marriage interrupted him. 'But too much pushing is oppressive, damn it. His spirits are low. I've seen it myself. He regards Gibbs as some sort of horror.' He turned to Lindsay. 'True, ain't it?'

38

'It is, your Grace.' Lindsay then spoke directly to the Prince Consort. 'In my judgement, Sir, it is essential for the Prince's happiness, for the success of the educational plans you have laid down, that Mr Gibbs be retired and someone else substituted.'

'Another tutor?'

'I would think, Sir, that at sixteen, almost seventeen, the Prince no longer needs a formal tutor to be in charge of him. Perhaps a Governor of his Household? – responsible to yourself and to the Queen?'

'I will think of it.' The Prince Consort stood up. 'That I promise. And, now, will you join me in a turn on the deck? I have not enjoyed so smooth a crossing on the Channel for many years.'

On Bertie's seventeenth birthday he received a long and imposing document from his parents. It was a manifesto of advice and revealed that a new dispensation was about to rule the last year of his childhood for, on his next birthday in 1859, he would be eighteen and therefore, as Prince of Wales, of full age, and in the event of his mother's death, he would succeed as ruler of Great Britain and Ireland. Between now and then he was urged to be temperate, sober, chaste and dutiful. His studies would be directed but not imposed, and after a visit to the Court at Berlin it was proposed that he should travel to Rome for several months. After that he would continue his studies at the Universities of Oxford and Cambridge, and in vacations go through the regular training of a soldier. Meanwhile he would be installed as a Knight of the Garter and formally enrolled in the Army as a colonel unattached. Accompanying the manifesto were gifts and messages of good wishes.

The boy read it through three times. He was obliged to in order to take it all in because his eyes were blinded with tears.

Later his Mama was much affected when she heard how he had shown such proper sentiments. It demonstrated that he had some beauty of character if not of person. The latter defect troubled the Queen. She confessed to her daughter Vicky that, at Bertie's installation as a Knight of the Garter, she could not understand why everyone thought him in the least good-looking. He had a small head, the Coburg nose, a receding chin, a strange hair style, knock-knees and unfortunately, he was short. Nevertheless, even without brains and beauty, if he could cry on reading Papa's noble manifesto, it showed he had a heart.

She did not know, perhaps she never did, that he cared for only one thing. He was to be freed of his Tutor. A Governor, a Colonel Bruce, was to replace him, and though he could do nothing without the Governor's permission, not even leave his own house, he was to be freed of his Tutor. The harrowing war with Frederick Weymouth Gibbs was over. After eight long years. Eight long, long years. He felt like a liberated galley-slave, an uncaged linnet, an animal released from a spring trap. . . .

It was this which had made him cry.

9

Oxford was all very well but, although the Dean of Christchurch had begged the Prince Consort to allow his son to live in as a nobleman-commoner in college, the Stockmar system of segregation had prevailed. The Prince of Wales lived in his own hired house with his Governor and Household.

Gibbs was actually there as Tutor, but he had no powers and was a spent force. Besides which, they had been separated for a long time and after a visit to Vicky and Fritz in Prussia, a four-month stay in Rome, and a summer and autumn in Scotland enjoying laboratory experiments with the Edinburgh chemist Dr Playfair, being prodded along in mathematics by a clerical tutor named Canon Heaviside, and helping Mama to receive at Balmoral four large omnibuses laden with savants and philosophers who had been meeting in the Scottish capital, the Prince of Wales had sufficient self-confidence to ignore his old enemy. Gibbs mattered no longer.

Frankly Bertie was disappointed by his sober welcome to Oxford, contrasting it unfavourably to his sister Alice with the reception given his favourite 'wicked' great-uncle, George iv, who had been feasted so handsomely that he could hardly sign the College Book.

He was a little disappointed, too, by his companions' lack of

40

go. True, they had been selected for him, and they included his old friend William Henry Gladstone; but, unhappily, the old William Henry, who had relished duels with bamboo swords and collecting grubs and insects, had become a sobersides. It was probably owing to his father's being Chancellor of the Exchequer and Leader of the Commons, that William Henry had determined to enter politics himself, and nothing – certainly not a stain on his university reputation – should stand in the way of his ambition. Bertie reflected sadly on the irony of their disparate circumstance: one thrust willy-nilly into statecraft, the other having to achieve it. . . .

November 9th brought the Prince of Wales his majority and the certainty that he would rule directly if anything happened to Mama. She complained habitually of her nerves, and had great fits of depression, but otherwise she seemed healthy enough, and, now that he was older and less subjective, Bertie felt more forbearing towards his parents even though they had crammed him so tightly into Stockmar's strait-jacket of an education system. Their relationship could never be as it once had been, but he got on well with Papa and respected him, and even Mama, who was so very bossy, had won his affection. Though his heart might thump when she made wild threats to abdicate, he had no longing at all for a throne which could only be obtained by her death. Yet he could not help remembering – it was the sort of thing which stuck firmly in his mind – that she herself had come to the throne only fourteen weeks after her eighteenth birthday. With his majority came a vote from Parliament that Marlborough House should be done up for his exclusive use, and a note from Papa that from henceforth he would wish his son to be associated with the intricate affairs of his estates as Duke of Cornwall, and that he was looking out for him a country house, not too distant from London. Birk Hall, an estate adjoining Balmoral, had already been bought for him and was being managed by Papa, who gave a faithful and exciting account of his stewardship. Certainly his advice was more pertinent and valuable than that of the famous John Ruskin who had the impertinence to remind him that the primary duty of princes was to preserve frescoes. . . .

41

It was tame, really, Oxford. Overdrinking never interested him very much, and there were still Stockmar-influenced diet sheets pinned to the kitchen door in his own private house, though he could smoke now and he did a great deal. And that winter was hard and there was skating and firework displays on Christchurch Meadow. Yet Bertie found it difficult to concentrate on his studies. His hot blood was stirring. If only they had let him have an Army career, but Mama had a dread of what she termed 'the objectionable life of cavalry officers'. It was precisely the sort of life he pined for. Once the riding-school stage was passed an endless vista of pleasure stretched before a young officer: the excitement of Uncle George's reviews, polo and hunting and steeplechasing; dashing about on glossy, thoroughbred chargers; paying careful attention to the niceties of dress and uniform; eating and drinking well in the mess, and flirting endlessly with pretty girls.

The Queen loved Osborne in the springtime. The weather was bland, the prospects soft and calming, walking or driving in the grounds and down to Whippingham so enervating, and the joy of being with Albert in the house which, like the new Balmoral, was entirely of his own design, made it a perfect refuge from the pestering of statesmen.

But from family troubles there was no escape and, in the spring of 1860, Victoria felt particularly burdened.

She and Albert sat at the twin writing tables in her sitting-room to discuss their problems together. The birth of Vicky's first baby, Willy, had been badly bungled by her medical attendants and the baby had a permanently dislocated left arm; but despite this, and despite clear and repeated warnings from her mother, Vicky was carrying another child. Leopold, their haemophilic son, was throwing himself about with all the energy of boyhood and stood daily in danger of his life. Alice was keen to marry Prince Louis of Hesse-Darmstadt, but Albert was not yet convinced that this was the best choice. Finally they had to decide whether Bertie was fit and capable of managing a tour of North America as his mother's representative.

It was the last which concerned them the most.

The idea had been suggested that the Prince of Wales should go to Canada to open a railway bridge across the St Lawrence at

Montreal and, at the same time, the new Parliament House at Ottawa, capital of the two United Canadas. Furthermore, President Buchanan had invited him to continue his tour privately into the United States, and it but needed the word of the Queen for everything to be arranged right down to the final detail.

On the whole Victoria was disposed to say yes. Her own father had lived in North America for a long time, indeed he had lived there with a Madame de St Laurent and given her children too, before circumstances obliged him to pension off the lady and marry Victoria's mother, and the Americans still recalled he had gone to one of Mrs George Washington's New Year receptions at the White House. It would be appropriate that his grandson, although incognito to satisfy militant republicans, should also be a guest at the White House. But Victoria was a little worried that Bertie would run wild and show her up by his inadequacies.

The Prince Consort's point was slightly different. Sufficiently hedged in so that he could not misbehave, Bertie ought not to make too much of a fool of himself. He simply wondered if the boy was up to it. Mature in so many ways, Bertie was very much the opposite in others. In contrast to his winning charm and courtliness was his adolescent, loutish behaviour to his valet and lower servants, which his father found deplorable; and, in contrast to his recently cultivated moods of resigned calm when faced with frustrations, were moments of strong passion – explosions of bad temper which puzzled and worried his father. As a father, the Prince Consort loved his son, but he was not proud of him at all, and he seriously doubted if he could manage such a mission. Nevertheless, the boy had to grow up. He had to be given some sort of responsibility. And Albert found himself beginning to agree with Victoria. Given the right suite, Bertie might manage it.

They agreed that he should go.

It was not unkindness, merely forgetfulness which accounted for the fact that the Prince of Wales himself was not consulted, nor even knew that he was going to North America, until plans were well under way.

That spring on his vacation from Oxford, he was visiting European relations, finding a pretty girl or two to kiss, staying at Coburg and enduring an opera composed and staged by his Uncle

43

Ernest the reigning Duke, and, with marked reluctance, visiting the aged Baron Stockmar, taking with him letters from the Queen. The old pedant eyed the young prince. Neither revealed it to anyone, but neither thought much of the other.

10

Not since that February day in 1852 when the Queen had explained his inheritance had the Prince of Wales so strong a feeling of his position.

For the very first time he was at the exact centre of all attention, and far from shying at it, he actually enjoyed it. He crossed the Atlantic from Southampton to Nova Scotia in a luxuriously appointed set of cabins aboard H.M.S. *Hero* of ninety-one guns. The escorts were smaller; the *Ariadne* of twenty-six guns, and the *Flying Fish* of six guns. He was nervous about the endless formalities which lay ahead, but, for the present, he was content to enjoy his exalted position. His strong sense of inferiority at being the brainless son of an intellectual, artistic father, and a gifted and imperious mother – a feeling hard-boiled by seven years of Gibbs' school-mastering – actually began to diminish.

As it turned out, Canada was not as boring as he had feared. He was genuinely interested in the bridge he had come to open, and so taken with the Niagara Falls and Monsieur Blondin's acrobatics on a tightrope that, had he had no suite to prevent it, he might have accepted the Frenchman's offer to wheel him over the falls in a barrow. And he was especially fascinated by stories of his grandfather's remote escapades.

With a sensibility which she appreciated, he sent sweetbriar cuttings to his Mama from her father's old garden, and with his equerries he chuckled over the late Duke of Kent's affairs. Had it been possible, he would have liked to get in touch with any half-uncles and aunts he still possessed, but the Duke of Westminster, who, being Secretary of State for the Colonies, represented the Ministry, and the Earl of St Germans, who represented the Queen, and his own Governor, now promoted to Major-General, were aghast at the idea. The newspapers, they said, would be bound to ferret it out; and if he did not already know then it was high time he learned that journalists were mostly men without honour or scruples who would, if starved of a story, shoot their dearest ones to contrive one. The Prince was surprised. By the end of the trip he was surprised no longer.

Politically the Prince's visit was not of vast significance. The Queen hoped that her subjects in the United Canadas would be gratified that she had sent her heir over the Atlantic but it did not seem to have occurred to anyone that the visit might be used by the Canadians themselves to forward their own political sectarian ends. This they did with a vigour and spirit which alarmed and outraged the Duke, who had ultimate responsibility for the Prince's safety and the Prince's dignity.

The two Canadas, French Roman Catholic and British Protestant, were about as amicable as the Irish Catholics and imported Scotch Protestants in Ireland, and, while on official advice and by his own inclination the Prince showed a scrupulous impartiality to both communities, the Orangemen of Upper Canada were determined to honour him as heir to their beloved William III .

Kingston, which was scheduled to receive a royal visit, undertook to receive the Prince with triumphal arches decorated principally in orange and with portraits of King William. The Duke therefore struck Kingston from the itinerary. The Orangemen who controlled the city were very angry. But the Duke and the Prince himself were adamant. Bertie stood at the rail as his steamer passed the Kingston landing place, hardly crediting that sectarianism – or racialism as it really was – could drive supposedly reasonable men to such bigotry. From unrepentant Kingston came the strains of provocative martial airs played by the town's band. 'Boyne Water' and 'Croppies Lie Down' floated over the waters of Lake Ontario.

The Orangemen were not quite in such power in Toronto, the capital of Upper Canada, and their threats to make a sectarian display of the Prince's visit were dropped by the Duke of Newcastle's particular request. But they cheated him. His sharp eye inspected the triumphant arches, and on one was a transparency of William III crossing the Boyne. At once the Mayor and Corporation of Toronto were barred from the Prince's Levée.

45

It was with some relief that the royal party left British territory at the frontier town of Windsor, and the Prince of Wales used one of his hereditary titles as Lord Renfrew when they crossed into the United States. There he was in the land of the Free to see for himself if, as his Mama believed, that the Americans really were as deplorable as Dickens and Mrs Trollope had depicted them.

His suite rather feared they were. There was much garishness, a distasteful lack of constraint in people's curiosity, and an inefficiency in the making of arrangements maddening to a courtier; but Lord Renfrew thoroughly enjoyed himself. He was young and he liked the confusion. He seldom took offence when people treated him like some prize porker paraded in a fair. Anti-British newspapers protested that only flunkeys paid honour to royalty, but no one seemed to pay any attention.

His private visit was a continuous triumphal progress as far west as St Louis and thence to Washington. At Harrisburg in Philadelphia he was requested to sit for a moment in the historic chair used by Hancock when signing the Declaration of Independence. It was a critical moment. More than a hundred reporters' pencils hovered over their pocket books, and perhaps only they showed any sort of chagrin when, with a charming smile, Lord Renfrew at once obliged and sat down.

The welcome he was given was warm and quite prodigious. The crowds were immense. Not an Irish-American voice was heard. And within the limits imposed by the rules of the house (dancing was forbidden even on the carpet) he enjoyed staying at the White House, as his grandfather had once done, as the guest of the President. Then he moved south and, after going to a prison and the opera in Philadelphia, fetched up in delirious New York.

Presidential elections were on at the time, and the furore was appalling, but apparently Lord Renfrew had abundant energy and resources. His suite, and especially the British Minister at Washington, were on tenterhooks. Mobbed by reporters who asked the most provoking, and often personal, questions, the Prince managed to be fairly discreet. There were, however, limits to his cordiality and he was at first repelled by their easy familiarity. Having been addressed all his life as 'Sir' or 'Your Royal Highness', it seemed extraordinary to be called Prince or even Albert Edward. He was genial about it because in theory, at any rate, his visit was a private one and he was Baron Renfrew, but underneath he did not like the boisterousness, the informality. One part of the Stockmar dicta which had penetrated very deeply into Albert Edward, Prince of Wales, was that royalty was a race apart. The reporter who actually called him 'Princey' – an address only ever used, and then in private, when he had been an infant by his dearest Laddle – received a chilled look from a haughty pair of Hanoverian blue eyes which made him squirm.

The reporters' questions seemed endless. Was there any truth, they asked, in the story that his sister Princess Alice was getting herself engaged to a German prince? What did he think about the Chinese war and the burning of the Summer Palace at Pekin? How had he felt on getting the news that his father's mother had died? that his other grandmother's health was beginning to break up? What – and this was the deadliest question – what did he 'as a royalty' think of the successful rebellion against the Bourbons of Naples? Which side was he on? With admirable good humour and tact Lord Renfrew struggled through the interrogation, and not without some success. General Bruce was proud of him and told him so. But what he had actually said or done bore little relation to what in the end was printed. Bertie was getting rather used to it, though he rather resented a report that one night he had slipped out and had 'disported himself riotously in the most luxurious brothels'. If only he could have . . .

Women certainly flung themselves at his head. He was not displeased. A frank appraisal of his own face in the glass told him that he had attractions. He was not as bad-looking as his Mama and sisters were for ever telling him in order, so they said, to take him down a peg. And, as it happened, he could be counted one of the world's most eligible bachelors. It was, therefore, hardly surprising that, at a ball given at the Academy of Music in his honour, for which three thousand guests had received invitations, five thousand people managed to cram themselves into the ballroom; nor surprising that a large part of the floor gave way. With genial good humour Bertie waited for two hours while the Americans showed their ingenuity in effecting instant repairs, in the process of which a carpenter was nailed in underneath the floorboards and there was a further delay while the frightened man was released. There seemed to be no end to their ingenuity. After luncheon at a military review an enterprising army sergeant sold the duck bones from the Prince's plate to souvenir hunters. No one knew who got

47

the genuine article. The amount of bones sold would have framed a score and more of ducks.

On the whole the Prince enjoyed himself. He certainly preferred America to Canada though, wisely, he kept that opinion to a few chosen intimates; and he took a liking to American women, which was important to their place in international society. Time had fossilized the protocol of many courts. Americans, Jews by religion, and parvenus, were not given the entrée into English society until the Prince of Wales' tolerance led the way to their acceptance. And the Americans certainly took to him. For all their pride in republicanism they showed strangely loyal sentiments to the great-grandson of their old oppressor, George III.

On 20 October the visit came to an end. Lord Renfrew, now the Prince of Wales again, sailed with his suite from Portland, Maine, aboard H.M.S. *Hero*.

It was Christmas time at Windsor.

Outside, as it ought to be at Christmas, it was very cold indeed. Twenty-eight degrees of frost, the Prince Consort had reported to the family, and there had been ice-hockey and slides on the frozen ponds and flooded water meadows. The windows were frosted over but there was sunlight outside and then moonlight, and indoors light from hundreds of wax candles and the big open fires of burning beech logs. On the sideboard at dinner was a huge baron of beef neatly garnished with the royal cypher in grated horseradish. And there were the other Christmas dishes. The favourite German ones, the favourite English ones.

It all looked too good, thought the hungry Prince of Wales, to be touched. But the meat was carved and the geese and capons, and everything was served in state.

In his new feeling of importance, Bertie showed an unaccustomed restraint about the delicious food as a good example to his younger brothers and sisters. They were all there, except Leopold and Baby who would be brought in with dessert, and Vicky, of course, in Berlin. And Alice's fiancé was there, Prince Louis of Hesse, a young man Bertie thought he would come to like. In a blasé fashion he talked to Prince Louis about his recent adventures.

The Queen eyed him sharply. She did not like blaséness. But her attitude softened. Really, the dear boy had done so well. Nothing but praise from the United States President downwards. She talked to him for a moment about Americans, and then about his transfer from Oxford to Cambridge, which was to be effected at the beginning of the Lent term. But she could not make him feel comfortable. He fiddled with his food while they talked. Poor boy! It had always been the same. She invariably failed in trying to treat him as an adult. But, then, her poor Mama had been the same with her. They had been against each other for years and years and only recently had they recaptured the old mother–daughter relationship. But with her mother so ill, it looked as if she was too late. What a pity it was. How foolish the wasted years when they could have been great friends – just as dear Albert had always wished.

She looked down the table to Albert. The covers had been drawn, and because this was Christmas Day, after dessert there were to be charades and games. In the autumn Albert had had a bad time after an accident with the runaway four-in-hand and though his recovery was exceedingly slow he had told her he felt much fitter. Certainly he was the dearest husband any woman could have. Christmas, a heady mixture of Dickens and German *Gemütlichkeit*, always made her sentimental. She watched little Arthur, whose ambition was to be a soldier, shoot at his father with a pop-gun. But Albert did not mind. As soon as nurse brought Baby in, he was swinging the child in a dinner napkin, up and down and round and round.

The Queen's eyes swam with tears: Windsor, Christmas, frost and snow and traditions of the time, and her dear family all but Vicky, with Bertie highly spoken of at last, and Albert so much better. So happy. So loving. She gulped in that thick, warm atmosphere.

11

Cambridge was no better than Oxford. But, then, it was no worse. General and Mrs Bruce supervised the Prince of Wales' establishment at Madingley Hall, four miles from Trinity, of which college he was a matriculated member.

Bertie made one single futile but very characteristic bid for independence, by catching a train for London. He had the wild idea of finding the famous Mott's, a haunt he had heard about where terriers killed sewer rats at a frantic speed, and pretty girls, called 'soiled doves', were as easily available and as expensive as the vast stores of champagne. It never seems to have occurred to him that a Prince of Wales buying a first-class ticket for Liverpool Street station was bound to attract attention. The telegraphs beat him to London. On arrival he was met by a royal chamberlain and a royal carriage and driven to the Palace. The Queen was not at all pleased to see him. She was worrying herself into a state – about her mother's illness, now diagnosed as cancer; about Albert's weakened constitution; even by the news that poor Miss Nightingale had just been inundated by a broken cistern, most of her furniture ruined, and she herself given a severe chill – and Bertie was given a piece of his mother's mind, not so much for breaking out from Cambridge as for actually using the railway. Did he not realize that rides on ordinary trains were fraught with danger? Her own newly appointed physician, Dr Baly, had recently been killed in a railway crash at Wimbledon. He had fallen through the carriage floor and been run over. Bertie really must be more prudent. She gave him tea and sent him back to Cambridge in a special train.

In theory writing essays for his supervisor Charles Kingsley, the socialist clergyman, or working at his books, Bertie was hunting with the Drag, or watching farces performed at the A.D.C., or playing tennis or cards with two of the original tea-party Etonians – Charles Carrington and George Cadogan – and a Jewish friend, Nathaniel Rothschild, of whom the Queen did not really approve. But Bertie was mostly dreaming of somehow getting himself into the Army. And, when he was not dwelling on derring-do as a soldier or on lechery with 'soiled doves' at Mott's, Bertie was idly thinking about Alexandra of Denmark.

It now appeared that this princess was highest on the list of marriage possibilities, and, while not over-excited at the thought, Bertie had not forgotten her portrait in Princess Mary Adelaide's sitting-room at Kew. At least she was ninety-nine per cent better looking than Elizabeth of Weid who had also been on the list until Bertie had seen her posed photograph and categorically refused to have anything to do with her whatever.

50

Why the Danish princess had gone into the lead Bertie did not know. He guessed it might be due to Mary Adelaide's persistence with his parents, or to Vicky's romantic interest – for Fritz's mad uncle had died and his father had succeeded and Vicky was now Crown Princess of Prussia as well as Princess Royal of Great Britain and a person whose views bore considerable influence. Oddly, it barely occurred to him that Alexandra of Denmark had been chosen for him by his own parents. Unknown to him his mother had expressed the rather tactless view that the English were weary of constant German connections and would find a Danish marriage more acceptable; and his father considered Alexandra the brightest prospect on a very limited horizon, who might do Bertie some good.

The Prince Consort was in fact making certain discreet diplomatic and family arrangements when he was distracted by the death of his mother-in-law, the Duchess of Kent. This, under ordinary circumstances, would not have deterred him for long. But the circumstances were by no means ordinary. In a storm of remorse because she and her mother had got on so badly for so long, Victoria went to pieces. Her hysterics and weeping and fits of sobbing and screaming were dreadfully alarming, and the Prince Consort had to use all his concentration on trying to keep her rational. It took a great deal out of him because he himself was suffering from poor health. Neuralgia and toothache and chronic headaches made him long for rest and quiet, but he could obtain neither while Victoria swooned and shrieked and said she longed to die.

A story ran through the Courts of Europe that the Queen of England was as mad as her old grandfather, King George III. Stockmar warned the Prince Consort of it. So did Vicky.

He was enfeebled himself, but by the sheer force of will power Albert made Victoria pull herself together. In the effort, Bertie's affairs, even England's affairs had to be given less scrupulous attention than they merited. He could spare neither time nor the mental vigour necessary, and without further question he agreed to Cousin George's suggestion that, in the long vacation from Cambridge, Bertie should go to the Curragh Camp in Ireland to do a little soldiering; and he agreed to Vicky's proposal that afterwards Bertie should be sent to Prussia, where she promised that by some romantic subterfuge or other she would contrive to arrange

51

a meeting between him and Princess Alexandra, and see how they got on.

Bertie was delighted with both plans. He was also delighted to hear that his father had contracted to prepare an estate for him in Norfolk, in a bleak place called Sandringham.

12

The Prince of Wales' training at the Curragh Camp was velvet and swansdown compared with that of the average subaltern. To begin with, he was already a colonel and carried that rank throughout. To go on with, he was received in Ireland and fêted as the personal guest of the Lord Lieutenant, and, instead of being given ordinary quarters, he was installed in the Headquarters Hut of the Commander-in-Chief in Ireland. There was no hardship in making-do with an establishment which contained a bedroom, sitting-room, drawing-room and a dining-room large enough to entertain a score of people.

Bertie was determined to enjoy himself.

He was attached to the 2nd battalion of the Grenadier Guards and he asked that, as a special favour, Frederick Stanley, Lord Derby's son, be sent to join him. Stanley had endured the Windsor tea parties and, like Cadogan and Carrington, had come out of them the Prince's friend. Moreover, like them again, but unlike William Henry Gladstone, he had not turned out a sobersides. Anything but. He was now a dashing and very lively subaltern in the Grenadiers.

General Bruce was there, of course. The Prince of Wales could not stir without his Governor. At least in theory he could not. But they had an attachment for each other which made their lives comfortable together, and, without informing anyone – not even Mrs Bruce – the General had decided the Prince was neither by temperament nor inclination the sort of man his father was, and could not be kept totally in gyves. If royal wild oats were to be sown, they were better sown discreetly.

Philosophically he allowed himself to be kept distracted by

officers who sympathized with the 'young Prince of Wales, and played dozens of rubbers of whist whilst his charge and young Stanley and the subalterns of the 2nd Battalion had the wildest of times.

Colonel, his Royal Highness the Prince of Wales, already knew from friends in Cambridge a good deal about the high life in London, but not until now had he heard it all, nor guessed at its magnificence. It seemed that, despite the energetic work of Homes for Fallen Women, and of enthusiastic amateurs like William Henry Gladstone's father, who went out in the streets at night on a regular round of reclamation, London was a veritable Babylon.

There was gaming of all kinds from card-playing to cock-fighting. There were the big occasions like a public hanging outside Newgate. There were jaunts to the opium dens of Chinatown and dockland. There were dog fights, boxing matches, all-in fights – both men and women, and there were night-houses of all kinds. London was thick with introducing houses, and Gladstone, or Old Glad-Eye as the girls called him, had a running battle with the madames of brothels in the West End. Indeed he'd made himself particularly unpopular in the Commons by interesting himself in the closure of a brothel which catered almost exclusively to Members of Parliament.

Greatest attraction of all were the famous demi-mondaines who led gaudy, cheeky, astounding lives and were photographed as pocket-Venuses and had ballads written about them. There was the famous courtesan Laura Bell who had saved hard, married a man named Thistlethwayte, and become a female evangelical preacher in some remote part of Scotland. There was the equally famous Nellie Fowler whose natural scent was so delicious and delicate that she drove her admirers frantic. There was the famous Polly Ash. Reigning supreme, at present, was dashing Skittles.

Born Catherine Walters in a Liverpool slum, she had won her nickname in a drunken row with some Guards officers – threatening to knock the lot down 'like a row of bloody skittles'. Yet she had little in common with the famous dockside whores like Black Sarah, or Poll Sellars, or the grotesque creature called the Mouth of the Nile. Skittles was exceedingly beautiful and she had a

53

presence. Moreover she had learnt to ride, and ride very well indeed, and dressed in a black skin-tight habit she was mesmerizing Rotten Row. Certainly she was mesmerizing the young politician, the Marquess of Hartington, who was even thinking of marrying her. One day he'd be Duke of Devonshire, too. Skittles was the most notorious of them all. She'd fought off Gladstone's reclamation, although he had given her a dozen pounds of the best Russian tea and a personally conducted tour of St Paul's; and she'd not minded being taken to the pantomime by the fabulously rich Miss Burdett-Coutts who had once had a crush on the Iron Duke and since had married a man young enough to be her grandson. Skittles was the thing. . . .

Albert Edward listened to the stories with starry eyes. And he joined in the drunken choruses:

> *Oh! dear girls, I love you more than honey,*
> *London is a funny place*
> *But costs a lot of money.*
> *Yes, London is a funny place*
> *Where rummy things are done,*
> *For in London Town they all must go*
> *The whole hog or more.*

There was no Skittles at the Curragh Camp. But a noted actress and discreet beauty named Nellie was smuggled over from London and popped into that luxurious bedroom in Headquarters Hut.

Nellie Clifden, as was her proper name, knew her job very well. She'd been warned about the peculiarities of this adventure and how to address her illustrious lover. But, she decided, it just wasn't possible. How could she 'your Royal Highness' a boy who was so dithery he could only say 'Oh, Nellie! Oh, Nellie!'

'Come, dear,' she said in the proper, usual way. 'Come, dear; it's all right. . . .'

Along the corridor, at a table with three fellow senior officers, General Bruce was winning at whist.

When the Commander-in-Chief, the Duke of Cambridge, came over to the Curragh Camp to review the troops he thought his young cousin and protégé was looking somewhat subdued. He

54

asked the Prince's Commanding Officer what was happening. Quite briefly he was told.

'My goodness!' The Duke blew through his bushy moustache. 'Good gracious!' Then he thought for a moment. 'Does his Governor know?'

The Colonel looked shocked. 'Major-General Bruce, Sir? Of course not.'

The Duke of Cambridge allowed himself to chuckle. 'Just as well, hey? Just as well. Just as well.' At that he put the Prince of Wales out of his mind and reverted to a topic which at present was causing him the gravest concern: the appointment of a most extraordinary fellow as War Secretary – a frightfully bright man who turned out classical *jeux d'esprit*. The Commander-in-Chief hurrumphed through his moustache. If the new War Secretary stuck to turning 'Hey Diddle Diddle' into Latin verse, and 'Humpty Dumpty' into Greek, as they said he did, he might be tolerable, but if he started poking about in the Horse Guards . . . The Duke turned scarlet at the thought.

The Prince's Commanding Officer had rightly surmised the Duke's reaction, but he was nervous of a projected visit by the Queen and Prince Albert. So was Bertie. He dreaded it. Already he was feeling remorseful and frightened and swore that it would never happen again.

But of course it did. And within six hours.

He clutched his head and he cried when Nellie had been smuggled out. It was like drink, laudanum, food: a craving. To calm himself he turned up the wick of the bedside lamp and he re-read Alice's letter.

Dear Alice. He could never tell anyone about Nellie; that is, no one in the family; but of them all, if they did find out, he felt that Alice would understand the most. She had written from Windsor to say that she and Papa and Mama had just been to visit the newly built mausoleum for Grandmama at Frogmore, and Mama had been surprisingly spirited. Everyone had feared that, at the sight of her mother's tomb, the Queen would have another *crise des nerfs*. But, Alice reported, Papa was not at all well. She was sure of it. Would Bertie study him carefully when they all came to Ireland, and study his features to see if he did not agree with her? . . .

In agitation Bertie began to ball the letter. He could not bear to

55

contemplate facing his father, not after what had happened. Those unnerving grey eyes, which he had once thought so kind, had a way of seeing things.

Nevertheless, when the royal party arrived from England, the Prince Consort was less observant than the Duke of Cambridge had been. Bertie saw at once that Alice was right. Papa was not at all well and only his care for Mama, and his strict sense of duty, was keeping him going.

It was not a happy visit.

Bertie was on edge all the time, though his father merely made the dismal remark that he and his friends appeared to take their soldiering in a very lighthearted fashion. He did not endear himself to the military by adding that it was as well for the Prince of Wales that afterwards he was to go to Coblenz to observe the autumn manoeuvres of the Prussian Army. Nor did he make himself popular with the common people of Ireland, likening them to the Poles in their constant political discontent. The remark earned him the sort of abuse he had not heard since just before the Crimean War. Seeing her dear Albert subjected to such an insulting and hostile demonstration, the Queen said she would never forgive the Irish, never. She was upset enough already. By misfortune, not malice, at a military review the band played a march composed by her dear, dead mother.

'*It entirely upset me,*' she wrote to Uncle Leopold. She wrote on 'the days of days', on her maligned and misunderstood but doubly beloved Albert's birthday. Unenthusiastically she commented on her heir's part in the military review:

> '*Bertie marched past with his company, and did not look at all very small.*'

It was a strange remark. Being tiny herself and married to a small man it was barely surprising that Bertie should not have been of average height.

Before they left for Scotland, the Queen made Bertie's shortcomings known to him. He was to concentrate much harder and please dear Papa. And when he went to Vicky's in Prussia, he was to mind his manners and remember that, in one sense, he represented England. She hoped he would write and say how things were with him and send his love and duty to his distressed, bereaved Mama. ...

He kissed her hand and her cheek and promised to do his best in everything. As the *Victoria and Albert* sailed from Kingstown his relief was so profound tears coursed down his cheeks. His parents had not the slightest suspicion. His secret was safe.

On 11 September he left the Curragh for Germany.

13

The autumn manoeuvres with his brother-in-law were far more energetic and less entertaining to Bertie than his soldiering in Ireland. Nevertheless he was grateful for the opportunity to get to know Fritz better. What he learnt and saw he liked very much. Fritz was one of the very few people alive who could or who did trouble to treat his brother-in-law as an equal. And unlike people at home in England Fritz was not for ever belittling what he did. He admired his knowledge of orders and uniforms, and his sense of correctness in wearing them, and he said so. Fritz also accepted what no one else seemed able to accept, that Bertie was not simply a replica of his clever father or his clever mother, but a separate individual. He was not the sort of brother-in-law who pushed books at you, or made you sit too long at concerts, or made an afternoon stroll into a botanical expedition, or a discussion an excuse for giving a monologue. Bertie admired Fritz very much indeed, and for the first time was able to see Vicky's virtues as well. From being a quarrelsome, self-indulgent nuisance of an elder sister Vicky seemed to be an entirely different person. She was not calm, of course. No child of Queen Victoria's could ever be entirely calm, but Bertie understood now what his tutors had called a full personality. Vicky was brave – and she had to be in a Court largely hostile to her English origin, and she was sensible and she was fun. Clearly she and Fritz adored each other.

In a moment of guilt Bertie coloured at the thought of what he

57

had done. Fritz the paragon, the paladin of paladins, the Galahad of Europe would never have soiled himself in such a way. . . .

Not far from Coblenz, about which the Prussian army was completing its manoeuvres, and even closer to Baden, where Bertie was Vicky's guest, lay the castle of Rumpenheim. And there, it being the biennial gathering of the family, no less than forty-three Rumpenheimers were gathered together in the many apartments of the white eighteenth-century house. Amongst them were Princess Mary Adelaide and the other Cambridges, and Princess Alexandra with her family.

Being first cousin to Alexandra's mother and first cousin to Bertie's mother, Princess Mary Adelaide might have been of some consequence in the flowering of this matrimonial alliance. But two things stood against it. One was Queen Victoria's determination that the Cambridges should have no influence over her son and her outspoken declaration that neither her aunt nor cousin was 'fit' to give Alexandra any sort of advice. And, secondly, there was an age-old antipathy between Princess Mary Adelaide and Alexandra's mother, Princess Christian; partly because the latter, with Rumpenheim directness, had once publicly and rudely drawn attention to her cousin's girth and gypsy love of jewellery; and partly because Princess Christian had recently called her an abominable flirt. With characteristic candour and gusto Mary Adelaide had retorted there was little for an oversize princess to do but flirt, though this had not improved matters.

For these two reasons Vicky did not make use of Mary Adelaide's well-known skills as a Rumpenheim intriguer. But Mary Adelaide was a good guesser and remembered her talks with Bertie at Kew, and she observed with silent amusement the antics of her cousin Princess Christian – a stately lady of limited talents and slight deafness – who was hard at it trying to achieve the impossible: that is, in preventing the majority of the family from guessing at the romantic plan for her daughter to meet the Prince of Wales.

It was a hopeless task. Either inside information, or an inspired guess, or, more likely, sheer inventive powers, had resulted in some press reports that the Prince of Wales' summer plans were probably connected with one or other of the ladies staying beside the river Main at Rumpenheim.

58

But Princess Christian did her best and was constantly suggesting diversionary tactics to keep everyone busy and happy.

The aged Duchess of Cambridge almost always commanded events at Rumpenheim. After all, as the last of the six children of the Landgrave who had willed it equally to his family, she was in a sense sole owner of the castle. But this year it was her niece Princess Christian who proposed the competitions, charades, amateur theatricals, expeditions, picnics and other family entertainments simply to keep everyone's mind off the Prince of Wales who was out with the Prussian army on manoeuvres. And she met with partial success. If she deceived no one else, she at least deceived her daughter.

On the morning of 24 September Princess Mary Adelaide was drinking over-sweetened hot chocolate in order to keep herself going until breakfast time when, to her secret pleasure, Alexandra came into the room to admit that she was muddled and troubled and would like advice. Papa and Mama, she said, had just announced she was to accompany them to Speyer to view the beauties of the cathedral. Could they have forgotten that she had seen the cathedral many times? And why, if they were going on a dusty, dirty railway journey had they told her to put on her very best dress?

Princess Mary Adelaide smiled. She spooned out the last of the sticky chocolate from the bottom of the porcelain cup. She had watched Princess Christian's expenditure of energy and ingenuity with wry admiration. It had been astounding. But really, she thought, as the girl's mother, she ought to have told Alix something. Not all. But something. And so she herself felt justified in rectifying the omission.

She gave a hint of what it was all about.

Princess Alexandra had a remarkable complexion quite unlike the pinks and whites of the British royal family. It was once described as entirely peaches and cream, and it set off quite remarkably her brown hair and blue eyes. As Mary Adelaide warned her that she might reasonably expect to find an extra diversion in the familiar cathedral at Speyer, and hinted at what it might be, her colouring deepened a shade. To be certain she had not misheard – for, unhappily, she had inherited a little of her mother's deafness – she asked for an explicit explanation.

But Princess Mary Adelaide put the direct question aside.

59

Pretty Alexandra must pocket her curiosity for the morning. Soon it would be satisfied. In fact Mary Adelaide was fond enough of Bertie not to wish to compromise him by appearing to be pressing his suit. Despite the interest he had shown in the photograph of Alix, she was not absolutely sure of his feelings. Nor did she know for certain what the Queen's wishes were, and her cousin Victoria, if crossed, could make life very unpleasant. Which would never do.

It followed that the only ignorant person as to the purpose of the Schleswig-Holstein-Sonderburg-Glücksburgs sight-seeing trip to Speyer was at the centre of it all; and, as the train rattled along, and her prettiest dress was threatened with the horrors of creases and, even worse, soot smuts, the sixteen-year-old Princess wondered who or what it was she was to see that day.

She was an unambitious, likeable girl, of parents who, despite their high-sounding titles, found it very difficult to make ends meet in the Copenhagen Yellow Palace where they lived in the winter and at the Bernstorff hunting-lodge in the summer. Of Prince Christian nothing worse was said than that he was dull. Princess Christian came of a family not noted for its sobriety or discretion, and there had even been a mild Rumpenheim scandal about her in her youth. Alexandra's brothers, too, were said to be fast, or, at any rate, wanting to be. But the family had Roman virtues of uncomplaining thrift, a contentment with their lot, a liking for simple pleasures, a respect for goodness and art and science, and they had a devotion to each other which made the family the very centre of their existence. Clothes were handed on; portraits of the children were not executed by professionals but generally by Princess Christian, who – lacking confidence in her ability to make a likeness – generally sketched her subject from behind; the simplest of toys, pleasures and entertainments had always been their lot. One day, of course, Papa would take over from that dreadful old man who now ruled Denmark, a much married and divorced King who had set up house in the Amalienborg Palace with a mistress. For this reason Alix and her sisters could not go to Court and had lived very quietly. They were, in the sympathetic description of Princess Mary Adelaide, Denmark's royal fieldmice.

Vicky, the Crown Princess of Prussia, would have hotly quarrelled with such a description. By now she was intoxicated by the romantic notion of marrying her brother to Alexandra and for days before the meeting in Speyer she had been bullying with all the energy of a resurrected Gibbs: emphasizing Alexandra's qualities, pooh-poohing her deafness and heavy Danish accent and the little scar on her throat caused long before by neglecting a cold, and making him learn up facts about Speyer cathedral so that he would have something reasonable to talk about. Bertie had them by rote: capital of Bavaria; population about 22,000; twice burnt to the ground by the French although the Cathedral – the object of their visit – had happily escaped. This was of red sandstone and considered one of the best examples of Romanesque architecture extant. The interior had recently been restored with splendid frescoes. . . .

When the day came Bertie gazed at the frescoes without the least interest, and begged his sister not to drag him about so breathlessly. They were supposed to be incognito and were now attracting attention. And he was right. The Crown Princess' chattering attracted attention. They were recognized. The Bishop himself arrived, panting in his purple robes, to give them a conducted tour. And in the coolness of the great building, before the altar of St Bernard, they met another party.

The Bishop was enchanted. A visit from Prince Christian and his family on the same day as a visit from the Crown Princess of Prussia and her brother the Prince of Wales! He, his clergy, and all the people of Spayer were honoured. . . .

Bertie instantly recognized Princess Alexandra. He had never forgotten the portrait in Mary Adelaide's sitting-room at Kew, and for the past few days likenesses and near-likenesses had been thrust under his nose by his aggravating sister. Having heard so much of her beauty he was frankly a little disappointed. Photographs and portraits had hidden from him the length of Alexandra's nose and the lowness of her brow. But after fifteen minutes' conversation he agreed with everything he had been told about her charm and liveliness.

At a little distance Prince Christian talked with the Bishop, and Princess Christian gossiped to Vicky about the misdeeds of Princess Mary Adelaide.

By chance both parties were going on to Heidelberg. By equal chance – so coincidental as to be positively embarrassing to the Prince of Wales, who was terrified of committing himself – both parties were spending the night in the same hotel. Vicky wisely did not try to push her brother; nor, with great courtesy, did Prince Christian.

Princess Alexandra hardly remarked on the strange coincidences. Mary Adelaide had done well to give her a trifle of a warning or she might have been alarmed. As it was, she was sixteen, confirmed, marriageable, and this young man, although he seemed so scared and lacked the panache of her elder brothers, and she knew very little about him except that he was to be King of England, she did not find unattractive. She had heard her young sister Dagmar say that Albert Edward of Wales was good-looking and a catch. She was predisposed to like him and she did.

Shyly when they parted she gave him a signed photograph of herself which Mama had produced out of a valise. Bertie bowed and thanked her. Prodded by the Crown Princess he produced a photograph of himself – also signed, and exactly the same size as the one Alix had given to him. With unselfconscious vanity he regarded it himself before handing it over. It showed him in his colonel's uniform, his hand on sword hilt. He rather liked it. And certainly he liked the pretty flush on Alix's cheek as she thanked him for the gift.

After this the chain of coincidences broke. The Schleswig-Holstein-Sonderburg-Glücksburgs returned to Rumpenheim. Albert Edward of Wales, after a tiff with his sister, in which he refused to commit himself to any sort of declaration, returned home and made his way up to Balmoral. He had sent a letter ahead to tell his parents of the meeting, but it was not phrased in strains of devoted passion:

We met the Prince and Princess Christian and the young lady of whom I had heard so much, and I can now candidly say that I think her charming and very pretty.

The Queen was inclined to be tetchy. Her extreme lowness after the death of her mother had subsided. Albert and Scotland had seen to that. Indeed, she was beginning to feel herself again and was thoroughly enjoying the carefully planned expeditions they made that summer – the most memorable of all their Scottish holidays; and here was Bertie holding back and risking the possibility of losing Alexandra to the Russians, who were also out wife-hunting. With uncommon candour for a mother, she bewailed his 'sallow, dull, heavy, blasé look', and prayed: 'May he only be worthy of such a jewel!' She wrote with more of hope than exactness in a letter to Vicky on the day after his arrival at Balmoral:

Bertie is extremely pleased with her, but as far as being in love, I don't think he can be, or, that he's capable of enthusiasm about anything in the world.

It was this which vexed her: her son's lack of vitality, his inability to realize that royal marriages can seldom be made in heaven, that they are hand-made, politically shaped, but they can become like her own, a profound and marvellous experience. She and Albert had learnt about love. Their marriage had ridden over a few uneven paths, most, she admitted, of her own making, but they had also been wonderfully happy. Their marriage was a living thing. Bertie's present attitude to it – with almost as much enthusiasm as a sheep approaching the dip – would get him nowhere.

Albert, dear blessed Albert, dealt with the boy. They talked together. The father noted a reticence in his son to make a positive undertaking. Before committing himself he wanted Alix and her family to be invited for an English visit, though he knew that, by meeting her in Speyer, he had already compromised her to some extent.

His father promised that he would not be forced into anything, but made him understand it would be ungentlemanly, to say the least, to jilt such a charming and pretty girl in the eyes of Europe.

'What a plague it all is,' exclaimed Bertie.

His father considered this explicitly non-romantic utterance as further proof that something was wrong somewhere, but he held his tongue.

Nothing had been settled before Bertie returned for the Michaelmas term at Cambridge, and the Prince Consort and the Queen made their last two outstanding expeditions of the season; one to Glen Fishie, Dalwhinnie and Blair Athole; the other to Cairn Turc, Cairn Lochan and Co-Ness.

Though he lived out at Madingley Hall with his Household, the Prince of Wales also had a set of rooms placed at his disposal in college by the particular request of the Master of Trinity. He used them as often as he could get away from his governors and tutors, and it was to those rooms that, on the darkest of all dank November days – and it was a striking fact that Cambridge streets seldom dried out between October and the following May – he sent for his particular Trinity friends Charles Carrington and Natty Rothschild. Both had been out following the Drag which Carrington hunted at Rothschild's expense, and both were muddy, wet and eager for a bath. But when the Prince told them the matter was urgent, and sported his oak to keep out casual callers, they forgot their discomfort. He gave them whisky and bade them draw themselves closer to the comfortable fire of coals.

'It's the devil,' he said morosely. 'My father's found out about Nellie.'

Carrington started. He and the Prince had been vying with each other all term for the attentions of dear Nellie. 'But how could he have found out?' he expostulated. 'You know Nellie. She'd not tell a soul.'

Bertie took a letter from his pocket. 'Do either of you', he asked, 'know a Lord Torrington?'

Rothschild immediately nodded. 'Youngish, a great club man, bit of an aesthete, and gossips like a dowager.'

Carrington also had heard of Lord Torrington, especially of his prowess as a prattler.

Bertie read out a part of the letter. His father said he was broken-hearted to hear that his son had established a liaison with an actress during his military training and that Lord Torrington, who had recently come into waiting and had his ear to the ground in all the London clubs, said that 'the liaison was still continuing. . . .'

'We must get her out of Cambridge at once,' interrupted Carrington. 'I'll see to it.'

'Thank you, Charles.'

Rothschild was less disturbed. 'There's no need, I feel sure, to rush things. No need at all. Play the game calmly. Every father expects his son to kick over the traces. The Prince Consort can't be all that different.' Then he stopped. To his acute embarrassment, for he was as shy as he was sophisticated, he saw that Bertie's eyes were swimming with tears.

Carrington, an oxlike figure, his clothes steaming before the fire, tried to help by being jocular. 'Now A.E.' he said – a name then used by the Prince's intimates. 'Don't get yourself in a taking. I'll take Nellie off your hands for a time.' He grinned. 'And gladly too. But you really must buck up. Your father won't do much. He can't.'

Bertie held out the letter. Rothschild took it. He and Carrington read it together. In the severest language the Prince Consort censured his son's disgrace. He was too broken-hearted to see him personally at present, but he required Bertie to give a full and detailed account of the relationship to his Governor without delay – together with an apology for having deceived the General.

'A full account!' exclaimed Carrington in astonishment. 'What can he mean?'

Bertie took a glass of whisky himself. It was unusual for him to do so. He shrugged. 'How I came to meet her, through whose agency, how she was got undetected into my room, and out again. Who did this, that, and the other....'

'Names?' said Rothschild shortly. 'He wants names?'

Bertie nodded.

'Well, you can't give him any,' said Carrington immediately. 'I'll help myself to more whisky, and, if you like, Natty and I will come with you to see General Bruce. But names, of course, are out of the question.'

Rothschild, exactly a year and a day older than the Prince, but in percipience a generation older, looked quietly at him and, meeting his eyes, looked quickly away again. Far less naïve than Charles Carrington, who saw everything in simple terms of black and white, he intuitively knew that the Prince had actually been considering betraying his fellow officers and friends; that in terror of parental and royal wrath he lacked the moral stamina to resist

65

his father's demands. Fortunately for him Charles Carrington had saved his character this time – but only just. Natty decided to be rather careful with A.E. in future. Overtrusting princes was not a Rothschild or a Jewish habit anyway, and to place much trust in one so light in honour, one so unaware it appeared of what could be done with decency and what could not, would be exceedingly risky.

Bertie's resolution was stiffened by Carrington and by the urgings of the disillusioned Rothschild. He was frank with General Bruce, but he refused to give the names he had been asked for. As Bruce had never been in ignorance of what was happening at the Curragh, and had won a considerable amount of money from his non-chaperoning rubbers of whist, the required apology, for having deceived his Governor, embarrassed him a good deal. He had to console himself with the reflection that he had no idea the Prince and Carrington had continued to enjoy Nellie's favours after their return to Cambridge.

To Bertie's surprise his father commended his refusal to name the officers and friends who had found Nellie for him, and, accepting his assurance that the affair was finished, he announced that he would be coming down to Madingley Hall – not as the University's Chancellor, nor as the Prince Consort of England, but simply as a father to see his son and talk about the future.

Agitated, pale, in an actual sweat of apprehension, Bertie again appealed for the support of his friends. George Cadogan was brought in as well, a good move because the Prince Consort liked his father. Carrington helped by being plain and straightforward – and the Prince Consort thought him a likeable lad. Nathaniel Rothschild helped by preparing Bertie for the fatherly talk which otherwise might have terrified him and made him truculent. At the art of cut and thrust in conversation, and in exquisite politeness, few could match him: but the Prince Consort liked him less than Cadogan and Carrington, considering him flashy and probably, underneath, rather fast – and this was odd because he generally got on with Jews and sympathized with their religious and social plight; indeed, an odd rumour had it that he had been fathered by a Jewish lieutenant in the small Saxe-Coburg army, and was, therefore, half Jewish himself.

Well-prepared as he was, and wishing to be accommodating to his father, Bertie was nevertheless upset and he showed it when his

66

father admitted that his first source of information had not been the gossipy Lord Torrington but a warning letter from Coburg, written by the aged Baron Stockmar. The Baron had reported the scandal was going about Europe and had urged the Prince Consort to check on the accuracy or otherwise of the rumours – which had been done through Torrington.

'The Baron,' said Bertie suddenly, in a peculiar strangulated tone, 'the Baron has never been my friend. Never. Never.'

His father realized it had been a mistake to mention Stockmar. 'There,' he said calmly, 'I believe you do him an injustice. But we need no further speak of him.' He drew his son's arm through his own. 'Nevertheless there are many things which we must discuss.'

'Should we walk out together?' suggested Bertie.

His father hesitated. He had a streaming cold and he felt weary. But if Bertie felt more comfortable talking out of doors, then he was prepared to walk out with him.

'Very well,' he said.

They began their walk. To mollify his son he said that, naturally, he had felt obliged to keep the affair from Mama. It was a sacrifice of the exact truth which he was reluctant to make, but for Bertie's sake he felt he had to. In fact, both as Queen and as Bertie's mother, Victoria naturally knew her heir had fallen, as she put it; she had accepted it with the calmness of a woman who is gratified to be proved correct in her worst suspicions, and of a woman who herself knew more about fleshly appetites than Albert ever would. Her strongest reaction had been a fear that news of his escapade might ruin Bertie's chances with the Danish princess.

The Prince Consort was correct in thinking Bertie would be more comfortable and confiding out walking. He got him to admit that his continued liaison with Nellie Clifden had made him reluctant to enter all at once into a formal contract with Alexandra of Denmark. And he was persuaded that marriage, far from being the imprisonment he had begun to fear it might be, was the very best thing for a vigorous young man with a strong and passionate nature. 'Which clearly you have, Bertie,' said Papa with unusual candour, and he went on and on and on as he sometimes did, while his son only half listened. Bertie was so relieved that all appeared to be forgiven and might, one day, be forgotten, that he mistook the way and inadvertently lengthened their walk by a

67

mile or two. It was a mistake which later the Queen thought important enough to record in her diary. His father had been thoroughly exhausted 'in consequence of Bertie's mistaking the road during their walk'.

The Prince Consort stayed the night, then returned to Windsor by special train, leaving behind a much happier son. He had agreed to do all he could to further the planned Danish marriage, and promised to do better in future. In fact his good resolutions were no more lasting than those of any other young undergraduate, and he was soon dreaming of Nellie's strapping charms again, and glad that his moralizing Papa had returned to Windsor. Life without parents and governors and tutors and equerries would be very jolly. Didn't Charles Carrington agree? Didn't Nellie?

The Prince Consort himself was much happier for this visit to Cambridge, but almost immediately his depression returned. His youngest son Leopold was having alarming and dreadful internal haemorrhages. His cousin, whom he had loved as a son, and who was King of Spain, had just died in great agony of typhoid. He himself felt so utterly dejected that he confided to his Secretary Sir Charles Phipps that he felt he could go on no longer. On December 2nd he collapsed.

Alice wrote a warning letter to Bertie, who was about to sit exams; but her mother forbade her to say how gravely ill the Prince Consort was.

'It was he, he,' cried the distracted Queen, drumming a finger on the arm of her chair. 'It was Bertie who so agitated my dear darling. By causing his Papa such distress by obliging him to go down to Cambridge when he was terribly unwell. . . . It was he who caused this awful suffering. . . . I will not have him here, Alice. I will not have him here. I will not. . . .'

Alice attempted to soothe her. Like everyone else, she guessed at what the Queen was going through. Her adored Albert lay in agony, moving from bed to bed, from room to room, refusing to eat, refusing to rest, incapable of resting, incapable of anything. It was a time of horror. The centre of Victoria's whole existence was slowly dying in great pain before her very eyes. It was no wonder she was distraught.

Alice personally nursed her father, and did all that she could for her mother, but on 13 December when her father was in a pitiable delirium, calling sometimes for General Bruce, at others shouting in French, shivering with cold despite his fever, and when she was warned by Dr Jenner that there could be no hope, Alice took it upon herself to telegraph her brother. Even then, fearing gossip and lack of discretion amongst the telegraphists, she did not state outright that the Prince Consort was close to death.

Bertie had been sitting exams, and took the news calmly. He reasoned there could be no urgency. By now Papa ought to have recovered. But he realized that his favourite sister was in some distress and needed him, and he decided to go. Nevertheless, not sensing the gravity of the situation, he dined well with Carrington and Natty Rothschild before catching the very last train from Cambridge. He arrived at Windsor, quite cheerful, and not in the least expecting what he found, at three in the morning.

He was amazed, frightened.

A large number of the family were there and everyone except the smallest children seemed to be up. The gentlemen of Papa's Household were all present. Even, in the background, he saw his old governess 'Tilla' Hildyard. He approached the Queen and kissed her hand and her cheek. Except that her lower lip trembled uncontrollably she was like a statue. She accepted his embrace in a way which sent a chill through him. Alice pressed him to her heart. Whispering, she took him to a tall, florid man who was presented as Sir Henry Holland, one of the four specialists who had been summoned from London. He stunned Bertie by bowing and saying in a grave, courteous voice that he feared the Prince Consort's condition was critical. He had rallied several times, but the crisis was not past, and there was very little reason to hope for a recovery.

Bertie asked Alice if he could see Papa, but she said no, not yet. In a little while, perhaps, but not yet.

'Alice,' he said quietly, close to tears. 'I must see him, and alone. There are things I have to say.'

'I know,' she said and looked at him full in the eyes. 'Yes, dear Bertie. I know. Papa has rambled a good deal. He could not help what he said.' She put her arms round him and tried to comfort him. Then she broke away. 'I must go to him,' she said and promised: 'You shall see him as soon as possible.'

He fled to the Prince of Wales' apartments in York Tower and when General Bruce arrived from Cambridge he spent hours talking with him, pacing his sitting-room, hoping anxiously for the summons from Alice or the Queen. His Governor was firm with him. His father had accepted his apologies and determination to do better, and the matter was done between them. It was finished with. Whipping himself with further remorse served no purpose at all. Not mincing his words, the General said: 'You must be manly about it, Sir. Tears shed now will help neither you nor the Prince Consort. We can best pray for a miracle.'

It seemed to be granted them. Early that morning the Prince Consort's condition appeared to belie every part of Sir Henry Holland's warning. Dr Brown, a local physician, even said there were grounds to hope that the crisis was passed. After weeks of restlessness and fever, the Prince Consort was tranquil. The anguish, the struggle were over. But still no summons came for the Prince of Wales and by early afternoon his father's state was worse than before.

Alice could not spare a moment to go personally to York Tower. She sent instead Jane, Lady Churchill, one of the Queen's permanent Ladies in Waiting, who had taken her post at the beginning of the Crimean War when Bertie was twelve, and who had never failed to be his champion at the centre of the Court. They had a great respect and affection for each other. Nevertheless Bertie flushed with distress when he realized she knew about his affair with Nellie Clifden. Not that she was censorious, or showed any sort of disgust. But she was a lady, and her knowledge embarrassed him. Lady Churchill was as kindly in a firm way as General Bruce had been. She would not have mentioned it, she said, had the Queen not also been aware of the facts.

Bertie started. Then he bowed his head in his hands.

'I only tell you this,' continued Lady Churchill, 'because her knowledge will colour anything she might do or say at this tragic time. And though your father's death will be dreadful for all your brothers and sisters it will be doubly so for the Queen.'

Bertie stared at her. 'He really is dying?'

Lady Churchill nodded. 'And you are to come and see him now.' She moved to the door which General Bruce opened for her. 'The Queen and Princess Alice and the family are expecting you.'

Victoria had doubted the wisdom of allowing Bertie to see his father. It might simply serve to excite her darling in his last hours.

70

But she was pleased to see she had been mistaken. Bertie took his father's hand and kissed it. Then he knelt at the foot of the bed with his sister Helena. The gentle pressure of Papa's fingers had been as expressive as any of the long talks they had ever had. Alice knelt at one side of the bed. Mama on the other. Vicky could not be there, of course, and Leopold had been sent to recuperate from his haemorrhaging in Cannes, and Baby Beatrice was too little. But the others came in to kiss Papa's hand, Affie in naval uniform, Louise at thirteen and Arthur at eleven. The Queen's half-brother Charles, Dean Wellesley, a knot of physicians, Papa's Gentlemen and Mama's Ladies, were grouped about the room. Bertie tried to pray with the Dean, but his eye was caught by the tragic face of Löhlein, Papa's valet, standing ice-white and crying in the far background. He looked so like Papa that everyone believed he was his half-brother, a by-blow of Duke Ernest I. He was in anguish to be standing by his master's deathbed.

At a quarter past eleven, Sir Charles Phipps, Private Secretary to the Prince Consort, telegraphed the Lord Chamberlain in London.

HIS ROYAL HIGHNESS THE PRINCE CONSORT EXPIRED PEACE-
FULLY AT TEN MINUTES BEFORE ELEVEN THIS NIGHT DECEMBER
14TH 1861

Shortly after midnight St Paul's passing bell tolled over London.

15

Since the death of his father the Prince of Wales had not gone contrary to his mother's slightest wish, and yet she was curt with him. He was briefly commended for his conduct at the funeral and told that henceforth everything should be done as Papa had planned or had intended. This included his own future. He was to marry soon, and Princess Alexandra of Denmark at that; and, to his surprise, he discovered that his father had planned he should soon go down from Cambridge and travel with his Governor in the Courts of Europe and in the Near East. The Queen explained shortly that the expedition would have to be subfusc now that she and the family and the country were in complete mourning, but it was to take place, and without delay. It was Papa's wish.

Meekly the Prince had agreed. Only the Grays who, by now, knew him very well indeed, his sister Alice and Lady Churchill, and Fritz, who came over for the funeral, saw the hidden misery.

To Fritz and to no one else he opened his heart, saying he could not bear the double load of guilt which weighed him down. It was bad enough to have been a cause, if only a partial cause, of his father's death, and that was what was being whispered at the Court as the Queen's opinion. Worse was the disgust he felt for himself because he did not seem to feel Papa's death as keenly as everyone else. Though, underneath, he had dearly loved him; for years and years he had found him too staid, and his hard grey eyes too penetrating, to be the companionable Papa of his early childhood; and, once or twice – to his utter horror – he had caught himself feeling relieved he would never have to meet those cold grey eyes again.

Fritz, a much older and wiser man, realized that his brother-in-law's present remorse was unsoothable. It had to smart, and go on smarting until its fire burnt down to a smoulder. He did what he could for Bertie, both in conversations with his mother-in-law, the Queen, and, when he returned home, in writing letters saying tactfully that Bertie did not deserve to be treated as a leper, and in urging Vicky to write letters in her brother's defence. Vicky often did this and with vigour. But the replies which came from Osborne made it clear the Queen was at present unmovable and inflexible. Bertie so grated on her nerves that he must be got out of the way as quickly as possible. Then, equally swiftly, he must take over Marlborough House and Sandringham, and marry Princess Alexandra.

Through private means the Crown Prince and Princess informed Lord Palmerston of what was happening, and, hearing how things were, Lord Palmerston made a brave decision. It was brave because he was in perpetual pain from gout, and he dreaded the rocking of a railway carriage, but he went down to Osborne

72

and saw the Queen for the first time since the Prince Consort's death.

Victoria was surprised to see him, and even more surprised when she heard what he had come to say. Lord Palmerston was frank. He told her that the country and the Ministry were concerned because she and her heir were not getting on, because there was trouble between them.

Briefly she explained the situation. Sitting about was not good for the boy. He would soon be going abroad. Lord Palmerston need not concern himself any further.

16

The Near Eastern trip was valuable to Albert Edward in that it kept him away from his mother.

She was in a desperately melancholy state: disinclined to break the solitude of her widowhood yet determined, as England's sovereign, to stick to her beloved husband's plans whatever happened.

Her Ladies were patient and marvellously understanding, especially Lady Churchill and Lady Augusta Bruce, sister to the Prince of Wales' Governor. So were her family, despite the fact that she clouded their lives with her lowness: Vicky, in Germany, bore the brunt of her mother's misery. Jeremiad after jeremiad poured in from England:

> *Has perhaps Princess Christian heard of the poor, wretched Bertie's miserable escapade – and thinks him a regular 'mauvais sujet'? . . . Oh, the whole thing is so disheartening to me! Alone! to do all this, and with B! If he turns obstinate I will withdraw myself altogether, and wash my hands of him. . . .*

> *Tomorrow is poor dear Lenchen's confirmation; it will be an awful day!*

> *Tell [Fritz] that when he comes for Alice's wretched marriage (which I wish were years off) he will act as my representative. . . .*

Poor dear Alice is very poorly! . . . It is most vexatious and I live
in fear of some further contretemps about that luckless marriage.

Mama's all-enveloping sense of tragedy was quite suffocating.
Bertie was well out of it.

Dr Stanley, Professor of Modern History at Oxford, was chosen
as the Prince of Wales' cicerone on his travels in the Near East.
Selecting him was one thing. Actually prising him out of his
Oxford shell proved extremely difficult. But, at the Queen's insistence, he gave way and surprised himself by enjoying the tour in a
modest way.

He joined the party at Alexandria. The Prince was already in
better spirits, having been entertained in Vienna and Trieste,
paid a furtive visit to Venice and another to Corfu, and shot
wild boar in Albania. General Bruce, too, although feeling his
responsibility as being in overall charge of the expedition, was
benign and tolerant. It was something to be out of England in
February. Professor Stanley felt sure that he would get on with
them both.

The Prince quickly responded to his scholarly air of distraction,
his steaming enthusiasm for antiquities, and what was so obvious,
his sheer goodness. And he showed his affection by politely feign-
ing an interest in what he termed in his journal 'tumbledown old
temples'; and, so as not to offend the Professor's religious scruples,
he limited his Sunday sport to the shooting of crocodiles, which
could be counted as pests. He also showed his affection in typically
boyish ways; provoking the shy Professor into smiling agreement
that a deeply pitted bust of Cleopatra really did resemble the
present Bishop of Oxford, and teasing him into accepting the fair-
ness of sharing their pleasures. In return for the respectful attention he gave to the Professor's lectures he asked that Stanley should
study a book which he himself adored. It was written by a Mrs
Henry Wood, and was entitled *East Lynne*, and astounded Dr
Stanley. For a scholar who regarded researches into the earliest
patristic writings as light enough reading, Mrs Wood's melodrama
was a severe penance. But he felt obliged to make it, and when
he catechized the Prince on ancient monuments, he in turn was
catechized on the deplorable *East Lynne*. 'Now, Professor,' the

74

Prince of Wales would urge. 'Tell me. Who said: "Dead, dead and never called me mother!"?'

General Bruce watched their friendship grow with amusement and pleasure.

Though, unlike the unworldly Dr Stanley, he knew quite well when the Prince was paying attention to a sermon or a lecture and when he was not, and he recognized what never would have occurred to the Professor that their charge was quite capable of slipping off on an escapade if he had the opportunity. But he himself kept a reasonably tight rein on the Prince and he was delighted to see cicerone and pupil get on so well together. He felt, therefore, a moment of anxiety when, on their return to Cairo from an expedition up the Nile, the Professor received news that his mother had died. He feared that Stanley might reasonably ask to be released from his post, but the Professor was sensible as well as stoical about his loss. He decided there was nothing effective he could do from such a distance and that he would remain with the Prince until the end of the tour. Bruce was very relieved.

The party moved on to Palestine, to botanize at leisure – Bertie pressing spring flowers and sending them to his sisters Alice and Vicky – and to shoot abundant game. But the chief purpose of the visit was of course religious and cultural, to see the ruins at Baalbek and the Holy Places of Christendom.

In the course of their excursions the Prince began to impress his cicerone with his talent for remembering names and places. It was a recently developed faculty which no one had yet noticed, and, knowing how valuable it would be to a reigning monarch, Stanley assiduously cultivated it.

Meanwhile letters from his wife in England were beginning to worry the General. People were saying that the Queen suffered brainstorms of melancholy. The old stories of last year, when she had shown such abandoned despair at the death of her mother, were again being whispered. Through a connection, Bruce heard Miss Nightingale's penetrating description of the Queen as 'the woman in the Greek Chorus, with her hands clasped above her head, wailing out her inexpressible despair'.

Bruce was also in touch with the late Prince Consort's Private Secretary Sir Charles Phipps, who now was the Queen's Privy Purse. Phipps was more cheerful than most about the Queen's

75

mental health, but he was not sanguine that she would apply herself as before to Government business. Some business she faced and dealt with out of respect for the known wishes of her dear husband. To others, she applied her own yardstick of what, under the circumstances, her husband might have advised. But it was becoming increasingly clear at Court that, from now on, she had decided to devote less of her energies to public affairs than to intense mourning in private seclusion.

As a result of all he heard, a serious speculation hovered in the General's mind. Should the Queen either abdicate, or lose her reason on account of her loss, the Prince of Wales would succeed, and the boy seemed totally unaware of the possibility. . . .

At their camp in the land of Dan the General took it upon himself to talk seriously with his royal charge. He confided his anxieties about the future, and stressed that the Prince should be ready for any eventuality.

The boy took all this in very slowly, several times asking the General to repeat himself. Then, abruptly, as though the keystone had been knocked upwards from an arch, confidences tumbled from him, frank confidences of his innermost feelings about his mother. . . .

Possibly it was inevitable. Sometimes he had resented the General's authority, his remoteness from his own generation, his interference – as he considered it – into ordinary life, and most of all, his unspoken criticism of any breach of good manners, but the Prince had grown to respect this Governor, and, in a sense, he was searching for a second father. The last few months had taught him to re-evaluate the dapper Grenadier Guardsman who had virtually ruled his life for three years. He was a natural confidant.

Amongst the things which had soured their relationship he mentioned the slippering the Queen had given him before all her Ladies; a type of public punishment which, he added ruefully, had been sharply administered at frequent intervals ever since. He bewailed his own stupidity and his mother's adroitness. He could never anticipate what she wanted or required and, as a result, he knew that he got on her nerves.

But against these scabrous memories there were better ones, the ones he liked to dwell on: memories of Mama on the lawn in her tent at Osborne, working with Papa at the despatch boxes; of

76

Mama taking them to pick strawberries under the gardeners' nets and allowing them to climb the mulberry trees to cram the fruit into their mouths; of Mama and Papa on yachting expeditions and on family excursions in Scotland; of Mama holding his head when he was ill, and comforting him when he met a slithery carpet of toads advancing over the lawns at Osborne in the year of the European revolutions; of Mama's bravery when she had been attacked by that brute with a cane; of her breathless description in the schoolroom eleven years before when gold had been discovered in Australia and California. . . .

The General listened in complete silence. He had thought he was already close to the boy but he had never guessed at these secret memories of childhood which, put together like built-up bricks, made his love for the Queen very real and substantial.

Though he was an undemonstrative man, he put his hands on the boy's shoulders. He was much taller and looked down into his eyes. 'You are absolutely right, Sir,' he muttered. 'Those are the memories to dwell on.'

This gesture of affection and understanding meant a great deal to the Prince. It was a reassurance. From now on, as long as he had such an understanding friend close at hand, things could not go badly at home in England. . . .

In a much happier frame of mind he talked of Marlborough House and Sandringham and Birk Hall on the Balmoral estate, and when he would be allowed to live in these houses. He talked of his marriage – if Princess Alix would have him? – when they should marry if she did? . . .

Then he saw the General's hands were trembling. Concerned, he asked if he was unwell.

Bruce shook his head. 'A touch of fever, perhaps, Sir. Nothing else.' He shivered. 'Nevertheless I admit I should not like to have been a Dannite living in these marshy upper regions of the Jordan. It is pestilent country.'

The General's fever did not improve but it remained low and it in no way interrupted the progress of the tour. The Arabs were ever-courteous but curiously obtuse. As a very special dispensation, the Christian Prince of Wales was permitted to enter the tomb of Abraham, but Sarah's was forbidden him, and, over endless liver-shrinking cups of coffee, Professor Stanley was advised that to penetrate the tomb of Isaac would be diplomatically inadvisable.

77

Nevertheless the party saw a great deal of the country, and the tour continued to Syrian Tripoli for a sight of the cedars of Lebanon, and thence to Constantinople and Greece.

At Athens the people had just driven out their king and were looking for another, but despite the unsettled state of affairs Dr Stanley directed a tour of the classical sights. In fact his head was so full of the glories of classical Greece that he seemed to be quite unaware of the agitations and upheavals going on below the Acropolis. But the General felt the strain. Things by now were too much for him. Though he had rallied well in Turkey the party's physician was concerned by a sudden increase in his fever. He was advised to hand over his responsibilities to Dr Stanley and telegraph for further instructions.

The Prince, who already depended considerably on his newly made confidant, was greatly worried. The General tried to calm him. The physician had assured a more thorough and rapid recovery if he returned separately to England to be nursed by his wife and sister. Carrying on with the royal party to France where the going was bound to be strenuous would only aggravate his condition.

Bertie saw the wisdom of this, though he was loth to say goodbye to his Governor when they sailed for Marseilles. Telegrams had passed between Athens and Windsor. Sir Charles Phipps, though himself far from well, was sent to deputize for the General and look after the Prince of Wales in Paris.

Owing to a stubborn oriental refusal to accept an incognito guest, the Ottoman Sultan had fêted Bertie to a formal and most extravagant breakfast in Constantinople. The Imperial French government showed the same disposition to treat him as heir to the English Crown. But Victoria would not hear of it.

In dear Papa's original plan [she wrote to her daughter in Berlin] *it was intended he should come home through Paris stopping only a day in order to have got over his visit to that Sodom and Gomorrah. . . .*

Once she had loved Paris herself but now, because France's ruler was a roué and she feared his contaminating influence, she extravagantly compared it with the Cities of the Plain. She loaded Sir Charles with memoranda of careful instructions. Points were underscored and underscored again. The Prince of Wales could be received quietly and privately by the Imperial family and buy trinkets and jewels for Princess Alexandra, but anything in the nature of a royal function while he was in deep mourning was out of the question (deeply underscored) and would be unforgivable (in capitals and underscored).

Unfortunately the Queen had forgotten her son's early devotion to the Emperor and Empress and their fondness for him. Naturally they had heard about his affair with Nellie Clifden, and knew that he was in disgrace at Windsor. They realized as well that to vex Victoria by flouting her known wishes would be no help to the boy, but they still wished to give him a good time.

Sir Charles Phipps kept three-quarters of an eye on his charge while he spent several days ostensibly at the British Embassy, and then he allowed himself to be distracted by the Empress, who held an informal soirée at Fontainebleau so that the Prince could meet some of the most attractive young ladies at her Court. In that one evening while the Empress and Sir Charles talked interminably together, the Prince encountered a number of charming women who were to be life-long friends: the Duchesse de Morny and the exquisite Duchesse de Mouchy, the Comtesse de Greffuhle, the Comtesse Edmond de Pourtalès, and, most important of all to him, the fabulously rich and daring and sulky Princesse de Sagan, who lived in splendour, detesting her unfaithful husband, M. le Prince de Sagan, Duc de Talleyrand-Périgord, an elegant dandy of dandies called in Society *Fleur des Pois*.

Sir Charles's eye noted with satisfaction that all the Prince's partners appeared to be married ladies. It was something of a consolation. Not much. But something.

Longing for her affection, Bertie was moved by his mother's welcome home to Windsor. He kissed her hand and her cheek. She returned his embrace.

'Dear boy,' she murmured. 'My dear, dear Bertie.' Her eyes filled with tears. 'Oh, if only your dear, noble father were here to welcome you at my side. . . .'

'If you will permit it, Mama, I should like to help you as he did.'

79

More gently than she would have done before, she rebuked his presumption. 'No one, no one could ever do that.'

Equally gently she asked if he approved of her asking Dr Stanley to remain as his companion and instructor. Eager to please her, he said yes, though he doubted if Stanley would wish to continue his exile from Oxford. This led them to talk of General Bruce, who had re-met the royal party on the coast of France to make a rough and unpleasant crossing with his charge. Bertie spoke highly of him and all he had done on the Eastern tour. The physicians had given a reasonable account of him and he was on the road to recovery, but was still too weak to continue his duties and had gone to his sister's apartments in St James's.

Their cordiality continued. The Queen took a mother's privilege of saying that Bertie looked unshaven. She asked if he intended one day to grow a full beard as Dr Stanley and several members of his suite had done in camp in Palestine. He told her, shyly, that he did; and, in fact, he kept to this resolution. He seldom used a razor in his life.

Then, because it was inevitable – a part of Papa's plan and therefore unalterable – they talked of his marriage. He reddened when, for the first time, she openly mentioned what before she had kept to herself, that she knew about his affair with Nellie Clifden. But his shame turned to irritation when she told him that his uncle Duke Ernest of Saxe-Coburg was strongly against the Danish match, and had somehow made Princess Alexandra's mother aware of what had happened. Apparently, out of sheer bumble-headedness, not malice, Uncle George of Cambridge had let out the same secret. But, said the Queen, he could be forgiven. Uncle Ernest could not. She shared Bertie's indignation. Interference into Papa's plans was not to be tolerated – and certainly not from his mischief-making elder brother who, if the reports were true, hardly led an exemplary life himself.

'He with his beams, to spread tittle-tattle about your mote !' she exclaimed angrily, much to Bertie's surprise.

He agreed with her suggestion that it would now perhaps be prudent for the wife of the British Minister at Copenhagen to confide the secret in Princess Christian with the assurance that there was to be no repetition and it had simply been a boyish scrape. An informal approach from the English Court might undo a little of Uncle Ernest's mischief.

Then they talked of Alice's approaching wedding, an event the Queen dreaded. Bertie, on less sure ground than before, mistakenly tried to help by encouragement. He was sure, he said, that Alice herself would make everything comfortable for her mother, and Louis of Hesse whom she loved so much, was really a most charming man. . . .

His mother interrupted him. She frowned. She raised a finger. She pursed her lips. Alice had been good. There was no denying it. During Papa's illness she had been an angel. But her haste in wishing to get away, to marry and leave her sorrowing mother, seemed almost indecent. At best it was inconsiderate. Had it not been beloved Papa's plan that she should marry in July, nothing on earth would have prevailed on her to permit it. The marriage was bound to be depressing. And as for Louis of Hesse. It was perplexing now to think what Alice saw in him. He had been writing her over-familiar letters, was far less refined in his manner than before, and his parents had been behaving outrageously over their future home. Moreover, continued the Queen, she feared that unless he was told not to, he would be bringing Alice into contact with his officer friends who so unfortunately lacked delicacy of feeling and conduct.

Bertie attempted to put in a word for Louis, for whom he had a genuine admiration, but this made things worse.

The Queen frowned: 'Contradictory,' she snapped. 'You were contradictory from the cradle. Contradictory. Laddle always said it.'

Bertie somehow got away without raising Mama's temper any further, but he was suddenly and acutely depressed.

He wished that he could have talked to the General about it. Sir Charles Phipps was a good and kind man, but he did not yet know him. A stranger could not be expected to be understanding. For consolation he turned to Alice, but Alice, though overjoyed to see her dearest Bertie, was in a state. She who had hardly ever grumbled before was now heaped with complaints. Mama had done this, and Mama had done that. . . .

Then quite unexpectedly came the news that General Bruce was dead.

To make and lose a close friend in such a short time was inexpressibly painful to the Prince of Wales. Never without supervision and attendants, willing and anxious for the most part to be at his beck and call, Bertie's life had nevertheless been a lonely one. General Bruce in the past few weeks had been rather like a ghost from the past – a reflection of Henry Mildred Birch. As a result, his death had a considerable effect upon the Prince.

He begged his mother to honour the General's memory by taking his widow into her own Household and for years after he was her constant correspondent. Resignedly he accepted General Bruce's replacement – another General, Sir William Knollys, who was his Comptroller and principal Private Secretary but, until he was twenty-one, was to have all the powers of a Governor: being responsible to the Queen and to Phipps, her Privy Purse, for all that the Prince did.

He did point out that he would have preferred to have had a younger Private Secretary, one closer to his own generation, and added wryly that while his particular friend the fifty-nine-year-old General Bruce had been in charge of him as a child, it was a shade unfair to give him a Private Secretary who was sixty-five to look after him as a man.

But his mother paid no attention. Papa would have wished it. Of that she was certain.

Very well then. Bertie accepted the appointment – and, as it turned out he never ceased to be grateful for all Knollys and Knollys' family was to do for him – but at first he was truculent and then he snapped when Mama announced that she considered it proper to familiarize the new Private Secretary with every detail of the Curragh affair. In fact, for the first time since he had grown up he actually lost his temper with his mother, but, with something – an indefinable air of authority, her autocratic personality, something – she crushed him, and he left her sitting-room feeling like a little boy.

Later he recovered his spirits sufficiently to defy her known wishes and went off to sulk by himself at Birk Hall, his property in Scotland, and afterwards he showed a determined measure of independence in moving backwards and forwards between Sandringham and Marlborough House.

Sandringham he loved. He liked the winter coldness, the wide expanse of sky, the firm sand blowing south from the North Sea. For the first time he tried out the estate's shooting potentials and found them capable of great improvement. He was the son of his mother in that he had a strong distaste for the press and enjoyed a brush with reporters. When a prying reporter from King's Lynn insinuated himself amongst the beaters he was quickly detected, but, as the Prince wrote to Mrs Bruce – *'I very nearly shot him in the legs as a rabbit was passing, and he very soon gave me a wide berth!'* He considered Sandringham House comfortable but too small. Already he felt he must have people about him, a great number of people. His liking for company was expanding with the increase of his energies. The house would have to be rebuilt on a much larger scale.

The Prince also was very fond of his London house, where Dr Stanley's researches proved an unending source of interest.

Marlborough House – a grateful country's gift of a town house to the great John Churchill – had been built on what was once the pheasantry of St James's. The Prince liked to refer to it by this deflating name. 'Come,' he would say to Stanley. 'Let us go to the Pheasantry to see how the restorers are getting on.'

Since the Prince Consort's decision to prepare Marlborough House for his son a great deal had had to be done. The place had been shut up when Queen Adelaide died there a dozen years before and it had fallen into shocking disorder. The grounds had become a jungle, the lawns overgrown and scattered with broken bottles and refuse, and the interior was in as bad a state. In the clearing and repairing a remarkable discovery had been made: that the walls of the two great staircases and the Grand Saloon were decorated with frescoes by Louis Laguerre. Moreover they were some of his best work; exquisite representations of all the Duke of Marlborough's battles and sieges. A careful restoration work, ripping off the canvas, paint, paper and panelling with which the frescoes had been covered, was still in process. It was interesting to

watch, the more so as Dr Stanley had an unusual power of narra-
tive and could make the frescoes come even more alive by
describing precisely what was depicted.

The Prince's Pheasantry had many other attractions, but the
one he enjoyed most at that time – perhaps on account of his
present misunderstandings with Mama – were the house's
historical associations. It was there that, after her bitter quarrel
with Queen Anne, Duchess Sarah had shown what she thought of
her sovereign. On Levée days she and her daughters had lolled
out of the upper windows in outrageous négligées, to demonstrate
their contempt for Court and Queen.

The Prince's relationship with the Queen was not a happy one.
Like the major part of an iceberg, it had to be mostly hidden, yet
it was obvious to those close to the centre of the Court that the
Queen was determined to keep her heir in his place, and she was
continually vexing him by making decisions about his future with
small or no reference to his own wishes.

In an unusually bitter burst of frankness to Dr Stanley, the
Prince said that had she been the plainest, most disreputable and
unprepossessing princess in Europe, he would have been married
off, willy-nilly, to Alexandra of Denmark: at which the Doctor
smiled and nodded his new spade beard and said that it was as
well, then, that Princess Alexandra happened to be very beautiful,
charming and of impeccable character. It restored the Prince's
good humour. He realized that in every sense he was a lucky man,
and he longed for an early marriage so that he would be entirely
free from his mother's influence and her doleful Court and so that
his desires for the bewitching, fascinating Princesse de Sagan and
the spectre of little Nellie, who still beckoned from where Charles
Carrington had set her up, would for ever be stilled.

But everything had to go at Mama's pace and at Mama's
direction.

Alice's wedding took place quietly in the Osborne dining-room,
on 1 July, 1862, and, as anyone could have prophesied, it was
overladen with gloom. But Bertie saw that Alice was happy. She
was concealing it for her mother's sake. She undertook to return
to England to have her first child – for the Queen supposed that
'poor, wretched Alice' would be subjected to Louis' gross appetites
without delay. And Alice's parting was a sorrowful one indeed.
Bertie realized that she was no longer pretending. She was

genuinely fond of her mother and did not like to leave her in her depressed state. But to be away from the sobs and the widow's weeds and the constant reference to what Papa might or might not have wished . . . To be away, and with her Louis, whom she clearly adored.

Bertie kissed her and wished her well. He would miss her sadly. She would always be his favourite sister. But he was glad, for her sake, to see her go.

Events proceeded. The Queen was living beneath the Cypress Branch but her vigour had returned. She needed it, dealing with all affairs in the Albert way. She had vetoed the Greeks' election of Affie to their throne. He was too immature. Moreover, like wretched Bertie, he had had a 'fall'. Had she bred a pair of lechers? She was frantic at this reappearance of Hanoverian high-living. Her chief consolation was Beatrice – asking the quaintest things, poor orphan Baby, if for example, her chicken at luncheon had been salted with Lot's wife. And there was Vicky, of course, to whom she unburdened herself in a stream of confidential letters about the most intimate matters. Amongst them were Bertie's affairs.

It was arranged by the Queen that her son's betrothal should taken place at Laeken in Belgium, under the eye of Uncle Leopold. The King of the Belgians was by now seventy-two and very unwell, but he was delighted to offer hospitality for such a purpose, and fell in with his niece's plans. Prince and Princess Christian, with their daughters, were staying at an hotel in Ostend and were invited to Laeken to meet the Queen of England. Travelling as Countess of Balmoral, the Queen arrived there herself on 2 September. She found that Prince and Princess Christian hardly matched up to her standards and Princess Dagmar she ignored. But she was very impressed indeed by Princess Alexandra. Two days later, pronouncing herself entirely satisfied, she left for Coburg where there was to be a large family meeting. On the same day, by pre-arrangement, the Danish family went to Ostend.

Exactly twenty-four hours later, the Prince of Wales arrived at Ostend. On 9 September he proposed in Uncle Leopold's grotto at Laeken, and immediately celebrated the betrothal by taking Alix to see the site of another English victory, the Field of Waterloo.

Photographs were taken. Telegraphs and letters despatched.

85

I frankly avow to you [wrote Bertie to his mother] *that I did not think it possible to love a person as I do her. She is so kind and good, and I feel sure will make my life a happy one.*

He followed his letter to Coburg. There, where the Thuringian forests met the Coburg plain, and the ducal castle of Reinhardts-Brunnen as well as the summer palace at Rosenau were full of his relations, he was told by his mother that Alexandra was a dear, sweet girl and he was a very lucky man. Evidently Mama, on her own account, was greatly in favour of the engagement.

So, of course, was Vicky who had engineered it, or tried to, from the very beginning.

She and Bertie walked together beside the storks' nests of Rosenau. 'The sight of them,' she teased, 'should bring you many children.'

He admitted he was very content to be engaged to Alix; far more so than he had truly expected. 'She was good,' he muttered, 'to overlook my disgrace.'

Vicky clapped her hands at this and called him a goose. 'All her life she has lived close to the Amalienborg Palace – the most shocking and sauciest court in Europe. She is a dear innocent, Bertie, but not ignorant.' She told him that Alix was already very much attached to him and advised him on how best to win her lasting devotion.

When he admitted how much he longed for the release that marriage would bring him, she warned him that he could never be free in the sense that other people are free. 'You are lucky not to be in Prussia. Our Court is so stiff. So correct. The protocol is absurd and drives anyone with imagination into frenzies. At least in England you will have some freedom, but you can never ever have the freedom of a private person, not even,' she added – as here she quizzed him with a faint smile on her face, 'not even with Madame la Princesse de Sagan.'

He coloured and would have said something, but she held her finger to his lips. 'Not a thing escapes our present ambassador in France. He is inhuman. Watch out for him. His name is Bismarck.'

Mama's decrees went out.

Alix – she had got over her first objection to the abbreviation of Alexandra – was to be schooled by her in private at Osborne and Windsor during the autumn.

Meanwhile, because engaged couples were better kept apart, Bertie would travel with Fritz and Vicky on a Mediterranean cruise.

The engagement would be a short one. Long ones were ridiculous and impractical.

On his return from the Mediterranean Bertie would be allowed to see his fiancée for a short visit – but it must be short.

The marriage would take place on the anniversary of her own wedding, February 10th.

The marriage would not be in London. She herself could not bear to appear in public at St Paul's or the Abbey. It would be solemnized at Windsor in St George's Chapel.

Even there she would not make a public appearance. She and her ladies would observe the ceremony as sad and silent witnesses from the hidden recesses of Catherine of Aragon's Closet.

The honeymoon would last fourteen days and would take place at Osborne House.

Being a determined woman herself and having bred nine determined children, the Queen's arbitrary decisions met with surprisingly little criticism from the family. True, Princess Mary Adelaide tactfully conveyed the Rumpenheim displeasure at Alexandra being inspected by her future mother-in-law like a prime heifer – and few people had more charm and powers of persuasion than she – but the Queen played a trick she had often used on complaining ministers, and checkmated the Rumpenheimers by totally agreeing with their views and totally disregarding them. It was also true that the disreputable King of Denmark sent the Queen a message to say he rejoiced to hear the marriage was to be held in England which held the implication that it was more usual for a bride to be married in her own country. Victoria was furious. Anger making her pepper the letter with exclamation marks, she wrote to her eldest daughter:

How impertinent. No answer will be given.

And then someone in the family daringly suggested to the Queen that Alix herself might wish to postpone the date, and was immediately snubbed with the practical reminder that if Alix was soon to conceive a child, it was better for her to have her lying-in the following spring. Vicky, who had given birth to her second son that August, had already received a piece of Mama's mind for carrying a child in hot weather:

Spring [she had been told] *is the only bearable time for these 'campaigns' and except four – all of you were spring flowers.*

The Queen was determined that her first daughter-in-law should not suffer on account of any ill-timed 'campaigns'.

As it turned out, Mama's plans were generally acceptable.

Rather than fidget and fret in this time of waiting, Bertie was pleased to use a royal yacht and travel in the Mediterranean, and Vicky and Fritz were not at all averse to escaping temporarily from Berlin. Like the Prince Consort, Fritz and Vicky were liberals who longed to unite the states of Germany by 'moral conquests'. And, quite without warning, the very worst had happened. The acute ambassador Vicky had mentioned to Bertie had been recalled from Paris to be made Chancellor of Prussia, and Bismarck was almost a caricature of the Prussian autocrat. He had brushed aside any thought of 'moral conquests', announcing that the great question of German unification would be decided 'by iron and blood'. Fritz and Vicky longed to get away for a time. Queen Victoria's plan made it possible.

Affie, nettled at the many lectures he had been given all that summer, was glad that Mama's mind could be occupied with other matters than his grievous 'fall'. Alice, who was herself carrying a child, and expected to present it to Mama as a spring flower at only a little time after Bertie's marriage, was also to be in England during Alix's visit – and looked forward to assisting in the process of making her into a non-political Princess of Wales and ironing out her Danishness. Bertie's other sisters – still in the schoolroom – were delighted at the thought of the arrival of a fresh face at Court.

Alix herself would have found life at Windsor and Osborne somewhat unnerving had it not been for them and especially Helena, with whom she struck up a great friendship, and Bertie's little brother, the haemophiliac Leopold. Affie was also at home at irregular intervals and then there was a good deal of what he called skylarking. Already he adored his prospective sister-in-law, and teased her by saying it was polite to ask the Queen each afternoon 'Have you enjoyed your forty-winks?' Gravely Victoria said yes she had, but on the third afternoon pointed out that such idiomatic language really would not do. She was alert already to Affie's devotion to Alexandra; and wondered if she had been wrong to veto Vicky's half-serious suggestion that Alix's sister, Dagmar, might do well for him. Certainly she regretted preventing him from accepting election to the throne of Greece. It would have kept him right out of harm's way. She confided her mild anxieties to his Governor, and kept a strict eye on all he said and did when he was at home. For Alix there was the excitement of a visit from Princess Mary Adelaide who arrived at Windsor to help plan the trousseau. It was a marvellous business; awesome to Alix, who calculated that her trousseau alone would cost more than her father's whole annual income. Most of it was to be made in England, but the lingerie was to be sent from Denmark, each piece embroidered with the initial 'A' and the royal crown of England.

Massive, merry Mary – as Affie affectionately called her – enjoyed herself a great deal, and was not in the least put out when the Queen made it clear that Alix was simply to be a Princess of Wales with no political affiliations at all. She was *not* to be the tool of the Rumpenheimers in general and the Cambridge family in particular. 'But of course! of course! of course! of course!' exclaimed her cousin Mary Adelaide in her most non-reassuring tone of voice, and oblivious to politics, returned to the delightful consideration of millinery, tailoring and finery of all kinds.

Alix had some leisure, but not very much, to keep pace with the delights planned for her by her new English family. She had serious work to do, her life being mapped out from dawn to dusk. She read English with Mrs Bruce, wrote English with the latest of the royal tutors, whose surname Ogg she found difficult to pronounce without introducing an insulting aspirate; also, surprisingly, she wrote English with the Princess' French governess, and she drew with the Queen's own drawing-master Mr Leitch. Careful walks, rides, early to bed and to rise, and determined not to mind the shadow of the Cypress Branch which overhung everything, Alix completely captivated her future mother-in-law. The good impression she had made at Laeken solidified into a loving regard. It was a pity, the Queen wrote, that the girl's mother's family was so disreputable, and she feared that Prince Christian was 'not very bright', but she was captivated by Alix, and exceedingly put out when her parents suddenly said she must be at home in the Yellow Palace for her eighteenth birthday. Such presumption!

While Alix's Englishing was taking place, Bertie was enjoying himself with his sister and brother-in-law. Sir William Knollys was there, of course, but already, by firmness and by the politeness taught him by General Bruce, the Prince had established a degree of independence which his elderly Comptroller sympathized with and respected. On general matters he corresponded directly with his mother; the more important business between them was effected by Knollys and the Queen's Private Secretary, General Grey.

But most of the correspondence during that time went on between those two indefatigable letter-writers, the Queen and her eldest daughter.

Vicky heard all about Alix's schooling at the English Court and gave a full account of their own travels: how they had been accompanied to Vesuvius' smoking craters by squads of tramping bersaglieri, how they visited the Blue Groto on Capri and she and Fritz and Knollys were drenched, how in Malta she had actually encountered Mama's half sister-in-law, Princess Leiningen, who had once eloped with an Englishman named Mr Spare and had then been cruelly humiliated when he married her own maid; how, on their return to Naples, Bertie had celebrated his twenty-first birthday and had been thrilled both with the fact that he could now take personal supervision of his hereditary apanage – estates which brought him at least £60,000 a year in addition to his Parliamentary grants – and equally thrilled with Mama's decision to make him a full general; how squalid and flea-ridden Rome was, after the salubrious south – Vicky had actually seen a monk blow his nose into an umbrella, so it was scarcely to be wondered that in such surroundings the Prussian minister to the Vatican had suddenly gone dotty, and could only be observed by his poor wife by irregular peeps through the keyhole of his room. . . .

Bertie left the party in Rome. Vicky and Fritz were to continue the journey until Christmas – not anxious to return to Bismarck's

Prussia – but Bertie had two duties to perform. One was pleasurable: seeing Alix and her parents in Dieppe and staying in their company two days as they travelled home – though he was forbidden to 'set foot' in Denmark where being 'so weak' his mother feared he would become embroiled with Princess Christian's awful relations – 'and that would never do'. The second was grim: observing the first anniversary of his father's death and then the transfer of his remains from the Windsor tombstone to the newly made mausoleum.

The Queen was exceedingly angry to hear from Vicky that she and Fritz would actually be travelling on the 'sacred day'. She sent a stern direction by telegraph to them at Venice

SPEND 14TH TRAVELLING FROM TRIESTE TO VIENNA IN STRICT INCOGNITO

– and she complained to her eldest son that at least they might have arranged for their carriage to have been backed into a railway siding for the day.

On the 14th December the Blue Room at Windsor where the Prince Consort had died was decked with flowers. His bust, surrounded by wreaths, was on his bed. Memorial services were held there for all the family and Household at 9.45, noon and again at 9.30 p.m. On the 17th the mausoleum was consecrated. Again attendance was compulsory. On the 18th the Queen and her children were present when the Prince Consort's coffin was placed in a sarcophagus.

Victoria was brave, but clearly deeply distressed. Bertie made no attempt to hide his tears. A year. Only a year. To him it seemed as if ten at least had passed since those grey eyes had closed for ever; ten years since he had seen Papa's most faithful servants place his stiff body in a coffin and carry it to the dressing-room already prepared with drapes of black cloth and drugget. Unlike his mother, who was resolved to remember everything, he would have preferred to forget the smaller, painful memories; but he knew that he never could.

18

In varying degrees of calmness the royal family had accepted Mama's arrangements for the marriage of her heir.

Naturally there were exceptions, notably a protest from the Grand Duchess of Mecklenburg-Strelitz, who was Princess Mary Adelaide's elder sister and who wished to know why, as a Princess of the Blood, she had not been invited to the wedding. She was not in the least appeased by Victoria's curious rejoinder that neither had the Hanoverian cousins been invited, nor any of Princess Christian's family at all. . . .

On the whole the Queen's family were content, but her subjects were far less amenable to her plans. The press, for which she had a particular and barely hidden abhorrence, was positively hostile. The loathed *Punch*, which had been so ungenerous to Albert, expressed the indignation felt by many people because so important a ceremony was being held 'in an obscure Berkshire village, noted only for an old castle with no sanitary arrangements'. The Queen felt herself hedgehogged with undeserved criticism and especially resented the suggestion that as the marriage was a simple one it should be announced as such in the columns of *The Times*:

> On the 10th inst., at Windsor, by Dr. Longley, assisted by Dr. Thomson, Albert Edward England K.G. to Alexandra Denmark. No cards.

On the day this was printed Lady Churchill used all her persuasion to calm the Queen, but met with small success. The Maids of Honour in waiting had the worst twelve hours of their lives. The unbelievable happened: a dish was condemned and returned to the royal kitchen with a tart message from the Queen. Servants quailed. Members of the Household melted away when they heard their mistress approaching. The royal children scuttled to schoolroom and nursery and stayed there.

It was almost as bad when the Established Church – *her*

Church as she liked to think it until someone had the courage to point out she was not its head and never had been – when her Church protested through the Archbishops because the chosen date fell in Lent, and set a bad example to her people who generally avoided that time. Lent! *Lent!* The Queen's robust unorthodoxy and indifference to the rules of the Church were well known. No matter what Canterbury said she would and she did communicate in the Church of Scotland. And it was not her fault that the date of the wedding fell in Lent. She had wished it to be on the anniversary of her own marriage, 10 February, and only a crowd of milliners and tailors and confectioners had forced the postponement to 14 March. Exceedingly angry with this unexpected and impertinent protest, she launched a broadside at her old enemies, bigotry, Roman Catholicism, and the British aristocracy which had never taken to her beloved Albert.

The objection rests merely on fancy on prejudice and on one in this case based on no very elevated view of one of God's holiest Ordinances. . . . [The Queen] would be very glad of an opportunity of breaking through a custom only in use among the higher classes and which she can't help considering as very Catholic. . . . Marriage is a solemn holy act not to be classed with amusements.

The Archbishop shuddered at her horrid unorthodoxy, but at once gave way. In the middle of Lent it should be.

Stirred up by this opposition, the Queen took the opportunity to give Bertie an extra warning or two. She did not do it directly, nor through the medium of their Private Secretaries, but chose to send for Lord Granville who led the Ministry in the House of Lords. A man of great political influence, highly respected by the late Prince Consort and by the Queen, and with a wide circle of friends, Granville made an impressive messenger boy. He bore his message tactfully for, unlike any others, he saw good in the Prince of Wales and they were on excellent terms. For the moment, he said evenly, the Queen had decided there was no need for the Prince of Wales to trouble himself with the societies and commissions over which his father had presided. Let him enjoy a year's marriage as a free bridegroom. And then he deliberately translated the Queen's strongly worded commands into a polite request. After the marriage, he said, would their Royal Highnesses be content not to go out to dinners and parties during the London Season, and restrict their social lives to occasional visits to the houses of higher-ranking ministers? and to a few of the very great houses like Apsley, Grosvenor and Spencer Houses?

Why yes, replied the Prince with a gracious smile, if it could be arranged, he and his bride would restrict themselves in just such a fashion – if it could be arranged. . . .

Granville smiled, too; and he accepted a glass of chilled hock, which was not really his drink; and saw the frescoes in Marlborough House; and heard the tale of how Duchess Sarah and her daughters had snubbed the Queen with their scandalous display of négligée, and went home chuckling to himself. As well expect a turtle to walk on its oval back as change that young man. Albert Edward was great-nephew to Prinny, and Sailor William, to the outrageous Duke of York and the infamous Cumberland. He was his mother's son. . . .

By the beginning of March London was decorated with triumphal arches for the Princess' short ride through the capital on her way to Windsor, and the Prince of Wales was in such a tense state of nerves that Carrington and Cadogan and Natty Rothschild and the young Duke of Sutherland and others of his friends had much of their time taken up in keeping him occupied and out of mischief. He had the most extraordinary energy, and was for ever rushing off here and there – to arrange things, look at things, do things – sometimes as H.R.H., more often incognito. Not a minute of the day, and few of the night, were left unused. If he sat down, he could not relax. If he slept, he barely rested.

He ended by working himself into such a state that, when the bridal party arrived at Gravesend, he was actually late at the quayside where the royal yacht had docked. In a high state of excitement he rushed about and quite informally kissed Princess Alexandra in the full view of thousands of his mother's subjects. They were delighted and roared their approval. He then greeted Alexandra's family; her father and mother, her brothers Frederick and William and Waldemar and her sisters Dagmar and Thyra. Waldemar was the youngest, being only five. He had been given a toy donkey to keep him quiet, and solemnly offered it to General

Knollys when the Prince presented the members of the Household. The Comptroller, with equal solemnity accepted the gift, and passed it to the Prince's Groom of the Stole. With grave and courteous expressions of thanks the donkey travelled via the Private Secretary, two Lords and two Grooms of the Bedchamber, the Librarian and General Knollys' son, Francis, before Waldemar seized it back again.

Alix had been sent details of the itinerary long before, but there was Bertie nervously plucking at his collar and explaining what was to happen and exactly when: that from the quayside they would first take a train and afterwards ride in state through London by royal carriage.

He looked at Knollys. Were they ready to entrain? They were.

Solemnly the Prince and his Household, the bridal party and their suite went down the gangplank and, to the cheers and roars of the spectators, took a train to Southwark.

All along the line were people waving. Houses, farm buildings, lamp-posts even haystacks were decorated with welcoming flags and bunting. At the Bricklayers' Arms Station where the carriage procession was to begin, the station was festooned with orange blossom and greenery, and outside, stamping in the cold air, were the horses which were to draw the royal carriages, and the escort of Life Guards with plumed helmets, shiny breastplates, and huge jet topboots, each as stiff as a ramrod on his charger.

To their chagrin the Queen had decreed that her children must wait to receive the Princess with her at Windsor. Therefore only her cousins were on the route to Paddington to wave a welcome to their fellow Rumpenheimers.

George of Cambridge had inherited Gloucester House from his Aunt Gloucester, and he and his mother and sister, and the ubiquitous Lady Geraldine with pencil poised over journal to describe the scene, waited to see Bertie and Alix and her family drive by. Wherever 'Fat Mary' appeared at the window the Londoners cried out and halloed and showed their fondness for her, and when Alix, as she drove past, saw the Cambridge party and blew them kisses, the uproar was tremendous.

Lady Geraldine's pencil flew. The official arrangements had been anything but satisfactory, the shabbiness, *extraordinary shabbiness* of the royal equipages had caught the eye, and because of friction between the City of London and the Metropolitan police, the crowds were not properly kept in order – in fact, at one point people swarmed round the first royal carriage hoping to touch the bride and many people were crushed and a way had to be cleared by the Life Guards with the flat of their sabres.

There was an even more hazardous moment, which Lady Geraldine knew nothing about, when an officer's charger took fright and by plunging and kicking managed to get its hoof in the rear wheel of the first royal carriage. There could have been an ugly accident. Bertie whitened. Princess Christian involuntarily gave a small shriek. But Alexandra herself saved the moment. Never frightened of horses, she leant out of the carriage and extracted the hoof.

Dressed in grey silk, with a violet jacket trimmed with sable and wearing a white bonnet with red rosebuds, the Danish princess went to the heart of the crowds. It was bitterly cold. She had to endure seven miles of incessant bowing to the crowds in London alone. She could not have been very comfortable. She was about to leave all that was familiar. But she won everyone's hearts.

Princess Mary Adelaide, bursting with pride – for had it not been at the back of her mind since Bertie had rowed upriver on summer evenings to visit them at Kew? – threw kisses and almost herself from the windows of Gloucester House.

Lady Geraldine wrote:

Charming *she was! bowing so prettily, so gracefully, right and left incessantly; winning* all *hearts.*

Tennyson, the Poet Laureate, had also contributed loyally to the occasion. His verses of greeting were scattered in broadsheets, flying on the cold wind, kicked up by the horses, trodden underfoot by the crowds, some kept for years afterwards to remember the arrival of Princess Alexandra.

> *Come to us, love us and make us your own:*
> *For Saxon or Dane or Norman are we,*
> *Teuton or Celt; or whatever we be,*
> *We are each all Dane in our welcome of thee,*
> *Alexandra.*

Trains from Paddington to Slough. Another procession and escort. More crowds. In darkness and sleeting rain to the castle, then to meet all her new brothers and sisters and Fritz the Crown Prince of Prussia, and that little figure in widow's weeds who was now to be Mama. . . .

It was a trying, hectic time for all of them, especially the Queen, the Prince and the bride. On the day before the wedding the bridal couple was taken to the Mauseoleum where, in the presence of Papa's remains, their hands were joined together.

'It was his wish, His design.'

The marriage was a wonder of colour after eighteen months of strict mourning. Half-mourning was permitted to the ladies – purple, mauves or white. The gentlemen were as gay as bantam cocks in their uniforms. Bertie especially – in the full dress uniform of a general beneath the mantle of the Garter.

Alexandra should have been wearing a dress of exquisite Brussels lace, the gift of ageing Uncle Leopold, but, sensitive to the feelings of her people, Victoria had commanded that she wear an English dress. This, too, was exquisite, silver tissue trimmed with Honiton lace, and, as was to be expected, she drew almost everyone's attention. But the sorrowing Queen, though apart, partly hidden, dressed still in the black she could never discard, was still at the centre of everything.

Bertie could feel it as he stood at the Altar with his bride at his side.

He pressed Alexandra's arm. She returned the pressure.

He looked up at Mama and he smiled because now he was free.

PART TWO

PART TWO

1

After a fortnight's secluded honeymoon at Osborne, surrounded by clipped evergreens and abundant memorials of the dead Prince Consort, the Prince and Princess of Wales returned to Marlborough House and there began a social reign which was to last for nearly fifty years.

1863 was the most brilliant London season ever known; at the head of it a young and attractive and apparently tireless couple who made the four months into a continuous Cinderella's ball.

At the recommendation of George of Cambridge the Prince of Wales had been given certain appropriate appointments in the Army. He was made Regimental Colonel of the 10th Hussars, and Captain-General and Colonel of the H.A.C., and so was able to indulge his liking for wearing uniforms. Under the discreet direction of his tailor, Poole, he also set modes in civilian dress which were quickly copied. This, too, gave him the highest feelings of satisfaction. Then, pressed by her family, the Queen permitted him to take a Levée and a Drawing Room on her behalf, which he did with great seriousness and greatly enjoyed. All his life he was to attach much importance to Court protocol and the desirability of exact ceremonial.

Princess Alexandra was more than content. After the limitations imposed on her by her family's strict economies, and the fustiness of life at the Yellow Palace, Bernstorff and Rumpenheim, the glitter of her first London season, at the side of a prince who was so self-assured and composed, seemed quite unbelievable. She felt like a liberated spirit.

All her worst apprehensions had subsided. Her father had warned her that the English were a very odd people with a European reputation for arrogance. To illustrate this point, he told her

101

the cautionary tale of a travelling Englishman so choleric and so haughty that in a dispute over a railway carriage seat he had belaboured people with his stick and was at that very moment in a Bonn prison. Yet since her arrival she had met with nothing but kindness from her husband's people.

The Princess had also expected to be lonely, for the Queen had not been very obliging about Danish attendants. But she quickly made devoted friends in a small circle. There was Princess Mary Adelaide, of course, and Princess Helena (whom she learnt, after the family habit, to call Lenchen). And there was Lady Macclesfield, her Lady of the Bedchamber, and the Prince's Comptroller's daughter, Charlotte Knollys, together with other members of the Prince's Household and a number of his friends. Amongst the later she was particularly attached to Charles Wood, one of the original seven Etonians who had gone to the Windsor tea parties to be bullied by Bertie or tremble beneath the gaze of his austere father. She and Wood were both serious about their religion, and both inclined towards what the Queen thought 'so bad for the Upper Classes', High Churchmanship, and he became her close friend. But the circle of her real friends was exclusive, and therefore it seemed to the enchanted public that everyone in England was her friend.

The crowds adored her and she managed their adulation beautifully and was equally successful in accepting the warm regard of English Society without letting it go to her head. This was not because she was naturally humble, but because she was rather absent-minded, and, with the charm of forgetful, easily distracted people, she found in each succeeding pleasure a new surprise. She had also caught from her mother the habit of the near-deaf who, fearful that they have missed something important in a conversation, frequently use beaming goodwill as a precautionary measure.

Alexandra had also expected to be homesick, but letter writing kept her in touch with the intimate details of family life in Denmark, and, for the rest, she simply did not have time for nostalgia. As she told her sister Dagmar, she was in a state of constant suspension, like an emulsion of oil and water, shaken all the time by event after event and never given time to settle.

She became devoted to her husband, and he to her. He so frankly worshipped her that she found his possessiveness a little stifling and a little embarrassing; but she was proud and not in the least abashed when the time came to tell him that in the following March she hoped to present him with a son.

All this time – at Windsor and Osborne, Balmoral and Osborne again, the Queen read her newspapers and wrote anxious letters and kept a sharp and not altogether happy eye on what was going on in London.

Since the Prince Consort's death she had attributed the lowering of moral standards in the kingdom to the loss of his influence for good. In this possibly she deceived herself. His own private code of behaviour had permeated everyone close to him, yet though his political influence had been strong – and of great use to England – the British aristocracy had refused to accept him socially and had gone its own way, never losing its taste for high living in the Regency style.

Albert himself, a model of chastity and monogamy, had not been totally lacking in understanding of those who were unlike him. Yet he had been concerned by the goings-on of the Manchester Set, as it was called, a group of the highest members of Society whose lives were a partially open scandal. It had gained its name from Louisa, Duchess of Manchester, who, on her arrival as a bride from Germany in 1852, had set herself up as a leader in Society, gone on the ran-tan ever since, and enjoyed herself very much indeed. She had even vamped Lord Derby and wheedled from him a promissory note that if he ever became Prime Minister he would appoint her Mistress of the Robes, and so, willy-nilly, the Queen had one day found herself being served by this unprincipled duchess in one of the grandest offices at Court. It had been mortifying, to say the least, to endure the company of one who did such dreadful, unladylike things; who had actually gone so far as to torment an adoring admirer, the Duc de Malakoff, by scaling a stile in a crinoline, and tripping deliberately so that she landed with hoop and petticoats over her head, revealing her nether parts clothed in a pair of her husband's scarlet, tartan knickerbockers.

It was either the promissory note, or that story of the scarlet knickerbockers – one or the other – which made the Queen refuse to invite her to the wedding of the Prince of Wales, an unprecedented slight to a former Mistress of the Robes. Now she was

103

very glad she had taken such a step because that fast and un-squashable duchess had recently been struggling with the notorious Skittles Walters for possession of the Whig parliamentarian Lord Hartington, and he – poor, weak vessel – forced to decide between a woman years younger than himself and a woman years older, had been driven to escape by looking in on the American Civil War. He had returned to make a handsome settlement on Skittles and choose Louisa Manchester, which was all very shocking – but at least they were consistently distant and respectful enough to one another in public. The duchess was called Lottie by her friends, and Hartington was always Harty-Tarty, yet Victoria understood that in their relationship they were never overtly familiar and addressed each other correctly by their titles. Their intimacy was not glaringly offensive, and at least was less flagrant than the open scandals of the day.

It appeared that many of the aristocracy either no longer cared about discretion or thought more of themselves than of family honour; that injured parties were no longer behaving with proper restraint. So much discreditable behaviour was made public simply because people went to law, and things which should have been decently covered up were repeated word for word by the press.

The Queen was appalled when she read in a newspaper that the Joint Hereditary Grand Chamberlain of England had dis-graced himself by stealing thousands of pounds from his French mistress and running off with her maid; when she read that the Earl of Wicklow had died in a brothel and that Lady Wicklow had actually tried to pass off their adopted child as his next of kin; when she read that Lord Euston, heir to the Dukedom of Grafton, had married a most unsavoury bigamist and could not rid himself of her because her first supposed husband turned out to have been a bigamist as well....

Seeing these things in print made them seem so much more fearful.

At one time the Queen herself had enjoyed a little circumspect tittle-tattle with her Aunt Gloucester who had been an eccentric, bawdy old lady; and she never lost her taste for saucy gossip; but, really, these present scandals, printed in indecent detail all over the pages of *The Times* – a newspaper she particularly abhorred – were rather too much.

Worst of all, as she read *The Times*, or had it read to her by Jane Churchill or another intimate – because, under no circumstances could she expect the Maids of Honour to sully their innocence by learning of such shameful affairs – the Queen began to understand that a good many of these disgraceful people were actually friends of Bertie and Affie.

This hurt and alarmed her.

She had a list of her sons' friends prepared for her inspection and studied it with growing concern.

There was nothing, of course, disreputable about the Rothschilds, but they were orthodox Jews and in commerce and not at all suitable company for princes. Then there was Lord Carrington. She neither liked nor trusted him. 'Get rid of him while you can,' she urged her son. 'It will be more difficult if you ever come to the throne.' She also begged him to give up the Duke of Sutherland although his mother the Dowager Duchess was one of her most intimate friends. Young Sutherland was extravagant, a profligate, and an eccentric, and he and Bertie had the shameful practice of rushing off with the London Fire Brigade to help douse fires if they happened to be free when the alarm went out. She was especially grave in her warning about Sutherland: 'He does not behave as a duke *ought*.' Two of Bertie's Oxford associates also commanded her particular abhorrence: the Marquess of Hastings and Harry Chaplin, nicknamed Magnifico – both handsome, both absurdly rich, both wild, and both very bad for Bertie. The Queen considered it a divine dispensation when the two fell out and became rivals. Magnifico engaged himself to one of the beautiful Pagets, but when he took her to buy luxuries at Marshall and Snelgrove's, the ungrateful girl slipped out of a back entrance and eloped with Hastings. The Magnifico had his revenge when the Marquess was persuaded to bet heavily against his rival's Derby entry and ruined himself by losing a fortune.

The Queen's fears, hopes and opinions were sent regularly to Marlborough House; generally through her own Private Secretary and General Knollys, sometimes by personal letters. In the main the Prince of Wales accepted his mother's rebukes, but not her advice. He respectfully reminded her that he was of age and had the right to choose his own friends. He had no intention of resigning the social sovereignty which had unexpectedly been thrust upon him and which he already relished. He was determined that neither Louisa Manchester who wanted social power, nor the Queen who had resigned it, should stand in his way.

The duchess barely made any attempt, but showed she was not to be browbeaten. When it became the custom for lists of guests amenable to their Royal Highnesses to be sent to hostesses before invitations could be sent out, she demonstrated a spirited independence. Imperiously she struck out one name listed by the Prince's equerry, remarking: 'I do not have the pleasure of *her* acquaintance'. And when as sometimes happened the Prince quarrelled seriously and lost friends and let it be known he would not accept invitations to houses where they were entertained, the duchess sent him a brief, brave message: 'I choose my own friends'.

On hearing this the Queen rather changed her view of the wicked duchess, but she knew there were very few people in Society who had a similar spirit and could stand up to Bertie's domineering ways. For herself, she was only too pleased to be relieved of those social duties which her Court ought to have performed but had failed to do so since 1861. She did not want Bertie's new position. She was in no sense his rival. And she was pleased to see how much he was enjoying himself; but she did want him to set a better example, and she did want Marlborough House to be a centre of proper conduct, not what it threatened to be.

If only Alix had not turned out such a surprise.

She confided in Lady Churchill that she had believed the Princess would have been a real force in the final shaping of her husband's character, but her hopes had been dashed. Alexandra appeared to be cast in a meek sort of mould and had Lady Churchill noted the exceeding smallness of her head? A phrenologist would surely find it worth an examination and it hardly augured well for her children.

Vicky, in Germany, was kept fully informed. By the end of May she was assured that, owing to her way of life and lack of stamina:

Alix, poor dear, is looking so sallow and is losing her 'fraîcheur'.

For the first time her deafness ('a great misfortune') was remarked on.

106

So was Affie's behaviour. He, with perverse silliness, had developed a simultaneous passion for salmon-fishing and his sister-in-law.

In confidence I may tell you [the shocked Queen wrote to her daughter] *that we do all we can to keep him from Marlborough House as he is far too much 'épris' with Alix to be allowed to be there without possibly ruining the happiness of all three and Affie has not the strength of mind (or rather more of principle and character) to resist the temptation, and it is like playing with fire!*

Very probably, had her circumstances been otherwise, Queen Victoria would not have been an unusually emotional and domineering mother-in-law, but, being the family's sovereign as well as its present head, she did not hesitate to act in a decisive fashion.

That is what she called it.

Affie when he was sent off packing back to sea, called it interference. Bertie when told a second time that he ought to choose his friends more wisely, keep better hours, and care more for his wife, called it the same.

Alix, who really cared for her mother-in-law, was disposed to be more understanding. She paid close attention to a long list of what Mama said she could and could not do. But, in telling her daughter-in-law to be more punctual, the Queen was going too far. Canute holding back a flowing tide had as much chance of success as Victoria stopping her daughter-in-law from being late. She always was. Always. And nothing could get her out of bed at a reasonable (English) hour of the morning.

At the end of that first brilliant London season, the Prince and Princess went down to Frogmore House, which had been placed at their disposal, and there they heard of the death of Baron Stockmar.

Bertie quite often puzzled his wife: by his abrupt explosions of ill temper and equally abrupt bouts of contriteness; by his extreme politeness one minute and what she considered complete boorishness the next; by his greed for food and cigars and cigarettes, but his virtual abstinence from drink; by a number of irreconcilable opposite quirks of character. But never in their short experience

107

had he astonished her so much as when he heard of the news from Coburg.

He sat there on an upright chair, his hands on his knees, clenching and unclenching his fists. 'So he's dead, dead, dead,' he said often.

She moved forward to console him, but stopped when he suddenly was on his feet, laughing, stretching out for her hands, and they were dancing together on the carpet, Bertie laughing and crying and saying again and again: 'So he's dead, dead, dead.'

She could never recall him mentioning Baron Stockmar again, but Charlotte Knollys gave her a partial explanation of his curious behaviour on hearing of the Baron's death. It seemed he had been an ogre of his childhood who had governed all he did.

Alix folded her hands over the slight swelling where her child now lay. None of her children, she vowed, should suffer as poor Bertie had done.

At the right of the double writing-tables in her sitting-room at Osborne the Queen was sealing a letter to Vicky. She used a wafer, not caring for new-fangled envelopes, and pulled the second bell beneath the ledge which was marked in gothic script PAGE.

Bertie and Alix are at Frogmore [she had written] *having over fatigued themselves in London as everyone has observed and stay there until the 18th when they came here for a fortnight, and I hope she may then bathe, and get a little fatter and stronger. . . . I send you dear Alix's letter I received this morning to show you that, though very affectionate and dear, she does not write well. . . .*
Bertie feels the dear Baron's loss – deeply.

2

In Scotland that summer there was a large and happy gathering of the family.

The Queen was at Balmoral, with Louis and Alice and their first baby, plus nursemaids and a black serving-boy named Willem, and Mr Gladstone as Minister in Attendance. At Abergeldie were the Prince and Princess of Wales and the Crown Prince and Princess of Prussia with their three children. After his single protest holiday as a bachelor at Birk Hall Bertie abandoned the place, far preferring the larger castle of Abergeldie which had belonged to his grandmother and which had a vaguely French atmosphere.

Not everyone was on Deeside simultaneously, for the Waleses travelled to Norfolk for the hunting and shooting, and Vicky and Fritz made a tour of the Highlands, but the households at Balmoral and Abergeldie frequently made joint excursions together, going for picnics and long tramps up the mountains. It was also the common practice that whilst the men went shooting and fishing and stalking, the ladies sketched and drove out and botanized.

As happens in all family holidays, there were squalls.

Vicky's eldest boy Willy caused the most. He was already notorious for his naughtiness at home, and he hardly behaved any better away from home – attracting attention to himself by doing outrageous things in public ceremonies, biting close relations, and insulting people of the most exalted rank by calling them names. The family conceded that, with his physical deformities, he had some excuse, but he went far too far that autumn. It was his grandmother's view that the famous pure air of Deeside had gone to his head because Willy was constantly on the rampage, refusing food, or throwing it on the floor, even at people, and the Crown Prince Fritz, his father, ordinarily a composed man, blushed with shame when Willy called the Queen and all her English relations a snub-nosed lot.

After that Alix got herself into trouble with Bertie by refusing to force her Danish manservant to wear the kilt. She argued that it would be as appropriate and as sensible as to kit him out in a waistcoat, baggy trousers, upturned slippers and a fez, should they happen to be travelling in Turkey. Her husband coldly pointed out that they were not 'travelling' in foreign lands, but resident in the Kingdom of Scotland. He sensed that she harboured the heretical notion that the kilt was an absurd garment anyway, and he managed to read into her remarks an implication that he, Albert Edward, by birth Duke of Rothesay, Earl of Carrick, Baron of Renfrew, Lord of the Isles, and Great Steward of Scotland, was by his exceptionally non-Scotch blood precluded from wearing

109

such a particularly Scotch dress himself. He insisted with increasing warmth and, realizing he was getting unreasonably angry, she gave way and set about persuading her man Neilson to agree. This was not easy. The Dane shared the views of his royal mistress. But he fell to her ruse when, having persuaded him to try the kilt, she exclaimed: 'Oh, I never saw you so handsome! I must have you photographed at once!' Thereafter the Prince and Neilson were satisfied. The Princess continued to be mildly amused.

Then Bertie bickered with his elder sister about who should have the provinces of Schleswig and Holstein when Alexandra's father inherited the Danish throne. He supported the claims of Denmark, she supported the claims of Prussia. Mama kept the pot aboil by stating that beloved Papa had favoured the claims of a third party, the Duke of Augustenburg. The political squabbling became acrimonious and was only at last silenced by the persuasions of Louis and Alice and Fritz and Alix, all of whom said that the subject had to be banned or it would ruin everyone's Scotch holiday.

After that there was a mild contretemps between Bertie and his mother. In his newly found independence he unwisely went so far as to criticize her favourite attendant, John Brown. Brown had been gillie to the Prince Consort which, so far as the Queen was concerned, gave him a special status in her eyes, but the Prince disliked his taciturnity and his short, abrupt manner. It appeared, complained the Prince, that this gillie was totally lacking in respect for anyone but the Queen herself, and his condescension to the royal family was both arrogant and insolent. Mama would have none of it. With Brown there she felt safe, and that was that; and, quick as a swallow in flight to defend herself by attacking, she asked what particular quality Mr Henry Mildred Birch possessed for Bertie to have appointed him as one of his chaplains. His first tutor had already been adequately rewarded by the valuable living of Prestwich. Bertie remarked that it was but a small return for all he owed to a clergyman who had always had his very highest regard; and he reminded his mother that Gibbs, for whom he had not cared in the least, had been given a C.B. and a fine service of silver plate by the Queen herself. On this occasion she chose not to argue. 'As it is done, it is done,' she said placatingly. 'But perhaps I should have been consulted in the first place.'

She was consulted – because in this case Bertie felt she had to be – when he and Alix planned to run over to Rumpenheim for a week. Directly afterwards, of course, they would return to Abergeldie. The Queen ruffled her feathers. Cousin Mary Adelaide was at the back of it, she was sure. She denounced the scheme as 'mad and very imprudent', forbade them to leave Abergeldie, and wrote to Uncle Leopold in Belgium:

They ought to be quiet and that Rumpenheim party is very mischievous for my poor weak boy's head.

Alix made no complaint. To mollify her ruffled mother-in-law she changed the subject entirely and digressed on the charms of Sandringham. Lady Macclesfield called it 'that cold, wild place by the Wash', but, really, it was very beautiful. She had planned the most interesting gardens and shrubberies, and the shooting promised to be excellent, as did the hunting. Being so devoted to hunting herself she regretted that, in her present condition, she could not hunt that season with the West Norfolk, but there would be other ...

'Hunting !' exclaimed the Queen – and, with hands held up in horror, she explained that whether the Princess was carrying a child or not, it was QUITE OUT OF THE QUESTION for her to hunt. The rules in England were strict. Protocol permitted her to drive over to a meet from time to time but on no account could she follow hounds.

Mr Gladstone caused another contretemps. He was considered a champion of the High Church cause, and, while it grieved him to see the Queen attend Presbyterian services, he annoyed her by using a royal carriage to travel fifteen miles to Communicate in an Episcopalian church. She made her displeasure felt and Gladstone was pained. He made no complaint but Charles Wood, who was in the Abergeldie house party, sensed the Minister's discomfiture. His High Church antennae vibrating, he sympathized. So did the Princess of Wales. The Prince – not himself an enthusiast in devotional matters – had declared nevertheless that if one day he did choose a religion, it would be of Charley Wood's kind.

The Queen was vexed. She felt she was the victim of a ritualists' plot, especially when the High Church Party took a long walk

111

together on the very day after she had complained to Mr Gladstone. She suspected they must be discussing advanced churchmanship. In fact her Minister in Attendance, whom she always herself found so very morose and ponderous, was showing a side of himself to the Prince and Princess and to Wood which few people ever saw. He walked them miles, because walking great distances was his passion, and at a rate which caused the Princess some anxiety until her crinoline swayed evenly and she could keep up with the tramping men, from Gelder Shiel to Glen Gurnoch and back to Abergeldie. And almost all the time he had them in tucks of laughter, telling them anecdote after anecdote of his early public life, and a few unlikely adventures in his private life too. His best, most startling story, was of how, fourteen years before, he had trailed an eloping couple across Europe in order to help a friend. In this quasi-private detective capacity he had run his quarry to earth on the shores of Lake Como where, hoping to gain admittance, he disguised himself and entered the villa gardens by night, rather like Mr Pickwick in the grounds of the establishment for young ladies in Bury St Edmunds. Again like Mr Pickwick, he was unsuccessful, his quarry slipping past in the dark in a carriage with the blinds drawn. . . .

The grave Minister, noted for his scholarship and oratory, his seriousness and apartness, was barely recognizable.

Certainly he would not have been recognized by his royal mistress, who scowled on his return to Balmoral and demonstrated her contempt for his High Church views by showing still further partiality for the Presbyterians. This was a pity. Having a keen sense of fun herself, the Queen would have enjoyed Gladstone's wry humour, but she never knew he possessed any.

Gladstone had laid the foundation of an enduring and rather unlikely friendship with the Waleses on that walk. But he seemed destined to wrangle with the Queen.

Only a few days afterwards she suffered a small accident which should have aroused his vocal sympathy and understanding. Owing to a drunken coachman driving on an unfamiliar road at twilight, the Queen and her daughters, Lenchen and Alice, together with Alice's black-boy and the ubiquitous Brown, who always sat on the box, were overturned into a ditch. Fortunately no one was seriously hurt, though the Queen wrenched her right thumb and bruised her face and Brown strained his knee, but the shock and then waiting in the cold for a rescue party played havoc with the Queen's nerves. On returning to the castle she deserved Gladstone's consolation and sympathy. But, fearful of neglecting his duty, he remained closed up and gave an impression of lack of feeling by solemnly warning his Sovereign that she should not expose herself to unnecessary danger. It was a warning which earned him a silent but exceedingly chilly response.

3

The Crown Prince and Princess of Prussia were invited to conclude their long holiday in Britain by staying at Sandringham for the Prince of Wales' birthday.

Vicky's eldest boy Willy would have spoilt the visit if he could. Indeed he tried to in the most aggravating ways. But he had reckoned without his uncle the Prince of Wales, who had strong patriarchal views as to the powers of a host and a close relation, and found himself banished to the nurseries with a severity which surprised even his own father and mother.

'Perhaps, my love,' Vicky murmured to her husband, 'that is exactly what he needs.'

Fritz thought not. He was a gentle, good-natured man; more sensitive than most to the fact that Willy's small deformities, and the constant attentions of orthodox doctors and quacks, were responsible for his very obvious deficiencies of character. But Fritz in no way resented Bertie's exercising authority in his own family and in his own household, and life was certainly more comfortable when Willy was impounded in the nurseries.

Bertie was a splendid host. Only two things marred his hospitality: that he hardly ever allowed his guests or his Household a moment to rest, and that he kept them up to the early hours of the morning. Fritz, mistakenly, thought these faults would even out with the passing of time. Meanwhile he enjoyed himself hunting, and, on a lesser scale, shooting, riding over the estate, gaming and playing billiards and eating a succession of heavy meals. He warned Bertie that his nursery nickname of Tum Tum would

113

soon be over-appropriate unless he watched his liking for rich food.

Because this was said in private Bertie laughed. He might not have done so had anyone else been in the gunroom at the time. None of his first friends had ever toadied to him, but he was making new ones in fast and rich and racing circles, amongst people who thought that princes required flattery and, unlike his mother who enjoyed and accepted flattery but under no circumstance allowed it to alter her judgement, the constant fawning of new friends was making the Prince a little vain. Being in private he did not mind his brother-in-law's frankness. Indeed he thought it a joke. He was small and thickening, and could hardly be described, like Fritz, as elegant; but he still had his good looks and his whiskers were developing into a thick, manly beard of which he was very proud.

He was also proud of Sandringham, and enjoyed showing Fritz his plans for improvements. The house was to be rebuilt entirely in a modernized Elizabethan style, and on a large enough scale to guarantee comfort. Whole villages were included in the estate, and these were to have schools, and clubs where the workers could get recreation and a certain amount of beer, but there were to be no pubs. One of the farmhouses was to be turned into an estate hospital. Of its kind, it was to be a model of the sort of thing the Prince Consort might have planned.

Though both were heirs to thrones Fritz was far less free than Bertie. In fact all the preparations for celebrating Bertie's birthday had to be upset because the King of Prussia, in a domineering mood, suddenly announced that Fritz, who had hardly come to settle at Sandringham, must leave for a tedious formal ceremony in Berlin. He went with a sigh, envying Bertie's greater freedom.

Vicky was left behind to lament on her father-in-law's overbearing attitude and talk with Alix about confinements and babies and layettes and nurses and nurseries. There was nothing, Vicky insisted, quite like a British doctor on these occasions. She had had hers at each confinement, sent out by the royal command of Mama, in spite of Prussian protests.

In the evenings there was whist – which Bertie adored; reading aloud – which he abhorred; tinkling music of the lightest kind; and endless talk about clothes, parrots, dogs, church appointments, the estate, the weather and family gossip.

114

Being something of an intellectual like her father, Vicky missed the opportunities for more serious music or intelligent conversation or something improving after dinner; but like any other woman, she enjoyed the family gossip.

Bertie admitted that he scarcely dared see Mama because Lady Augusta Bruce, one of her particularly favourite Ladies in Waiting, who, at forty-one, ought to have been entirely settled and dependable, had suddenly accepted the hand and heart of his cicerone in the Near East, shy Professor Stanley. Mama was in a great taking and appeared to think it was his fault. Something was being found for the Professor, probably it would be the Deanery of Westminster, and Lady Augusta had promised to continue in waiting when her turn came round, but she would not be Mama's perpetual companion and Mama was frantic. Vicky capped this sliver of gossip by declaring that Mama had been driven equally frantic by the harrowing discovery that she had been nourishing a viper, as it were, in her nurseries. Mademoiselle Hocédé had been discovered lending undesirable books to Lenchen (what books? Bertie immediately asked, but his sister paid no attention), and teaching Louise to be deceitful and disobedient. Naturally the viper had been dismissed, but her influence could not be wiped out in an instant. Louise was dreamy, introspective, and enormously vain, as well as sly, and already was something of a problem. As for Lenchen, her immediate future looked exceedingly bleak. Her lot had been cast by Mama's commands in a predetermined pasture. She was to marry a German princeling, any German princeling, who would undertake to live in England. It augured badly for poor Lenchen.

All three beside the fire at Sandringham deplored Mama's self-centredness.

The situation, declared Vicky, eyeing a needle with embroidery silk, was quite deplorable. She, far away in Berlin, could do nothing.

'And I have no say in anything,' said Bertie.

'Quite!'

'Thank God,' exclaimed Vicky after a moment, 'thank God for Jane Churchill and the dear Dean.'

So much depended nowadays on Lady Churchill and the Dean of Windsor. They were the only people who had any real influence, though the Queen took advice too from her Scotch Chaplain,

McLeod, and from the Marchioness of Ely, who was another permanent fixture at Court and the Queen's adviser on political affairs.

Bertie drew on his cigar. 'Even they', he remarked thoughtfully, 'scarcely matter as much today as that Scotch fellow.'

All three sighed.

After her carriage accident Mama had become yet more dependent on John Brown, and had decided to take him south as her permanent Highland servant. It had started a quiet buzz at Court. Brown lived in a limbo of his own, part way between the Household which would not accept him and the royal servants whom he would not accept.

'We can be sure,' said Vicky slowly, 'that there is nothing in the least improper in the relationship.'

'But it is surprising,' added Alix.

'Utterly mad,' snapped Bertie angrily. 'The man's uncouth – a gillie.'

Vicky studied the embroidery on which she was working. She could not help teasing her brother. 'Mama claims that Highlanders have no class system; they are members of a family, and all are nature's gentlemen. . . .'

'Gentlemen !' Bertie repeated angrily. 'The man's a lout. . . .'

'Possibly,' interrupted his sister. Then, quite seriously, she told them that on Deeside Brown was reckoned to have the gift of second sight. 'They are saying that Mama is using him as a medium.'

Bertie looked at her blankly.

Patiently Vicky explained what a medium was and told him about the new and spreading cult of spiritualism.

Plainly Alix thought it nonsense, but Bertie was exceedingly interested. 'You mean,' he asked Vicky, 'that through the right sort of medium and a planchette board, Mama can get in touch with Papa?'

'Of course not,' exclaimed Vicky and, emphasized her indignation by using a new English colloquialism. 'That is the greatest bosh !'

'Well I don't know. . . .' began Bertie slowly.

'It is also irreligious,' put in his wife, who very seldom interrupted him.

'Well,' he said at length. 'You had better look into it, Vicky.'

She was to go on to Windsor for a few days with Mama before returning to Prussia.

'I shall,' she said determinedly. 'And I shall certainly look into John Brown's place in the pattern at Court. We do not want Mama causing a scandal through her innocence.'

Whatever the Crown Princess found at Windsor she made no comment on it in her letters to Bertie and Alix. They took this as a good sign that Mama had herself, her Court, and John Brown exactly where she wanted them and was unlikely to offend the proprieties. Then, quite soon after Vicky left England, the opprobrious old King of Denmark died and Alix's father ascended the throne as Christian ix. Automatically he claimed sovereignty over the provinces of Schleswig and Holstein; and simultaneously Prince Frederick Augustenburg announced that, because he was the direct descendant in the male line, he was assuming the government of Schleswig-Holstein as Frederick vii. This inevitably caused a coolness between Sandringham and Neues Palais because Prussia, in the wings of this theatre of claims, prepared to seize the prize by force of arms, and both Bertie and Alix were scandalized. They were equally shocked because England appeared to be officially neutral. Earl Russell, the Secretary for Foreign Affairs, reported that Prussia's Chancellor, Bismarck, was behaving suspiciously:

It looks as if he was desirous of invading Schleswig by stealth.

Bertie and Alix had arranged long before to spend Christmas with the family at Osborne. Now they regretted it. They arrived to find that Mama refused even to hear their views on the all-important Schleswig-Holstein question, and in addition she refused to rebuke Brown who – so Bertie maintained – was seriously offending everyone by his impertinent silences. Bertie sulked. Alix wept. But the Queen was adamant. She told them she was not to be put upon and, as her dear children at this festive season, they ought to do all they could to soothe her nerves, not fray them. She was indeed in a great to-do; in such an agitated, irritable state that Sir Charles Phipps was persuaded – against his better judgement – to write to the Prime Minister that her physicians advised

117

a continuation of her seclusion, and that to open Parliament in person might do her a personal injury.

Lord Palmerston still kept what the Queen called his 'fancy-ladies', and was still capable of eating nine meat courses at a sitting. Nevertheless, at eighty, he was beginning to feel his age and the responsibilities of his office. He doubted the disinterestedness of Doctors Clark, Jenner and Watson in making such convenient recommendations that the Queen be left in peace, but he also doubted Victoria's ability to get control of herself yet awhile, and he refrained from prising her from the shell of her seclusion. In a polite reply he said he quite understood her position, and wished his sovereign a happy Christmas.

Happy! with Christian IX and Frederick VII and Otto von Bismarck hovering over Christmas like malignant vultures. Happy! when wretched Lord Elgin, her viceroy in India, lay dead as a result of exerting himself on a Himalayan swing-bridge. Happy! while her poor daughter-in-law Alix was in such a state, swooning and weeping and having a small burst of hysterics when the orchestra simply happened to play a piece of martial music.

Victoria worried a good deal about Alix, not understanding her peculiar languor, nor her deep feelings for her family in Denmark. She advised her to empty her head of everything save the fact that she was carrying the next heir to the crown of England, to practise deep breathing and to diet under Dr Jenner's guidance.

Alix politely thanked her, but continued to be anxious about her Danish family and her apparent inability to assimilate herself into her English family. Having had nine children herself, and seven without chloroform the Queen was not inclined to make any sort of fuss about maternity. Alix felt heavy and blown out despite her still slender figure, and the only concession she was allowed at Osborne was to remain in her room until ten in the morning – which was a whole hour before the time she usually got up at home. And she felt most uncomfortable because Mama ruled every item of her life from the number and type of her breakfast eggs to the choice of flowers and fruits for her rooms and the size of everything from the lowness of her décolletage to the precise length of Sunday sermons.

There was a brief release from Osborne in the shape of a compulsory three-day trip to Windsor for the annual memorial ceremonies for the Prince Consort, but Alix scarcely found this an

118

inspiriting experience, and Court disciplines travelled with them. She had a feeling, aggravated no doubt by her condition, that she did not yet belong to this closely knit, quarrelsome and often spiteful family, and she was discouraged by the realization that Bertie was not being as helpful as he might have been and that when he was not absorbed in his mother, he was entirely absorbed in himself.

She realized that Bertie's interest in Mama was because he was fascinated by her adroit handling of affairs. Next to Lady Ely perhaps no one was more clever at Court than the Queen and, in the nine months of their marriage, Alix had discovered that while Bertie liked a woman to have a pretty figure and was a particularly sensual man, he also liked women to be clever. It was strange, considering his own intellectual limitations, but it accounted for his special devotion to his most intelligent sisters Alice and Vicky, and his fascination for his mother.

The discovery had not upset Alix before. She had the normal accomplishments of a well-brought-up girl, but she never pretended to be in the same class as clever Alice and Vicky, and now she wondered what would happen when she could no longer hold Bertie with her physical and natural charms. The latter – to lose the quality of being endearing was something she particularly dreaded. If her charm was disparaged, it would curdle.

The thought of being unwanted – a plain and carping and boring wife – so alarmed her that she went in a panic to confide in her closest friend at Osborne, Princess Lenchen. It was an unhappy choice. Had she sought the advice of Princess Mary Adelaide at Kew, or that of her own wise Lady in Waiting, Lady Macclesfield, she would have been told that most of her present fears were caused by the fact that she was carrying a child and feeling ugly, and that, looked at from every rational point of view, her future in England was promising enough. As it was, Lenchen pessimistically recalled Bertie's 'fall', and Affie's too, and thought that her sister-in-law ought to be prepared for the endurance test of an unfaithful husband. Not that she would say anything so awful outright. Oh, no. Especially as poor Alix was in her delicate condition. But she dropped hints – intended to be light, but ending up as heavy – and then, not being very bright herself, seeing her mistake, she tried to retract altogether and puzzled and

119

alarmed her sister-in-law by saying that she wasn't to worry in the least. Everything was bound to be all right. Alix, she was sure, would go on being entrancing, a fairy-tale princess from over the sea, brimful with *bonté*, for the whole of her life. . . .

<h1 style="text-align:center">4</h1>

At the beginning of January the Prince and Princess of Wales were home again at Frogmore – if, thought Alix, Frogmore House could be counted as home like Marlborough House and Sandringham. Nevertheless she preferred to use this grace-and-favour house which had been Bertie's grandmother's, rather than the Prince of Wales' apartments at Windsor.

It left them a measure of freedom, though Mama *did* have that teahouse in the Frogmore shrubbery where, on occasions, she had the habit of breakfasting, and the teahouse *did* have a fireplace so that, in theory at any rate, it could be used in the wintertime. But Mama was miles away at Osborne and, in any case, Alix doubted if even her extraordinarily tough mother-in-law could use the teahouse that winter without freezing to death.

The ground was Russian hard. It rang like iron under the stamps of blanketed, impatient horses. The large surface of Frogmore lake – a pest in summer as, appropriately, the breeding ground of hordes of frogs and innumerable stinging insects – was now thickly frozen over.

On Twelfth Night Alix decided to give a children's party there, with traditional games and customs – a hotchpotch of Danish and English delights. There was a well-muffled-up band surrounded by braziers, and there were Chinese lantern in the trees, flambeaux on pole sconces round the lake, and heaped bonfires to warm those who temporarily felt the cold, trays of Danish pastries, roasted chestnuts and apples, gingerbread, hot potatoes and – a novel touch – buttered muffins, with a mild punch or hot chocolate for the youngsters and a fierce Prince of Wales invention for their elders. There were bobbing for apples, snapdragon, presents from a Christmas tree, skating, sliding, races, snowball-

120

ing, even Sir Roger done at quick time on the thick violet-coloured ice. And until the cold became too intense, even for the bonfires and braziers and young limbs in active circulation, it was the greatest success.

Afterwards the Prince of Wales congratulated his wife. She had done splendidly. It had all been the greatest fun, and the exercise had given him a hearty appetite for dinner. She smiled at his prowess as an eater. There were not many young men who could eat such quantities of Danish pastry, chestnuts, apples, gingerbread, hot potatoes and buttered muffins and still have a vestige of an appetite, and she was quite sure Bertie could more than manage the traditional Twelfth Night dinner, the very thought of which hung over her like a threat. But secretly she was concerned for him. Overeating on such a scale could not be good for him.

Lady Macclesfield had already become 'dearest Mac'. At the time of her appointment, a courtier had remarked that the Queen had put a watchdog in the Princess' Household, 'that dry old stick, Lady Macclesfield'; but very quickly they had taken to one another and, deprived of her mother, Alix used her Mac as a substitute. It was on Mac's shoulders that she wept when depressions and fears at her approaching confinement became too much for her. It was to Mac that she confided that evening her dread that her husband's increasing obsession with food would do him harm. Five sound meals a day, with extras in between, seemed not a bit too much to him.

Lady Macclesfield wisely put it down to the fact that the Prince had too little to do. It would be better, she said, later – when his year as a bridegroom was done and he was more closely associated with the Queen's work. Meanwhile the Princess was not to worry. From her own experience she knew that young men of twenty-two could stand almost anything. It was more important now for the Princess to consider her own health. If she really could not face going down to dinner, she would say so.

Alix gratefully accepted her advice and a tray was sent up to her sitting-room. The soup she pushed aside, but she pecked at a mousse of quails, not because she wanted it, but because dearest Mac, aware that it was one of her favourite dishes, had probably ordered it especially. . . .

121

Alix enjoyed Mac's mothering, but like any other grown-up daughter she was quite capable of disregarding her mother's advice. On the following day the weather seemed colder than ever, but Bertie proposed an expedition to see the ice hockey and skating at Virginia Water and Alix at once said yes. Lady Macclesfield cautioned her against too much excitement and activity. After all there were only two months to run before the ritual of a royal confinement took place. It was wiser to be careful. But the Princess brushed her advice aside. She had sables she said and wore layers and layers and layers and layers of wool, and she would sit only for a time in a sleigh-chair to watch the skating.

As she and Bertie drove off through the snow she told him how pleasant it was to be able to get out each day. There was talk in the family that her sister Dagmar was to marry the Tsarevitch and she pitied Dagmar those long Russian winters walled into gorgeous palaces by ice. It was more comfortable to be in England – she clasped her husband's gloved hand and squeezed – more comfortable out in the open air, even though there was an undeniable bite in it.

Virginia Water, scattered with skaters, some of them playing ice hockey, others waltzing to the music of a German band, was beautiful, quite beautiful. Bertie, naturally, found the ice-hockey irresistible. Impulsively his topcoat was thrown aside and he was on the ice. Alix watched and smiled. She loved his enthusiasm because it was absolutely natural; the energetic good-looking young prince of fairy tales, not the sober statesman which the Baron and his father had trained him to be and which, with the increase of his responsibilities, would inevitably make him cautious and seem older, if not any wiser.

The afternoon wore on. People were lighting fires and flares as the cold intensified and the short day died. Bertie had abandoned the hockey but was still energetically skating backwards and forwards. The Princess, as warm as toast, though the very tip of her nose was chilled and made her think of Dagmar again in those steely winters in St Petersburg, was wishing that dearest Mac had not been quite so thoughtful the night before. A twinge in her stomach told her that the quail mousse had been, perhaps, a little off; or, more probably, too rich for her at present. Or was she being unjust to Mac? Possibly it had been unwise to eat gingerbread as well as buttered muffins at the party. Then she recalled that her breakfast coffee had been rather strong – and once before she had given herself a bilious attack with coffee. She mentioned it to Bertie as they drove back to Frogmore through the frosty night. Full of *joie de vivre* he said cheerfully it was unfortunate they could not divide his astonishing digestive powers in half and share them. There would still be quite enough for each. . . .

Lady Macclesfield did not appreciate the joke as she should have done when the royal party reached Frogmore and the Princess repeated what her husband had said. She shooed her charge upstairs and began to ask questions. Then she felt the Princess' stomach, tut-tutted several times, and watched her face when next she said she had felt a twinge of pain. She said it quite brightly, assuring dearest Mac that it was not in the least severe. But Lady Macclesfield had had no less than thirteen successful confinements herself. She knew precisely what was happening.

She left the Princess, undressed and in bed, her head propped against an extra supply of pillows, and then went down to the library where the Prince was enjoying a cigar. He turned pale when he heard what was happening. 'Now, Sir, you are not to agitate yourself. Nor are you to visit her Royal Highness, please, unless you can undertake not to upset her with your nervousness.'

'But what, Mac, can I do?' he asked.

'I would suggest, Sir, that you arrange for the Home Secretary to be telegraphed. He ought to be here. After that,' she added, 'perhaps you could send for your Equerry and play billiards.'

'Billiards!'

'Billiards,' repeated Lady Macclesfield.

She summoned a footman and told him to run at once for the Windsor physician, Dr Brown. She summoned a maid and sent her to the local drapers, Caleys, for some yards of flannel. Mrs Knollys was consulted, but, though a mother herself, on being asked if she could assist as a nurse, gave a shrill squeak of terror and fainted away. Afterwards, she apologized but said she really could *not* be of any assistance; though she believed she had a sheet of wadding by her if that would be of any use. It would, said Lady Macclesfield, and took it with her, and her own flannel petticoat, up to the Princess' room.

Outside the door was the Prince. Evidently billiards was out of the question. The Home Secretary, he told her, could not be

123

expected for a long time, but Lord Granville was a house guest and as Lord President of the Council could bear the necessary testimony. 'That is . . .' said the Prince. He swallowed. 'That is, if all goes well with the Princess and the baby.'

Lady Macclesfield took him by the arm. 'Be sure it will, Sir,' she said to hearten him. 'Now if you will ask Lord Granville to step up and seat himself outside this door, you may then come into the room and help me.'

He looked at her in shocked amazement.

'I shall be the nurse,' she said firmly. 'You will do all that you can to cheer and encourage the Princess.'

And that was how Bertie's son and heir was born: everything being capably managed by Lady Macclesfield. Dr Brown arrived too late at Frogmore House. By then the tiny baby had been delivered by Lady Macclesfield, who used her petticoat as a receiving flannel. And, though only three and three-quarter pounds, the boy had a lusty voice.

The Prince said everything was marvellous, marvellous, marvellous. He kept saying it and kissing Alix's forehead. He probably kissed Lady Macclesfield as well, though this was not recorded by either; and, in his joy, he might well have kissed Earl Granville who bore the necessary solemn testimony that a high and mighty Prince of the Blood in direct succession to the Throne of England had been safely delivered of the Princess of Wales.

Alix looked lovingly at her excited husband. To dearest Mac she had murmured throughout the delivery, 'as long as I see your face I am happy'. She gazed at the infant, wrapped up in a bit of Caleys' flannel, and said to herself 'How odd.'

Lady Macclesfield, who knew her Dickens well, felt not unlike Mrs Gamp and, after what she had inadvertently gone through, could have shared that odd lady's taste for pickled salmon and a lot of gin with considerable pleasure. She drove everyone from the room, including the Prince. The Princess, she said, was exhausted and must be left to rest. But the Prince eluded her vigilance. When she returned herself later to peep in at the sleeping Princess, she found her still awake in her husband's arms. Both were crying with joy.

And with relief.

.   .   .   .   .

That same American Minister to the Court of St James's who had described Princess Mary Adelaide with acerbic skill, remarked on the prince's birth:

As the event was not expected for two months and no prepara-
tions had been made for it, the public feeling is a mixture of
agreeable disappointment and ill-suppressed risibility.

Everyone, of course, was astounded. Not least the Queen, who hastened from Osborne to Windsor and thence to Frogmore to examine personally what she called 'the Heir-but-One'. She was gratified to find that, though small, the child was perfect, with a good deal of hair and all its nails, and was wrapped literally in cottonwool lying in its cradle beneath a full-length portrait of the Prince Consort in mediaeval armour. It all augured well for the future, she told herself, and commemorated the event by planting a small holm-oak which, she informed Vicky, in a despondent mood,

'will be a striking tree – if it lives.'

Naturally, it being the general prerogative of mothers-in-law, and in particular of regal ones, a few faults were hunted out. There was trouble about a nurse: the one recommended by the Queen turned out to be, as she admitted,

'cross, grand, and a great nuisance'.

There was concern about Alix's inability to sleep soundly:

'I fear Bertie's late habits have caused this.'

But the most serious fault-finding was with regard to the naming of the Heir-but-one.

Victoria, in her wish to perpetuate the memory of her husband, had a fixed resolve that all future male sovereigns should be named after him. Bertie would be Albert I; therefore, it followed that the Heir-but-One would, one day, be Albert II. The intellectual Lady Ely warned her royal mistress that dynastic ambitiousness could lead to excess. She reminded the Queen that this

125

had been the custom in the Princely House of Reuss – and in five centuries Friedrichs had reigned in abundance from Friedrich I to Friedrich LXXIII. But the Queen was not impressed. She urged Bertie, directly and indirectly, to promise he would reign as Albert the First.

To her surprise – perhaps, a little, to his own – he preferred not to commit himself. He would not even undertake to follow the prevailing foreign custom of doubling up his names, as Louis Philippe and Victor Emmanuel had done, and reign as Albert Edward. He would much rather, he said, wait and see.

This bold front vexed the Queen a good deal, but she, in turn, vexed the Household at Frogmore and especially Alix.

Baby Beatrice, who by this time was a precocious six-year-old, arrived at Frogmore and announced pontifically: 'Albert Edward Christian Victor, that's what Mama's decided to call him.'

Not possibly for the first time, but certainly for the first time in which she deliberately used Bertie as her knight errant, Alix complained to him about Mama's lack of consideration. Bertie was quick to defend her and wrote to the Queen:

I felt rather annoyed when Beatrice told Lady Macclesfield that you had settled what our little boy was to be called before I had spoken to you about it.

Lady Churchill, who was handed the letter by a stony-faced Queen, so that she might see how wilful and ungrateful her son had become, was secretly delighted. Evidently the young Prince was no longer afraid of his mother as she and everyone at Court had thought was the case.

But Bertie was not prepared to make an issue of it. With all his limitations he had a kindly streak in him and he knew that it was a bad time for his mother. She had just lost a dear friend in the agonizing death from cancer of the Duke of Athole. She was frantically anxious about the political situation in Europe. With good grace he gave way. The chosen names should stand, and amongst the baby's godparents should be his sister, the Crown Princess and Prince of Prussia, and Alix's father, the King of Denmark, and as if to mediate between dissenting parties, the old King of the Belgians.

The Queen had a full account of the christening sent to Vicky

126

by the Chamberlain who had stood proxy for her. To it she added her own tart comments:

I never felt more thoroughly shaken than I was all through. The poor baby roared all through the ceremony – which none of you did. Alix looked very ill – thin and unhappy. She is sadly gone off.

Sadly gone off or not, it was Alix who, in the end, bested the Queen. Edward was the name she had wanted and Edward she was going to have. By repeatedly calling the baby Eddy she caused everyone to follow suit, and in the family it was always his name, even used after a time by the Queen – though officially he was always known as Prince Albert Victor.

5

The proxies of Prince Eddy's Prussian and Danish godparents who stood side by side at his christening in the private chapel at Buckingham Palace were soon at sword's length. The Prussian Chancellor Bismarck had made a non-interference pact with Austria which guaranteed Prussia's rear if she walked into the provinces of Schleswig-Holstein.

To the Queen's distress her family at once aligned itself into separate camps and she knew that the impending war was going to be fought out at Windsor as well as in Schleswig-Holstein.

Angrily she demanded that Lord Palmerston and Lord Russell do something, but they were classic Whig grandees who took small account of their sovereign's wishes. They calmly reminded her of the Prince Consort's policy of English neutrality in the internal affairs of Germany, and told her that it was not her Ministry's policy to encourage self-determination for the people of Schleswig-Holstein. Why not, demanded Victoria, if it kept Prussia and Denmark from each other's throats? Moreover, how could Palmerston and Russell be so provokingly inconsistent? If they thought self-determination good for the Italians, why not for the Holsteiners?

Because Albert had at some time favoured it, she supported the claims of the Duke of Augustenburg, and this gave her a pro-German bias which none of the English liked. Lord Palmerston reproved her gently for lending her name to a hopeless cause. One of her former ministers had the impertinence to criticize her in the House of Lords. The press, as usual, was hostile and very clamant.

Bertie was heart and soul with Alix in the quarrel. And so were the people of England. Neither he nor the Princess troubled to hide their immense satisfaction that it was so. They agreed with Mama on only one point: that Bismarck was a brute. Papa would have thought so.

Vicky, deeply in love with Fritz, and determined to be loyal to her new country, found herself very much criticized by the family in England. Bertie remarked bitterly that she appeared to have succeeded in becoming a thorough Prussian. Even her mother, after the invasion of Holstein wrote:

I had hoped that this dreadful war might be prevented but you all (God forgive you for it) would have it!

Vicky responded with spirit. She was hotly on the defensive when, on 1 February, the Prussians swarmed into the provinces and seized them from Denmark. Aunt Feodore, Mama's half-sister, and ordinarily a quiet sweet person, was terribly angry in defence of Augustenburg's claims. For a time she was vitriolic both to Vicky and to Bertie. Then, on the wise advice of Uncle Leopold, the Queen banned any further discussion of the Schleswig-Holstein in her household. Papa would not have wished it.

Then there came a crisis.

On 10 March, 1864, the anniversary of his wedding to Alix, the Prince of Wales ceased his year as a bridegroom. Thenceforth he was prepared to take his proper place in affairs.

It was generally understood in England that he had already taken it. His visible presence at Marlborough House and down

128

in the country, and his strong and widely circulated remarks on behalf of Denmark being thoroughly approved; and it was suggested – by no means for the first time – that this was a suitable time for the Queen to abdicate in his favour. Though not as clever as his sisters, the Prince of Wales was believed to have a grasp of international diplomacy which promised well for England's future. His position as the sovereign of Society had already been assured. Now perhaps was the time for him to take over from his mother, so that she could continue to enjoy her quiet isolation as a private person.

However subdued it was, few things irritated Victoria more than criticism of her conduct as a widow, and the sudden rash of press commentaries on her invisibility and inaudibility; together with caricatures and the publication of aggressively rude broadsheets; together with the pinning of a notice to the railings of Buckingham Palace that the place was for sale or to be let 'in consequence of the late owner's declining business', inflamed her antagonism to alarming proportions.

Unhappily, just at that very time Bertie wrote a polite and formal letter to ask if he might have direct access to Foreign Office despatches and other Ministry affairs. Now that his apprenticeship was over and his year as a bridegroom concluded, he was ready, he said, to share her work and wished for the privilege of a key to despatch boxes.

In response a salvo was fired from Windsor, not directly at Sandringham or Marlborough House, but (insultingly as Bertie thought) through the Foreign Secretary. Lord Russell was instructed by the Queen's secretary to inform the Prince's secretary that the Sovereign did not wish her Heir to enter into separate and independent communication with the Government. In other words, she doubted if her son had a balanced judgement, especially about such provocative matters as the Danish and Prussian war, and she doubted his discretion to hold his tongue.

When Knollys gave his master this information, although he had sweetened and diluted it, he was quite alarmed by his reaction.

The Prince clenched his fists until the knuckles whitened. His face grew red and the veins stood out at his temples. Another vein, in his already thickening neck, was visibly throbbing.

The Comptroller begged the Prince to be seated and was

ignored. Again he begged it, and was told with extreme rudeness to get out of the room.

It was no way for anyone to address an elderly and highly respectable Comptroller of sixty-six, and Knollys had difficulty in controlling his own tongue. Nevertheless, because the Prince's distress was so obvious, he said nothing, obediently did as he was told and left the room. He went directly to the Princess' sitting-room. A white parrot flew freely about the room, and as General Knollys was announced, it flew to its perch and glowered at the intruder. In too great a state of agitation to be entirely tactful, the General told the Princess what had happened. She listened quietly, thanked him, and told him that she herself would go to see the Prince.

She found Bertie, still standing before the fireplace of his room, evidently working himself into a great rage. She said nothing but put her arms around him. Slowly, the German guttural rolling of his r's more pronounced than ever, he unburdened some of his fury. He had been treated shamefully, shamefully, and so angry was he that he could not express himself with a coherence she could understand. He talked of his odious tutor Gibbs, and his lonely horrible childhood . . . of being unjustly accused of causing his own father's death . . . of being sent away in disgrace . . . of the humiliations he had suffered . . . of the domineering, cold dictatorial attitude of his own mother . . . even of the impertinence of her Scotch factotum. . . .

But, though incoherent, Alix sensed the strength of his resent-ment, and deep down she was alarmed that her generally easy-going but sometimes bad-tempered Bertie could become so pulsing with anger. She calmed him as well as she could, and when he had command of himself again, he kissed her forehead, and thanked her; but there was a sharpness in his tone, a certain bird-brightness in his eye for several days.

He confided in no one; not in his wife, nor in his intimate friends, nor in his Comptroller, the General. Nevertheless Knollys judged the Prince was schooling himself to submit to the Queen and carry on as before, to being content with the social sovereignty he had already earned for himself and which for a year had seemed so important to him. He was mistaken.

The Prince had determined to show how deeply he felt his humiliation, and he did it by contemptuously disregarding his mother's wishes and championing the Danes with all the fervour and publicity he could.

The Queen froze with displeasure when she heard of his head-strong abuse of Prussia and all things German, and she could hardly contain her anger when, simply to thwart her, Bertie visited the Italian revolutionary Garibaldi, who was then in London. She wrote, through her own Private Secretary, a severe censure of General Knollys, whom she held responsible.

Bertie instantly defended his Comptroller who, he said, had been unjustly blamed.

I fear he feels it very much as he is not, and cannot be, responsible for my actions. I have now been of age for some time and am alone responsible....

The Queen gazed at this sentence in her son's letter as though hypnotized. The underlined word 'alone' held her eye for over a minute.

Bertie relentlessly returned to his public attack on Prussia. After a temporary armistice, the war had been resumed and Alix's father had appealed to the Great Powers. The Prince of Wales suggested that in his unique position he might make a useful channel of communication between the Danish Court and the Ministry.

Nothing stung the Queen more than this. Was her heir about to steal her prerogatives? Was he setting himself up as an Absalom in her kingdom?

She sent a message to Marlborough House by Lord Clarendon.

The Prince respected Clarendon. He also liked his ready wit and enjoyed his company; but when the old earl made the purpose of his visit clear, the Prince's cordiality underwent a quick change. Sugar-icing aside, in its naked form the Queen's message was this: Her son's offer could only be accepted, if at all, with extreme caution. In other words, it was refused. His immediate response was to unite all those in the Royal Family who supported the Danish claims.

He went first to the Cambridges. Princess Mary Adelaide and George of Cambridge were presented with his views. Russia would not help the Danes. France could not. And England could, but would not because, as Lord Derby said, the Whigs had a

131

crazy policy of 'meddle and muddle'. 'Just so,' agreed Uncle George; and, at Mary Adelaide's promptings, he and the Prince of Wales went to see Lord Derby, leader of the Tories. For the first time in his career the Prince was imitating former Princes of Wales by threatening to entangle himself with the Opposition.

It thoroughly frightened the Queen and to add to her worries Bertie chose that very time to make a formal protest at being denied a key to the royal despatch boxes. But she knew her son better than he knew himself and judged that if he was pressed hard enough he would give way.

To show him a taste of her power she sent for George of Cambridge and gave her cousin ten of the most uncomfortable minutes in his life. He was *her* Commander-in-Chief, she said, and he would lose his appointment if he led her son into mischief. Princess Mary Adelaide would not have been beaten so easily, but the Duke of Cambridge lacked her robustness. Cowed, and determined to extricate himself from the affair, he told Bertie what he had gone through and advised him to be careful.

It was a shrewd move.

Bertie's bad temper quickly evaporated in the face of his mother's powerful personality. Even though he felt right was on his side he dared not provoke her too far. When she replied to his protest that her mind was made up, her decision was final, he showed signs of giving way.

Alix would have goaded him further but General Knollys had no difficulty in persuading him that a political confrontation between the Sovereign and her Heir was not desirable. They would be playing into the hands of socialists and republicans. . . .

It was a way out, and the Prince seized on it as a reason for not persisting in his claim. All his hopes of being politically involved in affairs were shattered for the present but, no matter how bitter his disappointment, he could not face up to his indomitable mother.

She, in her turn, having re-established her authority, chose to be generous.

When Alix asked if they might visit Denmark as soon as possible she gave her consent. She made only three conditions and these she considered reasonable: that the strictest incognito should be observed, that they travel through Germany on their

132

way home, and that the baby should be sent home with its nurse in the royal yacht after an absence of three weeks.

The Prince agreed to all the conditions. He agreed, as well, to the limitations she imposed on his visit to Aldershot that July, that he would 'exercise nothing of the sovereign's authority or sovereignty'.

Wise Uncle Leopold heard of these developments and felt uneasy. He was old and he was ill but he had never failed to advise his niece Victoria in her own best interests. He urged her to be less rigid, and he begged her, for her own sake, to sacrifice a fractional part of her seclusion. She must be more in the public eye. Therefore, with the greatest reluctance, she faced the ordeal of riding out in London that summer in an open carriage for the first time since the Prince Consort's death. She was rewarded by the warmth of her people's response. She was an honest woman and, in a triumphant letter to Uncle Leopold, she made no attempt to conceal her jealousy of Bertie and Alix's popularity amongst her subjects.

Naturally for them *no-one stops, or* runs, *as they always did, & do* doubly now, *for* me.

It was not this acknowledged jealousy which had made her put Bertie in his place and deny him a key to government despatch boxes, but a sincere regard for her country and its defences. Now that he had shed his puppy troubles and had grown up she rather liked him, but there was no denying his impossible lack of circumspection. She had heard recently from her ministers an extraordinary example of his undependability: a secret telegraph message, decoded and given to him at dinner, had so excited him that he read its contents to everyone at the table. It was horrifying. Quite simply he could not be trusted.

Rightly or wrongly, though, her decision was to have a profound effect on the Prince of Wales' character and on his way of living for the rest of her reign.

6

It was Alix who rebelled once they were out of England. If to exercise her independence and not always be at the beck and call of her mother-in-law was to be that undesirable thing 'a political princess', then she would be one.

By what right, she asked Bertie, had the Queen offered the Gladstones Abergeldie House that autumn without reference to her? By what right had she obliged them to accept such conditions before permitting them to leave the country? By what right had she such a powerful say in all that went on in Eddy's nursery?

Her indignation fermented Bertie's own feelings. Mama at a distance was far less formidable. He too felt they had been imposed upon. Nevertheless he was nervous when the Danes refused to accept their incognito, acclaiming them as the Prince and Princess who throughout the war with Prussia had always been on their side and had led English public opinion in their favour. They could pretend to be Duke and Duchess of Rothesay if they wished, but all Denmark knew and welcomed them as the Prince and Princess of Wales. His uneasiness was soothed when the Danes did exactly the same to the Tsarevitch who was in their country to woo Princess Dagmar and took no notice at all of his incognito. Mama, he felt, would understand.

She did, though she was not pleased, and held her tongue.

But then Bertie became bored with the tame family life at Fredensborg Castle. He could not abide the tedium of the endless games. Loo and parchesi were the most exciting. Nor, after a few days, had he a word of praise for Danish cuisine. Each meal, he said, appeared to end with a helping of currant jelly. And so, when the King of Sweden invited him over to Stockholm he jumped at the opportunity, especially as he and the King had many tastes in common. Bertie was soon writing confidentially to his brother-in-law back in Fredensborg about the charms of 'Miss Hannah' and 'Miss Ida', two noted Swedish beauties, and he and the Swedish

134

King went on an elk hunt which became a greatly publicized event.

Queen Victoria was aghast. She disapproved profoundly of the fast courts of Sweden and France, and could not understand what her son was doing in Stockholm. Nor could she understand why, after repeated requests for his immediate return, her grandson was still in Denmark. She telegraphed her views to Bertie.

In reply she received a surprisingly blunt letter.

His morale boosted by the elk hunt and the Swedish beauties, Bertie wrote that it was natural for a young mother not to wish to be parted from her firstborn but Eddy should be sent home as soon as possible. Unwisely he added an uncalled for and clumsily expressed excuse for not maintaining strict incognito. It would have required, he said, staying in an hotel or in the stuffiness of the English Legation—

> *and I have no intention of letting Alix be uncomfortably lodged if I can help it. . . . If I am not allowed to use my own discretion we had better give up travelling altogether.*

Pained by this petulant note of defiance, the Queen reacted characteristically. Aware that Bertie loved France and that he and Alix were planning to return incognito through Paris, she telegraphed a curt order that they were to return instead through Belgium.

No one seemed to approve of this headstrong decision; neither the Prime Minister, nor the members of the Queen's Household; nor even Uncle Leopold who, though saying he would be delighted to see his great-nephew at Laeken, doubted if Victoria really possessed the authority to make such decisions.

Nevertheless after a scene with General Knollys, Bertie gave way.

His wife was thunderstruck; shocked by his craven attitude; enraged by her mother-in-law's autocracy; in tears at having to give her tiny baby into the care of Lady Spencer, who took him in a royal yacht to England; understandably upset at having to part from her family and especially from her sister Dagmar, who was now officially engaged to the Tsarevitch.

Bertie felt at a disadvantage because he had slipped off to Sweden on his own, and because his mother was so obviously at fault, and he was amazed by Alix's fury. In fact he was in an unenviable position. To the world his wife gave an impression of calm and dignified repose, of an unshatterable sweetness. Now he was learning that the unruffled placidity of her nature could be whipped into a storm of extraordinary power.

When they left Denmark for Germany Bertie found his wife's obstinacy unbearable. She refused, point blank, to call on the Queen of Prussia, who was a friend and a regular correspondent of Queen Victoria. Nor would she go to the Prussian capital. Only after visits to the family in Hanover, and to Alice and Louis in Darmstadt, would she even consent to meet Vicky and Fritz in East Prussia. Even then she was glacial to the Crown Prince and his A.D.C. because both were in uniform and both were wearing a medal ribbon earned in the recent war against the Danes.

Bertie was puzzled by his wife but absolutely loyal to her. He complained to Vicky of Fritz's lack of thoughtfulness, and Vicky made an old nursery quarrel of it, writing to Mama in England:

Bertie is become quite unmanageable. . . . and Alix, good as she is, is not worth the price we have to pay for her in having such a family connection.

But Vicky never bore ill will for long and she was far too sensible a woman not to see the importance of getting on with her brother and Alix. She took her sister-in-law on one side and tried to soothe her ruffled feelings. Then while admitting that Bertie could not be the most easy of men to live with, and Mama's overbearing nature must chafe her nerves, Alix must for her own peace of mind try to be more tolerant. Mama was right in one thing. Political princesses never had a moment's joy or peace; and Alix had to be 'English', just as she had to be 'Prussian'.

Alix was pacified, though not entirely persuaded.

Fritz, good-natured as ever, apologized for any distress he had inadvertently caused her, and he took immense pains to entertain Bertie. . . .

When they returned to England, travelling as ordered by Belgium, both the Prince and Princess of Wales were in a different frame of mind, but neither looked forward to collecting their little son and going down to Osborne to face Mama's wrath.

She, however, had been put under considerable pressure by

136

Uncle Leopold and Vicky and Fritz, and she had come to the conclusion that any sort of breach between her and her children would be both inadvisable and uncomfortable. She barely scolded them at all, and the warmth of her welcome was obviously sincere. Both Bertie and Alix felt this, and they were so relieved that they actually enjoyed their short visit, though they could not be persuaded to stay for a second family Christmas. They wished, they said, to establish a custom of always spending Christmas at their Norfolk home.

7

Calling himself thenceforth the family 'canal-bridge-and-railway opener', the Prince of Wales took upon himself all the social duties which his mother refused to carry out, and he knew next to nothing of what was happening in Whitehall. On rare occasions he attended the House of Lords, but this was discouraged by his mother. Yet, despite rumours to the contrary, they remained on reasonably amicable terms.

The Prince also began to set up a routine which for parts of the year excluded his wife and permitted her to visit relations in Denmark. From Christmas until mid-March both were at Sandringham. Thence he went to France *en garçon*, visiting friends – in particular Madame La Princesse de Sagan at her properties in Cannes and Deauville, and Mello – with a few days in Paris at either end of the visit. From the end of April to the end of July both the Prince and Princess were at Marlborough House reigning over the London Season. At the end of July they were at Cowes for the regattas, staying aboard the Prince's yachts, though occasionally at Osborne House. And afterwards he would go to take a cure at a German or Austrian spa, sometimes with the Princess, more often without. Early in October both went to Abergeldie for a month's deer stalking.

Since Alix's totally unexpected explosion of temperament on the first trip to Denmark, their relationship had undergone a subtle change.

The Prince's affection for his wife had been strengthened and deepened. No one else could have tried his patience as she did and not suffered the edge of his tongue. Atrociously unpunctual, a lover of informality and entirely illogical, she constantly irritated him, and yet he bore with her, and showed a warmth of devotion towards her which was touching. He was a dependent sort of man who needed to lean on others.

Alix on the other hand, had the natural independence of those who are deaf and those who are vain. In order for her to hear properly she should have used a hearing horn, but although she had many – of tortoiseshell and mother of pearl and buffalo horn – she was too vain to make use of them. She could hear Bertie, for he had a deep clear voice, but she missed a good deal of what was going on about her. To moderate her vanity as a girl her parents had frequently told her she was not in the least pretty – to which she had precociously replied that, if not pretty, at least she was very good – but there was no denying that by the standards of her time she was a beauty and vain with it. Bertie found her enormously attractive physically, but it was to be expected that during the first years of their marriage, she would be frequently carrying a child, and she feared that, on account of his strong appetites, he would be tempted to stray elsewhere. And she had a deep affection for him. She told someone that had he been a cowboy and not Prince of Wales she would have married him just the same.

Pride prevented her from discussing her doubts and difficulties with anyone in England. She could not even confide in her dearest Mac. But Dagmar, her sister, was a help. She tried to explain in long, rambling letters something of what she felt – that her marriage, which had seemed to her so solid and enduring, was being threatened; that one day it might fracture like a diamond under the great weight of her own fears and possessiveness. Dagmar had consoled her with the very sensible remark that while, admittedly, diamonds were less valuable if broken, the pieces still had a high value and they continued to be very, very hard. And it was Dagmar who, by her own courageous example, reminded her that political marriages were made in courts and chancelleries on earth and not in Heaven. At about the time of the birth of Alix's second son, George, Dagmar's fiancé died of consumption, but the Russian and Danish royal families considered it politically expedient for her to be betrothed to his brother Alexander, the new

Tsarevitch. With calmness and great dignity Dagmar had adjusted herself emotionally to consent to this new proposal and she had succeeded beyond anyone's expectations.

The confidential letters between the two sisters at this time helped Alix more than anything to face her own fears with the same sort of calmness and dignity. She had the great consolation, too, of being a natural mother. Unlike Queen Victoria who confided that when she was carrying a child she had felt too much an animal, too little a human being; but very like her sister-in-law Vicky, Alix enjoyed motherhood. She revelled in what Mama described with disgust as the sluggish cow-like feeling while waiting for her confinements. But she never had to wait as long as other women. She seemed destined always to have premature children. But all save one soon recovered to grow into healthy children; the very centre of their life being not their nurses, nor a casually selected servant – as was often the case with royal children – but Alix herself. All their lives they called her by the affectionate compound name of Motherdear.

The Prince of Wales' routine permitted him a great deal of leisure. It was hardly ever sufficient. His unbounded energies consumed the hours. Often he was not in bed until three in the morning, and would be up again at nine to eat a heavy breakfast alone – the Princess never appearing before eleven – and to smoke a cigar or two before getting down to necessary business with his Comptroller.

Business was both public and private. From Knollys and from précis of newspaper reports and the boiled-down bones of government despatches which he resented so much, he kept himself informed on some of the more serious national and international events, and with Knollys' help he accepted or refused invitations to open this, that and the other.

Then there were always serious private matters to attend to. Alix, having come from a family where every penny counted ought, surely, to have been economical; but, on the contrary, she was wildly extravagant, and keeping up with his own taste for high life and low company, and his ambitious schemes for Sandringham, Marlborough House, yachting and breeding bloodstock, were causing havoc in the accounts of his Privy Purse. General

Knollys frequently suggested exactly what economies should be made and how. The Prince agreed, and then forgot all about them. A fiat had at length arrived from Osborne. Mama had heard from Lord Palmerston (and who could have told the Prime Minister?) that the Prince was drawing extensively on his capital in order to pay gambling losses. Knollys blamed the alterations at Sandringham for the collapse of his finances. Palmerston generously wanted Parliament to vote him a larger income, but the Chancellor, that strange, inscrutable Gladstone, said the Queen must pay. And she would not. So there he was, stuck, as Knollys put it, between Gladstone and the Queen, and in an uncomfortable financial pickle. Such serious considerations were better put aside.

When business both public and private became too unbearable to contemplate the Prince had a happy knack of blanking his mind to them and thinking of other things. His aptitude for concentrating on small and curious details was a helpful distraction. He was interested in the most unlikely things: in receipts for supper dishes; in the construction of an American bowling alley at Sandringham where the conservatory had been; in the gossip that it looked as if, at last, his cousin Mary Adelaide had trapped a husband – unfortunately only the son of a Middle European morganatic marriages – but a prince and a handsome man for all that; even in the fact that his much-disliked tutor, the barrister Gibbs, had published a book entitled, of all things, *Once a Clergyman Always a Clergyman*.

There were other distractions too: Paris in the springtime – a secret *vie orageuse* with delicious cocottes, and kingly dishes in the restaurants . . . lobster soufflés, cutlets with foie gras, cucumbers en demi Devil, chaufroid of ham and ortolans, croûtes à la marinière . . . all exquisite; sailing at Cowes in his new yacht *Dagmar*; hunting with Alix, for she had quietly forgotten Mama's prohibitions and now followed hounds as often as her condition allowed; being much impressed by Alix's tact and charm when the family gathered *en masse* by Mama's command at Coburg for the unveiling of a gilt-bronze statue of Papa, and where she, and only she, was able to soothe the Queen and douse the family squabbles which inevitably flared up; and then there was always the distraction of Mama's Highland Servant, the ubiquitous Brown who clung to his post at the centre of the Court and could not be dislodged by anyone or any means.

But a fresh family war threatened to be the most considerable distraction from routine at this particular time. It was caused by Lenchen's marriage prospects and the family was split right down the middle because her suitor was a mild, bald, elderly German princeling who matched up to Mama's requirement that he must be prepared to live in England. Prince Christian of Schleswig-Holstein-Augustenburg was Mama's choice, and she was supported by Vicky and Fritz and other German relations. The rest of the family, led by Alice, declared that Lenchen's entire happiness was being sacrificed to Mama's convenience. Affie and George of Cambridge agreed; the latter rather quietly because of his delicate position as Commander-in-Chief. Louise was so enraged by Vicky's attitude, as though the matter were already cut and dried, that, when asked what she would like to give Lenchen as a wedding present, snappily replied: 'Bismarck's head on a charger!' Bertie and Alix's feelings were no less forceful, though their objection to the match was primarily because Prince Christian had taken Prussia's side in the Danish–German war and that was quite unforgivable. Bertie declared that if the objectionable marriage took place neither he nor Alix would attend.

It was Lenchen herself who decided the issue. Shy, wanting in charm, and not especially pretty, she knew that it was Prince Christian with his bald head and country-bumpkin ways or nothing.

The wedding was decided on.

The family, for her sake, pretended to be reconciled, but Lady Geraldine spoke for the anti-Christians when she described it as:

'an abominable, disgraceful *marriage with a miserable starveling German Princeling.'*

Vicky and her mother were no less spirited in championing the amiable Prince Christian, and the Queen, appalled by the open rebellion from Marlborough House declared:

Alix is by no means what she ought to be. It will be long, if ever, before she regains my confidence.

It was not as long as she expected because Alix suddenly gave way. She had been persuaded by her old friend Lenchen. 'It might be my only chance,' said she with a candour which dumbfounded

141

Alix. And Bertie was persuaded to do the same because all at once Mama had too much to put up with. In quick succession she lost Lord Palmerston, Phipps her Private Secretary, and Uncle Leopold. Their deaths brought on a *crise des nerfs* which was pitiable, and Bertie would not add to her pain by quarrelling any further about his sister's wedding.

There was no family quarrel about Princess Mary Adelaide's marriage. Indeed there was general relief that she had found herself so suitable a partner: an exceedingly handsome Serene Highness, four years her junior, whose father would have been heir apparent to the reigning King of Würtemberg had he not forfeited his rights by making a morganatic marriage. Given the title Prince of Teck, Prince Franz had grown up in Vienna as the particular pet of the Emperor and Empress. His demerits were obvious because, being extravagant, he was penniless. But his assets outweighed them. Like Prince Christian he was prepared to live in England and he was tall, well-built, elegant, with beautiful eyes, the darkest of blue-black hair, waxed moustaches and a tuft of an imperial; very good looking indeed, in fact known in Viennese court society as *der schöne Uhlan*.

During the short engagement the Cambridges and the Prince of Teck himself busied themselves in trying to improve his status and fortunes. The King of Würtemburg undertook, one day, to make him a duke. The Queen permitted them the use of the apartments in Kensington Palace where she herself had grown up, and gave him the Order of the Bath, but she would not alter his title. So far as she was concerned Mary Adelaide's own title was more than anything that could be specially made up for the occasion, and that was quite sufficient. And she set the seal of her approval of the match by appearing in person at the wedding.

Kew Church was packed and overflowing for the occasion. So were Kew Green and the village. Everyone wanted to see Fat Mary and the Queen. The former, mountainous in white lace, wept with happiness. The Queen smiled at everyone and nodded, and for a moment felt quite her old self again, though she commented in her Journal on the handsome bridegroom's nervousness. She also added a cryptic note which remains unexplained to this day:

The Fracas with the China caused by the Bp. of Winchester was considerable. Such *an absurd thing to happen!*

142

Both Bertie and Alix saw off the bridal couple for their brief honeymoon. It had to be brief as Prince Franz was being called to his regiment in the Austrian army. It was 18 June and Bismarck was in the middle of another of his underhand wars. Within a few days of that happy day in Kew the Tecks were on their way to Stuttgart, leaving behind a family of speculation as to who would ultimately be the dominant partner in this unexpected and unlikely marriage. Mama's half-sister was firmly of the opinion that the Prince of Teck would soon be *'unter dem Pantoffel'*, as she put it, and Bertie was inclined to agree with her. But Mama and Alix were of a very different opinion.

Then the much-disputed marriage between Lenchen and Prince Christian of Schleswig-Holstein took place in St George's Chapel at Windsor. Not only was the Queen there in full state, but she also gave away the bride. It emphasized her view in a very pointed way. Bertie was relieved to discover his new brother-in-law was a mild-mannered elderly prince with nothing more than a senti-mental regard for his old home in Germany. To give him some-thing to do the Queen made him the Ranger of Windsor Park, where he was to indulge his passion for planting trees and con-struct a lovely garden about Cumberland House. He came to England with the progeny of doves from his old house in Germany, and a load of cuttings from the roses there. In fact he was a kind, if dull, middle-aged gentleman and did not really deserve Alix's tart rebuke that she wondered he had not followed the example of Franz of Teck and gone off to join his regiment – but on the other, hated, Prussian side, of course. . . .

Bertie took her to task for this unnecessary rudeness. He was determined that, if possible, she should at least try to accept her friend Lenchen's husband. He begged her to apologize; and, abruptly giving way, she did, thereby embarrassing poor Prince Christian who was already embarrassed enough by his connection with this extraordinary English Royal Family. There was not in the least doubt who was going to be *'unter dem Pantoffel'* at Cumberland Lodge.

Had he time to go, Prince Christian would have been too late to fight in the Austro–Prussian War. Even the Prince of Teck who did go, was too late.

After the conclusive defeat of the Austrians at Sadowa the Prussians quarrelled amongst themselves as to what terms they should demand. Bismarck, though only a lieutenant in the reserve, had got himself hastily promoted to major-general so that he could be on the scene in person. The victorious King of Prussia wanted to inflict severe terms on Austria but leave her allies largely alone. Bismarck wanted the unification of Germany. He could only achieve it at the expense of those princes who had sided with Austria. He tried all his tricks of persuasion on the King. He threatened resignation, affected hysterics and broke crockery. It was only when he said that he would do away with himself by jumping from a high window that his royal master gave way.

It so happened that the Queen and the Prince of Wales were together when they heard the peace terms. Hanover was lost to the royal family for ever, together with the King's considerable private fortune. The Grand-Duchy of Hesse-Darmstadt, where Alice's Louis was in succession to the throne, lost a large part of its territories. Alix's uncle, the Landgrave of Hesse-Cassell, lost everything except the right to live as an exile on the border of his former possessions. . . .

Bertie raged against Prussia, in particular against Bismarck.

Victoria, white-faced, stood there holding the despatch. She herself was much alarmed by the swift changes which were taking place. The map of Europe was now altered beyond recognition and in the British Isles, simply to catch party votes, the franchise had been enlarged so that the self-interested and the ignorant had a say in affairs. Why, Mr Lowe, an advanced Liberal, had himself said that to enlarge the franchise was madness; and when it had been done, and he had been shifted to the less dangerous benches of the House of Lords, he had remarked with asperity that 'now we have given the vote to so many our prime duty is to educate our masters'. . . .

The Prince's political thinking coincided almost precisely with his mother's, and he was upset but not surprised to see her in such a trembling state of alarm after Bismarck's rape of the German principalities.

When news came at the end of the month that a mob, forbidden to hold a meeting in Hyde Park, had broken down the railings and worked havoc in the flower beds, settling there for two whole days, he went down from London to dispute with the Queen's new Private Secretary, General Grey, the wisdom of giving her full details of the violence. Eventually General Grey persuaded him that the Queen had a remarkable robustness in facing misfortune, and it was decided that she should be told everything.

She reacted as Grey had prophesised. Democracy, she said, would be the ruin of them all.

'Just so,' her son agreed.

8

The Prince and Princess of Wales had fallen into the habit of making White Lodge in Richmond Park their Saturday to Monday retreat, and Mary Adelaide of Teck sensing, quite correctly, that it was but a temporary arrangement, and having her own eye on this grace-and-favour house as a most suitable country retreat, quite frequently dropped hints to her old friend Alix. But she discovered that Alix, either because of her deafness or her imperfect grasp of Mary Adelaide's flood of hints, failed to detect her real intentions, and so, one February day in 1867, the Princess of Teck called at Marlborough House to make her meaning abundantly plain.

She had already enjoyed a substantial tea to fortify her for the drive through the cold, clammy air, and she would not hear of fresh tea being made for her. 'But a negus, dear, yes a negus, would be very welcome and warming.' She held her hands to the fire while the hot negus was being ordered, prepared and brought, and nibbled at ratafia biscuits and garibaldis. Then, at a suitable moment she asked outright for Alix's word in the Queen's ear should the Waleses ever think of giving up White Lodge. The place needed doing up, of course. She believed it had scarcely been touched since Bertie had lived there as a boy surrounded by clergymen and soldiers. But it really would suit her, being conveniently near to London and yet in the country, and it so happened that her Francis had a most wonderful knack of arranging houses to make them very comfortable and laying out gardens. It was the only away, she lamented, in which he could make himself useful – for the Queen had no thought of employing him, nor had her new Tory Ministry led by the genial Earl of Derby and that bright lizard amongst statesmen, Mr Benjamin Disraeli.

Mary Adelaide was so preoccupied with making her point and sipping the steaming negus and eating biscuits that she hardly noticed Alix had said neither yes nor no nor anything else since the topic had been introduced. When she did eventually notice she stopped eating and said that she hoped she had not offended by asking.

'Oh, no, no,' reassured Alix. 'It is just that, at the moment, I can't . . . I can't concentrate.'

Mary Adelaide was immediately concerned. She was carrying a child herself – which at her size and at her age was something of an undertaking – but she was far more anxious about Alix who was due to be confined of her third child in little over a month's time. 'You feel unwell, dear?'

Alix gave a dejected nod.

Mary Adelaide took her hand, which was trembling. She felt Alix's forehead and found it burning with fever.

A dresser was called, then Lady Macclesfield, the Princess's monthly nurse, her physicians.

The Princess of Teck supervised their examination with the authority of a close relative, an old friend, a matron, and a woman who had wheeled the Princess of Wales in her pram many years before. It was to her that the physicians reported, with unconcealed alarm, that the Princess appeared to have rheumatic fever. . . .

The Prince of Wales was sent for.

At one time he had been wary of Mary Adelaide, and not been absolutely sure that he could count on her discretion. She had ears which caught the secrets of Society like clams collecting sand, and a tongue which tittle-tattled. But, to his relief, she had been absolutely fair. Anything she might have known about his indiscretions – and, being Mary Adelaide, she probably knew them all – she had kindly kept from Alix; and she was a capable woman in emergencies. He was very glad to see her there on one side of Alix's white bed with Lady Macclesfield on the other.

Dearest Mac was comfortable and sensible; Mary Adelaide equally wise and doubly imperious. It was the latter, not the Prince

146

of Wales, who sent telegraph messages to the Queen and the remainder of the family. Then she used her authority as his close relation to make Bertie square up to the facts that rheumatic fever so close to a confinement was exceedingly dangerous. Alix's parents had to be sent for. Straight away.

Queen Victoria was exceedingly anxious. Despite Alix's gadding and her maddening air of insouciance, and her habit of answering back, she was growing very fond of her again. She sent telegraph after telegraph of inquiry and wrote to Bertie and to Alix's parents. Eventually she received the good news that in spite of everything Alix had been prematurely delivered of a healthy child, her first girl, and was herself responding well to treatment. Her physicians were sure that although recovery would be prolonged, it would almost certainly be complete.

Entirely reassured, King Christian finished his private visit and went home to Denmark, but Alix's mother remained.

Victoria was not best pleased. She recognized Queen Louise's rights but dreaded that she would make trouble between Alix and Bertie. Even the Danish Queen's features seemed to have destined her to be mischievous for she had beautifully sad, reproachful eyes and the pointed ears of a Puck, and, having suffered a good deal on account of malicious gossip about her own family, she sought revenge whenever she could, probing into secrets, uncovering indiscretions, tittle-tattling and moaning about other people's deleterious behaviour. It was not inappropriate, Victoria remarked to Lady Churchill, that the Danish word for queen was *droning*. In its English sense the word seemed particularly apposite. Droning Louise's place might be justly with her daughter, but, aware that Bertie's private life could hardly stand up to the careful scrutiny of his mother-in-law, Victoria, for her own part, would just as soon introduce an asp into Marlborough House.

Her fears were abundantly justified.

Droning Louise naturally saw a good deal of her fellow Rumpenheimers, and milked them for information. Mary Adelaide was too accomplished a gossip herself to give anything away which she wanted to keep to herself, but her sister Augusta, who was over in England, was child's play to the clever Danish Queen. So was her mother, the half senile Duchess of Cambridge. And as for George, a little comradely chaff about boys being boys would start him off on a chain of genial reminiscences, and, should he come to

147

himself and realize that he was, maybe, being uncircumspect, a little push from the spiteful Lady Geraldine, who hated the Waleses, was sufficient to set him off again. Several of Droning Louise's suspicions about her son-in-law were fully confirmed.

The previous autumn he had attended Dagmar's marriage to the Tsarevitch, and being alone – Alix's condition made it impossible for her to go to the wedding – he had consoled himself with certain Russian ladies noted for their wildness but not for keeping a still tongue in their heads. And the Prince's behaviour in Paris was equally scandalous. Last year he had been entertaining the magnificent Emilienne d'Alençon, a courtesan who used heliotrope scent and rode in a carriage upholstered in heliotrope-coloured satin. And now, hissed Lady Geraldine, he was head over heels with the Schneider girl. Positively head over heels. . . . Droning Louise looked dismal. She remarked that it was abominable of the Prince. While poor dear Alexanda lay immovable in Marlborough House, her satyr of a husband was constantly running over to France – ostensibly to the Great Paris Exhibition, in reality to prink himself out and wait like a common subaltern in Hortense Schneider's dressing-room while she thrilled Paris in Offenbach's latest operetta as the Grand Duchess of Gerolstein.

The nimble-witted Mary Adelaide noted that Alix's mother seemed to relish the gossip, that it gave her a gloomy satisfaction, that she was actually going to shatter her own daughter's illusions. What the result would be Mary Adelaide did not care to imagine, but, if possible, she intended to be at hand to offer Alix her help.

To everyone's surprise, for her child had not yet been born, the Princess of Teck took to driving each day to Marlborough House. Ostensibly she was inquiring after her dear young friend. In fact she was looking for evidence of distress in Alix's face. At last, and it was not long before Droning Louise's departure for Denmark, she saw signs of what she had been looking for. Despite her husband's admonition to take care or his son and heir would be born in an open carriage or at Marlborough House, Mary Adelaide continued to make herself available as often as possible in case, simply in case Alix wished to talk.

But unaccountably she remained silent.

Then Lenchen's confinement seized everyone's attention. She had a son, named for his father, and old Christian was happily planting trees all over Windsor Great Park to mark the event. And after that Mary Adelaide herself was delivered of a baby girl, called at first Mary, but afterwards May. Contrary to all expectations, she bore the child easily, painlessly, and, ironically, in view of her terrible unpunctuality, on the exact date her physicians had foretold. After her lying-in, she returned to her custom of visiting Alix who was still kept to the house, one knee permanently damaged and her deafness increased. It was not until 3 July that Alix could be wheeled out into the garden for the first time and little Princess May was taken to see her.

Alix again was showing signs of distress, though she pretended it was because she had been looking forward to attending a military review and it had had to be cancelled on account of the murder of the Emperor of Mexico.

Mary Adelaide's hands flew in the air in horror. She warned Alix with great emphasis to avoid all reviews until she was in absolutely tiptop condition. Her own poor mother-in-law in a moment of weakness at a review had been thrown by a startled horse and trampled to death by a squadron of heavy chargers.

Alix's eyes filled with tears, but whether out of sympathy for the victim of a cavalry charge, or for other reasons, Mary Adelaide had no means of knowing, and all the time – sharp as a bird – she watched her young friend. That she was suffering on account of Bertie, Mary Adelaide felt rather than observed, and then one afternoon, when the two friends and Lady Macclesfield were playing five-card loo together in the Great Saloon at Marlborough House, she accidentally discovered that her intuition had been right.

Their game was temporarily interrupted by Charles Wood, who said he had daguerreotypes for the Princess to see. They were of the Prince, who much enjoyed having his picture taken.

She laid down her cards and looked at the photographs in turn, passing them to Lady Macclesfield. Lady Macclesfield barely gave them a glance before passing them on. She was a great card-player and was wondering how best to use the 'Pam' which good fortune had dealt her. Mary Adelaide also gave them scant attention. She had half an eye on the photographs but half on Alix because a tear was stealing down her young friend's cheek. She dashed it off with a quick impatient forefinger because it betrayed her feelings. But the tear and the gesture told Mary Adelaide her

149

worst fears had been justified: that despicable Danish queen had felt it her sorrowful duty to inform Alix about Bertie's *vie orageuse*.

In the great Teck bed at Kensington Palace Mary Adelaide told her Franz what had happened. He was himself a great brooder on misfortunes and therefore would feel for Alix and know what to do. To her amazement he advised her to say and do nothing.

'While poor, dear darling Alix suffers?'

'Exactly.'

She sat bolt upright in bed. 'Franz, you have no heart.'

'I have one,' was his reply, 'and a head as well. Keep well away from both Alix and Bertie.'

She lay down again and thought. Before she went to sleep she believed she had found the right solution.

The Queen was invited to Kensington to view the new baby. She accepted, partly to satisfy her duty to the family, but mostly because the Tecks lived in that part of Kensington Palace where she herself had lived as a child. The old unhappiness, loneliness, the feeling of being cut off, the intrigues of her mother's lover, the endless war between her mother, whom she loathed, and the governess she had loved, were all now forgotten. Only the happy memories remained.

She admired baby May without reservations. Really she was a fine child. And Franz, though so gloomy and sulky because he had little to do, had made their apartments very comfortable. He was sent off to do something or other and then the two cousins sat on a sofa to talk.

Victoria had intended to say tactfully that Aunt Cambridge and George were anxious about the Tecks' extravagance; and that to avoid rousing petty jealousies, she really could do no more for Franz, excellent and dear man though he was; and that the running expenses of White Lodge, which she now knew her cousin was after, would surely topple them into still more money difficulties; but Mary Adelaide came straight to the point and the Queen forgot everything else.

'Poor Alix,' she said softly. 'I suppose it was inevitable but I do

150

feel for her so much.' Then, with some asperity she continued to give her opinion of Louise of Denmark.

'There is no proof. . . .' suggested Mary Adelaide.

'Proof? Stuff! I knew she would cause trouble. I told Jane Churchill so. And she has.'

'She certainly has,' agreed her cousin unhappily.

'And we must do what we can to put things right.'

Mary Adelaide looked at her with great relief. It had been a risk to confide in her. But evidently the Queen shared her own feelings for both Alix and Bertie, and only she had the authority to interfere in their lives.

'I shall speak to Bertie,' continued the Queen after a moment's reflection. 'And he will listen because he has to. But only Alice has any real influence on him. It was always the same and perhaps it still is.' She smoothed her white collar and added firmly: 'I shall write to Alice myself. She and I, as you know, dear, have not been on the best of terms recently, but I feel certain that for Bertie she will rally. Yes, she will rally. Meanwhile,' she continued, 'you will do your excellent best, dear Mary, to encourage Alix? It is outside my province as her mother-in-law.'

Mary Adelaide undertook to do all she could.

The Prince of Wales did not enjoy the strongly worded letter he had from Darmstadt. His favourite sister acknowledged that gentlemen, and especially rich and royal ones, frequently formed relationships outside the bonds of marriage – but to be flagrant, and flaunt his affair with a French actress while Alix was lying seriously ill at Marlborough House, ought to make him feel ashamed. He was, she scolded, a cad. She also formally complained of his conduct through his Comptroller, which was a final touch of acid.

Nor did the Prince of Wales enjoy his private luncheon with the Queen at Windsor. She was not in the least vehement but the cold way in which she underlined the facts was very telling. She reminded him that though moribund, republicanism still lived. She reminded him that the press cared for neither of them – as witness the snide though never quite libellous comments on Mr Brown of Deeside and Miss Schneider of Paris. And she told him that to be inattentive to his wife during the time of her illness and be for ever running across to France was scarcely kind. She suggested he take Alix for a cure abroad and look after her. The royal physicians had already recommended Wiesbaden, a famous spa and with a comfortably mild climate at the foot of the Taunus Hills.

Alix said with a little of her old spirit that she would have preferred to go to a watering place which was not in Prussian territory – for Wiesbaden as the capital of Nassau had been filched by Prussia in the war the year before – but she was glad to get away from the scene of her illness, where she had hated her restricting debility and lameness and had hated even more being an object of unexpressed pity. She had brought herself eventually to speak to Mary Adelaide about her bruised feelings, and Charlotte Knollys, too, had been taken into her confidence. But neither, she guessed, could measure the depth of her misery, although both now saw how well she had concealed the jealousy and possessiveness which had tormented her. Yet, though it was a relief to get away from London, and the doctors held out a real hope that the Wiesbaden cure would do wonders for her spirits as well as for her game knee, she wished that Bertie had not insisted on accompanying her there. It was not that her affection for him had lessened, but it had altered. She loved him as much as before it became abundantly plain that he was keeping mistresses, but she did not yet want to see much of him in private. In any case, holidaying with the energetic Bertie was invariably exhausting, and she felt herself totally unable to have a frank talk with him as Mary Adelaide had suggested. And so she chose to protect herself by inviting her sister Dagmar and the Tsarevitch to join her, and asked her mother as well.

Bertie kept it to himself but he did not care much for his mother-in-law. Her mournful face, her habit of bleating complaints alternating with astringent remarks on what she thought was wrong with young and modern princes, grated on his nerves. But he did like Dagmar, now re-named Marie Feodorovna, a petite and vital version of Alexandra and minute beside her huge husband the Tsarevitch. And once he had overcome the initial feeling of inferiority which a small man naturally experienced in the presence of so enormous a prince – for the Tsarevitch had the beard, build and morose temperament of his ancestor Peter the Great – Bertie did his best to get on with him, too. But the

Tsarevitch was as shy as he was big. He appeared to lack initiative. He was a bore.

Queen Victoria was concerned. However beneficial its curative waters, Wiesbaden was far, far too close to Rumpenheim and far, far too close to Baden; facts which she had overlooked when her physicians made their recommendations. She quickly wrote to Bertie warning him that Baden society was disreputable:

No one can mix in it without loss of character.

She said nothing, and could not, of Rumpenheim, but then to her dismay she discovered that the mischief-making Droning Louise was at Wiesbaden and that wild young Lord Carrington in the suite of her son. In an agony of suspense she bade Vicky do what she could to bring pressure to bear on Bertie. Vicky obliged her. But Bertie was bored and when bored he was bad tempered and not inclined to accept bossiness from his elder sister. Guessing the source of her strong advice to behave himself, he wrote directly to the Queen at Balmoral.

I know that Vicky has written to you on the subject,
but one would imagine she thought me 10 or 12 years old,
and not nearly 26.

And then he and Charles Carrington went to Baden for a week. This brief display of independence over, and much lighter in pocket and heavier in frame, because the restaurateurs of Baden had put themselves out to please so notable a gourmet, the Prince of Wales returned to Wiesbaden to do his dull duty as a husband. He regarded his ailing wife and his mother-in-law with a dull eye, the huge Tsarevitch, too. Boredom settled on him like blanketing fog. But then, suddenly, a situation arose which demanded all his attention and entirely dispelled his boredom. The King of Prussia telegraphed to say that he wished to visit the Prince and Princess of Wales there at any time convenient to the Princess. He was by no means obliged to, but was being diplomatic and remembering that his daughter-in-law was the Prince's sister; the King was being friendly. But he had not taken into sufficient account the bitter hostility of the Danes to Prussia. The Princess of Wales refused point blank to see him or even to reply to the approach. Her mother solemnly approved. But General Knollys did not. He was horrified. He spoke privately to the Prince, emphasizing the appalling diplomatic situation which would arise if the King's courteous offer was met with such rudeness. Somehow or other the Princess had to be persuaded to receive him.

The Prince agreed. He and Knollys, other members of his Household and even 'dearest Mac' and the Tsarevitch did their best to make the Princess change her mind. But, steeled by her mother, Alix was obdurate. She remained so even when Bertie personally asked her to consent as a great and particular favour to him. She refused.

Feeling acutely self-conscious about his failure he telegraphed the King to say that his wife was still too unwell to receive visitors.

At the Prussian court tempers flared. It was well known there that the Princess of Wales was much better, and that she was often receiving visitors. Great offence was taken, but the King of Prussia, determined to end this deadlock between the Hohenzollerns and the English royal family, ordered Fritz to telegraph another offer. It was magnanimous from the reigning sovereign of an autocracy. If the Princess of Wales would name a date and time – any date or time – for the King to call on her and pay his respects, he would be there.

Telegrams showered in on the Prince of Wales: from Vicky in Berlin, Alice in Hesse, from Mama in Scotland, from the thirty-eight Rumpenheimers in residence at the Schloss. As a last resort, the Prince and his Comptroller went to Droning Louise and begged her to use all her power as a mother to persuade Alix to be less rigid. At first she refused. Later however, she said she was prepared to sacrifice her own feelings. When warned of the diplomatic troubles which might follow her continued refusal, she would meet the King of Prussia herself, and she hoped that Alix might too.

Bertie already knew his wife better in one sense than her mother knew her. Unless actually commanded Alix would do no such thing. He would have to order her compliance.

He took a telegraph form and on it he scribbled an invitation to the King of Prussia to breakfast with the family on the following day. Then he went to Alix's room and showed it to her.

She read what he had written. Her chin set. Her cheeks trembled as though she was about to cry. At this odd moment Bertie suddenly noticed that she had rather a long nose. He rang for Knollys and asked him to despatch the telegram without delay.

Alix, supported by her husband, her mother and her brother, the King of Greece, who had just arrived at Wiesbaden, met King William of Prussia the next morning. The King was so gratified with the success of his visit that he stayed to luncheon too. Alix was a little distant but polite. Vicky and Alice reported in great excitement that the King had been delighted with her, that he had declared his own relief that the family feud was over. . . .

Over?

Princess Alexandra was not a woman to forget. Those *Pikelhaube* Prussians might deceive themselves and everyone else, but she would remember.

She would remember as well that twice that year her husband had hurt her pride. It bled like an internal haemorrhage, invisible but serious.

9

Mrs Disraeli, bewigged, bejewelled, painted, ancient and as frail as Brussels lace gave a reception on 25 March, 1868.

It was not at No. 10 because although her adored Dizzy was now First Lord of the Treasury and the Queen's first Minister, she considered No. 10 shabby and damp and probably overrun with mice. In fact she felt too old and ill to move from her comfortable home in Grosvenor Gate and so everyone was bidden to celebrate Dizzy's accession to power in the Foreign Office.

For some time now Dizzy had had the Queen's ear and affection and few, except Gladstone who hated him, could resist his charm. The charm might be put on and all humbug – as Gladstone, glowering, averred – but there was no denying its potency and on his arm at the reception on that wet, sleeting, horribly cold

155

day was the equally charming Princess of Wales. His shrivelled appearance and his charm allied to the Princess' youth and *bonté* made them a perfectly contrasted couple; just as Mary Anne Disraeli's great age and her lace-like frailty contrasted well with her partner, the Prince of Wales.

The Prince was just at an important turning point. Very soon over-eating would make his nursery nickname of Tum Tum hurtfully apposite, but at that moment he held himself well and had an air which made his attendance on Mrs Disraeli the apogee of her social life.

Mary Anne had come far: some said from a run-down farm in Devonshire seventy-six years before, where she had been known as 'Littly Whizzy'. Now she entertained London Society as Dizzy's beloved wife. She noted that even the Gladstones were at her reception, plotting, no doubt, the ruin of her darling; and 'Soapy Sam', the Bishop of Oxford, scheming, perhaps, to improve someone who simply wished to be left alone; but the main topic of conversation amongst the serious-minded at her party was the outrageous conduct of the Irish.

Mrs Dizzy was not in the least serious-minded herself, but she knew her duty as a hostess and she deplored to the Prince the Fenians' threats to his mother. Not long before Christmas a plot to kidnap the Queen had been uncovered, and this was followed by news from America that eighty American-Irish assassins had embarked at New York determined on flushing Victoria from the Isle of Wight. They had never arrived to penetrate the defences of Cowes and Osborne and it was now accounted a newspaper rumour, though Mrs Dizzy warmly told the Prince that she herself hoped there lay at the bottom of the Atlantic a boatload of eighty American-Irish assassins. And recently his poor brother Prince Alfred had been shot at by a discontented Irishman in Australia. Happily the wound had been slight but waiting for bulletins from the other side of the world had been nerveracking to the royal family.

Mary Anne was all sympathy. Lightly she touched the Prince's arm with her fan. 'You wait, Sir,' she prophesied. 'My Dizzy will do for them. He'll do for them.'

As he was already aware of Mr Disraeli's plan for doing the Irish – a plan which involved his going with Alix on an official visit to Ireland – the Prince made no audible reply.

On their way home from that remarkable reception Bertie pressed his wife's hand. He often made such spontaneous signs of affection, which she very much valued. They talked in low voices of the Disraelis' happiness and how they deserved it.

It was said – at least the Whigs and Liberals said – that Dizzy had married Mary Anne for her money, but her care for him and his appreciation of it, their obvious compatibility, and their mutual affection which was never paraded but quite impossible to hide, made them one of the most envied couples in society.

A year before, when he had been Chancellor of the Exchequer, Mama's sudden liking for Disraeli had caused a ripple of anxiety in the family, but Mary Anne had cheerfully accepted the friendship and now he was the friend of all her children from Vicky in Prussia to Beatrice in her schoolroom.

Alix felt that Mary Anne's tolerance of the relationship might well be a lesson to her.

As for Bertie; he was amused because Disraeli invariably greeted him with a low bow, saying aloud, 'My dear, dear Prince'; and once he understood that Mama and her minister were attracted because they were so very different, he was pleased at the influence Disraeli could bring to bear on her for the good of his own race and other foreigners who did not have the entrée to Court. Mama still stiffly maintained that the Orthodox Rothschilds were *not* the same as her Baptized and Christian Prime Minister, and that her good friend had natural rights which other Jews, American and parvenus could not expect to enjoy, but her resolve was weakening. And meanwhile both were enjoying a romance which in any other couple but Queen Victoria and Benjamin Disraeli would have been grotesque and scandalous.

As they drove home to Marlborough House Alix analysed their strange relationship. Though not intellectual in any sense she had an intuition for this sort of thing and saw that Dizzy admired Mama's vitality, her grandeur, and her plain common-sense. And, while she adored the flattery which he offered her with an almost oriental extravagance, neither was affected by it.

'They both find it soothing,' remarked Alix.

Bertie chuckled. 'Their feet on the ground and heads high in the air?'

'Exactly.'

Again he pressed her hand.

157

It encouraged her to hope that perhaps he might decide not to go to his club. She asked.

'No, White's can be damnably dull. Their smoking rules are as archaic as Mama's. I'll play billiards with an equerry while you lie down.'

She made a moue. She was again carrying a child and her physicians had laid down certain strict rules. Lady Macclesfield made sure they were carried out.

Seeing her grimace he said gently: 'After your rest, join me in the library and we will look at maps of Ireland. And perhaps we will look at other maps. Mrs Dizzy appeared to think it an excellent plan for us to enjoy ourselves. After duty pleasure. She suggested we took a long holiday together during the coming winter.'

At that moment the carriage stopped. Footmen leapt to let down the steps and hold umbrellas.

Inside the Great Hall was warm. Mantles, coats, hats, gloves were taken. The Princess smiled at her husband. 'It would be wonderful,' she said, and took his hand.

Very seldom did she spontaneously show great pleasure. Now, the thought of a long holiday alone with Bertie, away from the fogs of London and the cold winds of Sandringham, somewhere in the sun, made her do so.

Queen Victoria had doubted the wisdom of the Waleses Irish visit. It seemed lunatic to send her heir to Ireland while her second son was recovering from an Irish bullet wound. But Mr Disraeli persuaded her that, politically, it was highly desirable, and she felt that if the young people had the courage to make such a gesture at such a worrying time, then she ought not to prevent them.

Both Bertie and Alix were nervous as they approached their first reception to Ireland. Their welcome might be less cordial than Disraeli had prophesied. After all he had never been there himself – indeed, although his policies had such a profound effect on the country, he was never to go to Ireland in his life.

It might be cheers, raised hats and the fluttering of handkerchiefs.

Or it might be catcalls and rotten fish – worse still, a dead silence.

Worst of all, if the Ribbonmen were out of hand, the Prince and Princess actually stood in physical peril of their lives.

Happily Disraeli's prophecy proved correct. It had been based on the Viceroy's reports, his own intuition that all would be well, his confidence in the Princess' reputation for charming people, and the Prince's reputation as a roisterer and race-goer. Wily Disraeli knew the Irish willingness to accept a good fellow, and a pretty, unaffected woman.

The Prince was feasted, taken from jollity to jollity, and caught the people's highest admiration by his keenness and mad extravagance at the Punchestown Races. As for the Princess, she found in the Irish a natural sympathy.

They were unpunctual as she was, they loved informality as she did, they were maddeningly illogical in all things, as she so often was; and, being from a little country herself, she felt immediately at home amongst the Irish. *The Times* – on this occasion accurate – described the visit as '*The Danish Conquest of Ireland*', and ever afterwards the Irish had a place in Alix's affections. Bertie though, for all that he had enjoyed the junketings, knew that the Irish were as fickle as they were full of fun, and General Knollys impressed on him that they were a forgetful people. Very probably, before the royal yacht had docked at Southampton, the Irish would be busy again with their home-made bombs and cutting each other's throats into the bargain.

When the Waleses went to Osborne to report their Irish progress and collect their three children they found Mama in a highly nervous state. Her congratulations were warm for all they had done, and she was sincere when she said she admired their courage; but she was alarmed about the increase of republicanism; about renewed attacks upon her secluded life as a widow – and about other matters. . . .

The way she mentioned 'other matters' told Alix that Mama wished to be left alone with Bertie. Tactfully she asked for permission to withdraw so that she could speak to the children's nurses.

'Dear Alix,' the Queen murmured, kissing her on both cheeks, and offering a small tight little hand for her to kiss.

When Alix had gone Bertie coughed. It was a nervous cough, and he felt nervous; but he had the directness of his mother.

'Yes, Mama?'

The Queen gave a deep sigh. From the drawer in her desk she took a marbled cardboard folder, opened it, and passed it to her son. Inside was a large collection of newspaper cuttings about La Schneider.

He had, of course, seen them all before. General Knollys' son Francis made it his business to collect any useful information and certainly all newspaper cuttings which referred to the Prince and Princess of Wales. *The Times* and other newspapers were now openly associating the name of the heir to the throne and the star of Offenbach's operetta.

He handed back the folder and his mother returned it to the desk drawer and locked it. 'You are *so* imprudent!' she said, and not angrily but sadly.

'Mama, they make things up. You know they do.'

She nodded. 'I do indeed. And as much, perhaps more than you, I have suffered from the newspapers. But unless they are stopped, unless you pull yourself together and give no hint of scandalous behaviour, you will harm the throne. Indeed,' she added, 'there will be no throne for you to inherit.'

She declared the situation was so serious that he must somehow keep himself out of the public's eye. 'Come with me to Scotland,' she suggested.

'But it is the beginning of the Season!' he protested. 'Later in the year, yes. With your permission Alix and I plan to visit Egypt and find a little winter sun. But I cannot leave London now. Not at the beginning of the Season. It would arouse more comment than ever.'

'And Mademoiselle Schneider?'

'Our friendship, Mama, is over.'

She nodded. There was relief in his eyes. 'I still think you should come to Scotland. My birthday is on May 24th. Come for my birthday. It could not possibly arouse adverse comment. Alix, I feel sure, will not mind. It would give you and me a chance to be together in private for two or three days for the first time for years.'

To her vexation Bertie still would not commit himself. But he did undertake to mention the matter to his wife.

Alix, when she heard the suggestion, was perturbed. She did not know the real reason why the Queen wanted Bertie to forgo a part of the Season and decided that it must be to get him alone at

Balmoral and thoroughly under her thumb again. He was at last living and thinking independently of the Court and that, according to Alix, was how it should be. She told Bertie so. She told Mac. She told Charlotte Knollys. She told Princess Mary Adelaide. Urged on by Alix, Bertie wrote to the Queen that it was necessary for Society, trade and public affairs that someone should lead the London Season and, as she herself refused to appear, he would have to do it for her.

It was an offensive, thoughtless reply to someone who was greatly concerned for the future of the monarchy in England, and Victoria, having a violent Hanoverian temper, almost told her son he was being unco-operative, rude, silly, and clearly failed to understand the importance of keeping out of the public's eye. But simply because of this importance, she strangled her anger, and continued to write severe letters, touched here and there with an appealing melancholy, begging him to change his mind and go up to Balmoral. To Alix's indignation Bertie found Mama's appeals irresistible. He actually missed the Derby and went up to Deeside for a short three-day stay. The Queen appreciated it a great deal and went out of her way to please her son. She showed him the new retreat she had had built for herself beside Loch Muich, a place so still and remote that it met her need for complete seclusion. The double cottage which she and Albert had built together was to be allowed to tumble into disuse. It marked a milestone in her widowhood which Bertie understood and appreciated. He also more distinctly understood her concern for the throne, not simply as a sign of power but as a sacred trust. In the short time she had available she worked on his impressionable nature to slow him down a little and teach him the necessity for even greater circumspection. She gladly gave her permission for his projected winter holiday with Alix and advised him to make it last several months so that the furore whipped up by the press would have a chance to settle and perhaps die.

In July, again prematurely, the Princess of Wales was confined of her fourth child and second daughter, Princess Victoria. Her strong maternal feelings were still further strengthened. Could she not, she asked Bertie, take the three older children when they went to Denmark at the beginning of their long holiday?

161

Through Knollys and General Grey the question was put to the Queen.

Certainly not, she wrote to her son, and Alix was selfish to consider that the Princes Eddy and George and the Princesses Louise and Victoria were her private property. They were the 'children of the country' and must be left in her care.

Alix wept. She said nothing against Mama or Mama's decision. She just sat there, the letter in her hand, the tears trickling down her cheeks.

Bertie was deeply touched. He did not want to risk damaging his new and highly valued relationship with Mama, but he still would not have Alix bullied by anyone. He went directly to his desk and wrote three drafts of a letter before he was satisfied with it. In essence he accepted Mama's decision as the Command of his Queen but he added a protest:

None of us are perfect and she [Alix] may have her faults; but she certainly is not selfish and her whole life is wrapped up in her children. It seems hard that because she wishes (with a natural mother's pride) to take her 3 eldest children to her Parents' home, every difficulty should be placed in her way....

The Queen knew when to yield. Those who would topple the throne would only be kept at bay if she and the family gave an appearance of being firmly united. She gave permission for the children to accompany their parents for the first part of their trip abroad; to France and Denmark and Sweden, but she asked that they be sent home early in the New Year and she kept a keen eye on what Bertie and Alix were doing; larding her maternal letters with sharp questions:

What was Bertie thinking of allowing himself to be initiated as a freemason by the King of Sweden? Secret societies were indefensible.

Why had no governess been sent with the children in the royal yacht from Copenhagen?

Why had Alix *again* behaved so uncivilly in Berlin – addressing the Queen of Prussia as Your Majesty instead of calling her Aunt Augusta as she had been told to do?

Why had they broken their incognito in Vienna?

162

Why was Lord Carrington in the Prince's party, and Colonel Oliver Montagu? Neither were the steady, reliable men who ought to accompany princes. And was it true that that very fast young Duke of Sutherland was waiting in Egypt to join the party?

Bertie fired a shot or two on his own account. He defended his choice of friends, and he suggested that Mama went up to London more often to show herself to her subjects. But, considerately, he became more amenable when he heard that Dizzy had been replaced as First Minister by Gladstone. Mama would be in no mood to bear teasing, however mild. And out of genuine thoughtfulness for her because she so loathed extravagance as well as to protect himself from her wrath, he supervised and censored the bulletins of news about their holiday in Egypt.

He mentioned that the Khedive was treating them handsomely, as was only right, but he glossed over the fabulous luxury of their trip. The stark truth would have excited all Mama's hatred of prodigality and excess. A fleet of dahabeahs and tugs and steamers had been placed at their disposal by the Khedive for their voyage up the Nile and no expense had been spared. There were striped awnings, bright rugs and chairs on the decks; panelled staterooms below with beautiful carpets and heavy English furniture especially imported for the occasion. The Prince and Princess with their Ladies and Gentlemen, valets and dressers travelled on a massive gold and blue dahabeah *Alexandria*, and the rest of the party were accommodated on a large steamer *The Ornament of the Two Seas*. There were also a kitchen steamer complete with four French chefs and their assistants; provision boats for the transport of ordinary necessities and an undreamt-of number of luxuries, amongst them caged quails and ortolans, tanks of lobsters, three thousand bottles of champagne and four thousand of the finest claret; a laundry, plus French laundress and her family; and, as far as the First Cataract, a dahabeah stable of half a dozen horses, a mule, and a special white donkey for the Princess.

With superb food, in excellent company, and miles from anywhere, their holiday was something neither the Prince nor the Princess ever forgot.

The Princess especially was very happy. She spent a great deal of her time doing nothing in the shade of the striped awnings, and

163

much appreciated that, for the first time in her married life, she was not bound by too strict a routine. Breakfast and luncheon and tea were eaten in the oddest circumstances and at the oddest times. Informal expeditions were decided on and carried out all in an instant. Nevertheless, because Bertie was Bertie and by nature and training extremely punctilious, there had to be some sort of routine. A happy compromise happened rather than was decided on. Having brought his favourite gillie Peter Robinson to supervise the slaughter and collection of duck, cranes, cormorants, crocodiles, herons, hoopoes, flamingos and spoonbills, the Prince spent a great deal of his time out with the gun. He also started to collect curios – an energetic pursuit under the Egyptian sun. But he was not for ever organizing people save in the evenings when, after a formal and exquisite dinner aboard *The Ornament of the Two Seas*, he liked Sutherland's piper Alister to play to them, or he would have Alix sit at the piano and he himself would lead the company in choruses until one and two and sometimes three in the morning.

They penetrated a thousand miles into the yellow desert before turning back, and for the last stages of their voyage, the Khedive placed his own luxurious yacht at their disposal. The *Mahroussa* was fitted out like a palace, with tapestries, crystal, gold and silver plate, services of Sèvres china, and silken hangings. And after that, in Cairo, the Esbekiah Palace was handed over to them. It had been especially refurnished and decorated for their reception – but on so massive and grand a scale that it was actually uncomfortable. The royal bedroom, for example, was over fifty yards long, held twin beds of solid silver and furnishings of beaten gold.

Alix was invited to the Khedive's harem and there met a substantial number of his four wives and five hundred concubines, all of them gorgeously dressed and dripping with jewels and scent. Her description of the gardens, fishponds, eunuch guards, and fantastic riches made Bertie gape, and seeing this, she laughed to herself. Poor Bertie, the life of an oriental despot would suit him so much more than trying to be a respectable Prince of Wales.

The party embarked for Constantinople at the end of March. It had been a long, long holiday. By way of the Grand Porte and Paris they were to make their way back to England and what Bertie dolefully called an eternity of bridge-canal-and-railway openings.

164

Alix smiled to herself, guarding her secret. Bertie had a vast number of souvenirs – stuffed game, no less than thirty-two mummy cases, a complete sarcophagus, cratefuls of beaten trays and copper pots and jugs, a black ram and even a ten-year-old Nubian who was to be baptized in Sandringham and afterwards pour out his coffee there. She too had her souvenir of that happy holiday. Either far away on the turgid, yellow Nile, surrounded by nothing but yellow sand; or in the silken splendour of the Khedive's yacht; or, more likely, in those impossibly uncomfortable solid silver beds at the Esbekiah Palace, she had conceived her fifth child.

10

The Princess of Wales was safely, but again prematurely, delivered of Princess Maud, in the November of 1869. She held the baby in special affection and to Bertie she called her the Fruit of the Nile. But her happiness was soon dulled by the dreadful events of 1870.

At the core of her own personal troubles was Bertie's irresponsible wildness. It sprang from his restlessness and his dread of boredom, and she was forced to agree with Mama that it was stimulated by a good many of his friends. Their long holiday had kept him out of the public eye and his failings had been forgotten; but, except for a lapse when he quarrelled with the committee of White's about their smoking regulations, resigned, and founded his own club, the Marlborough, he had led a very quiet life indeed for months. Then stories began to leak out of wild parties at Gunton Hall in Norfolk, a house he had taken while Sandringham House was being rebuilt, and the Prince of Wales had been heard to declare that he cared not a damn for the snivelling Liberal Nonconformists who were trying to squeeze the juice out of England and out of him as well. Pontificating and humbug he loathed. He seemed determined to flout the conventions and marked this by beginning to use hansom cabs when he went to assignations. People who carped that the heir to the crown was living in a world of fast women, jade and lobster were appalled to be told by the unrepentant Albert Edward that he liked fast women, jade, and lobster.

Something or other had got into him. Alix tried her best to calm him and warn him. So, from a loftier and far more serious plane, did his mother.

Nemesis, said the Queen darkly could not be far away.

As usual she was right.

In February a partially subdued Bertie confessed that a divorce case was coming up in the courts and he had been subpoena'd as a witness. He assured her of his innocence and this she at once believed, but she was thunderstruck when he rambled on unhappily that the defendant's Counsel would be bound to try and show him up in an ugly light. The truth was, he had written the lady a number of trifling letters. . . .

Victoria's blue eyes flashed. She was horrified by his callowness. Surely, surely, by now he had learnt never to commit anything to paper at any time?

She took advice from the Lord Chancellor, and then set Mr Gladstone on to Bertie. Though she could not forgive him for taking Mr Disraeli's place as her First Minister she considered he was just the man to deal with her son and heir. He was an acknowledged friend of the Waleses – a fact which she privately deplored – but she knew that, in his official capacity as Prime Minister and Leader of the Liberal Party, he could be counted on to disapprove of Bertie's stupidity. She was correct. Gladstone did not approve of Prince Albert Edward's frivolousness at all.

He asked if he might call at Marlborough House and in the privacy of the Prince's private sitting-room he immediately broached the matter of the divorce case. He did it with an openness which the Prince appreciated. He was not quite so frank as to call the young man an idiot for having landed himself and the royal family in a distasteful position at a time when the republican clubs were growing and spreading, but his meaning was clear. Then, with his acutely analytical mind, he summarized the probable course of the case.

Sir Charles Mordaunt was filing a petition for divorce against his wife for adultery with two named gentlemen, and a cross-petition was being brought on account of Lady Mordaunt's feebleness of mind. Her counsel, predicted Gladstone, would almost certainly proceed thus, and thus, and thus.

'You will be asked, Sir, quite openly in court, if you have committed adultery with Lady Mordaunt.'

Bertie paled behind his cigar.

'And you must say with firmness and the utmost conviction what is the truth. That you have not.'

When it came to the point, and all turned out as the Prime Minister had foreseen, Bertie grasped the edge of the witness box and made his firm declaration. But he was sincerely glad that he had been warned of the likelihood of such a question. It had never occurred to him that anyone would ask a Prince of Wales such an outright question in a public court, and the unexpectedness could so easily have caused him to hesitate and thus appear to be prevaricating. He was grateful, more grateful than he could say, to Mr Gladstone.

That evening, by a pre-arrangement, he and Alix dined at 11, Carlton House Terrace (Gladstone like Disraeli merely used 10, Downing Street as an office). It seemed to set the official world's approval on his behaviour in court, and certainly all who were present noticed his calm affability and the Princess' composure.

The Prince expressed his private thanks to their host for the warning, and settled to enjoy himself. It was a pleasant meal of simple well-prepared food which, because it was such a startling change from his usual fare, the Prince found delightful. And he enjoyed the company of Mrs Gladstone, related as she was to his old governess, Lady Lyttelton, though dear Laddle at that moment was seriously ill – probably, Mrs Gladstone feared, on her death bed.

At the other end of the table Alix talked quietly to Mr Gladstone. She was as much at home at 11, Carlton House Terrace as she had been in the unpretentious Yellow Palace in Copenhagen, and, as far as was possible under the circumstances, she found herself very comfortable.

The Mordaunt Case was over, but not quite done with. Although the Prime Minister was so obviously gratified by the result; though the Queen and her family were too; and so presumably was the Princess of Wales, it was noticed that she sometimes looked thoughtful and sometimes sad. Inevitably so, of course, but the press took it up, as they took up everything and anything which might be in the interest of increasing sales.

Reynolds' Newspaper wanted to know why His Royal Highness had not been put to a more thorough, pressing and stringent examination in the witness box. This carried the suggestion that things had been arranged by those in high places. *The Times* actually ran a leader which bade Prince Albert Edward walk in his father's footsteps and avoid even the semblance of levity. *The Times* also, and without anyone's permission, printed a copy of one of the Prince's letters to young Lady Mordaunt – hoping perhaps, to do him some disservice, but in this case failing because its very ordinariness seemed to press his innocence.

From the press the hostility to the Prince seeped out into the country. In London it could be felt. When the Princess appeared in a box at the theatre she was warmly cheered, but the cheers died when she was followed by Louisa, Duchess of Manchester, and turned to hisses when Prince Albert Edward appeared. He flushed. Possibly it had been unwise to go to a play at that juncture with the scandalous Louisa, but it was not the thing to hiss at royalty. Not at all the thing. He quietened them with his scowls.

A particular annoyance was the sale of broadsheets. They were scurrilous rather than bawdy. One contained a cruel jab at Lady Mordaunt's undoubted madness and swiped, in passing, at the Prince of Wales:

> *This lady's appetite,*
> *It really is enormous,*
> *But whether wrong or right,*
> *The papers will inform us,*
> *She is fond of veal and ham,*
> *To feed she is a glutton,*
> *She got tired of Charley's lamb,*
> *And longed for royal mutton.*

This sort of thing put the Prince in a sultry rage for days. He was driven mad by the suggestion that because of his supposed infidelities the Princess was off to Denmark earlier than usual, indeed that she had already gone. Why, there she was at Chiswick – a house lent to them temporarily by the Duke of Devonshire –

leading a sedate matronly life for all to see. And when the provincial newspapers started to perform like gadflies after cattle, he was vexed beyond endurance.

The *Sheffield Daily Telegraph* actually reported that he was to be cited as co-respondent in a divorce case between the Seftons. As soon as he heard of this the Prince moved. The Crown lawyers were instructed to sue that newspaper for criminal libel. But there was little satisfaction in the certainty of getting a conviction.

Learning how the hounds of British moral outrage kept a man at bay was utterly depressing him. He even found himself feeling sorry for Arthur Clinton, a son of the Duke of Newcastle, a man whom he'd known for years and who committed suicide that June because the police were bringing an action against him for having a criminal relationship with a soprano stockbroker. Ordinarily the Prince would have been puzzled, possibly shocked by such *outré* behaviour. Now he simply felt sorry for poor Lord Arthur because he was another prey of the hounds of British moral outrage.

They didn't let up for weeks. It was felt generally that the Prince had gone too far and had behaved badly. In the proletarian slang of the day they told each other he deserved his unpopularity. 'That's a cough-lozenge for him,' they said. 'That's a cough-lozenge!'

The Prince's worst hurt was given him at his beloved Ascot. And he really did love Ascot, regarding it as his own small kingdom: Ascot where the maddest wagers had been made, where for £5,000 a lady had ridden round and round and round covering a hundred miles in ten hours while her husband, for another £5,000, undertook she would eat a whole leg of mutton and drink two bottles of claret to top the event off; Ascot, where he himself had chivvied people into strengthening and brightening up the rickety Royal Pavilion. It was there, at the centre of his own particular universe, whilst driving down the course with Alix beside him, immaculate in what Poole the tailor had determined was the correct dress for Royal Ascot, that the Prince found he was actually being booed by the crowds.

He did not expect, nor did he particularly wish, to be popular with the middle classes: especially the so-called respectable chapel-going, education-crazy, lower-middle-class egalitarians whose voting power made Gladstone involuntarily toe the Nonconformist line and caused him no end of trouble. But he did care

169

about the masses; the stinking, jellied-eel and cockle-swallowing race-goers who had always been so friendly. That they should boo him bit very deeply indeed, and only his natural good-humour prevented him from becoming permanently soured and aloof.

At that very same Ascot meeting he was able to overcome his rancour and smile simply because the mob was so absurdly fickle. When one of his horses won a race, the same stinking jellied-eel and cockle-swallowing crowd roared with delight.

He cursed them genially. He was glad, he shouted at them, that they'd got themselves into a better frame of mind, and they roared the louder.

And he could smile when Oliver Montagu and Carrington told him that down in the Charing Cross Road, where hostile broadsheets and pamphlets were going like hot cakes, the suppliers could not keep up with demand – and a prurient buyer of a book which the cover promised *'will contain a portrait and biographical memoir of the young and extremely pretty Lady Mordaunt, with many pleasing reminiscences'* was back in the shop wildly complaining that he'd been done. Only the cover was real. Sealed inside was a copy of Dr Watts' Hymn Book.

11

On the broad lawns in the grounds of Chiswick Lodge two mothers, attended by their Ladies, and eight children, attended by nurses and nursery maids, the whole served by a knot of liveried footmen, enjoyed a June afternoon tea.

There was tea itself, in four varieties and with what the stouter mother declared was a Rothschild abundance of varieties of sugars, milks and creams, sorbets and fresh fruit, and the essential plates of bread and butter which, as surely as Matins preceded the Litany each Sunday, had to come before scones and droplets, tarts, sponges, biscuits, pastries and substantial cakes.

The Wales children were wilder than the Tecks. Eddy now eight, George aged seven, were older than the rest. Louise of Wales came next, then May of Teck, then Victoria of Wales, then

Adolphus of Teck (invariably called Dolly). The babies in their prams were Maud, Fruit of the Nile, and Prince Frank of Teck, who were almost of an age.

The hubbub was awful until tea finished when the babies were wheeled away, the Ladies in Waiting, nurses, nursery maids and footmen withdrew, the little girls played with rag and china dolls under the Duke of Devonshire's prime cedar, and the boys went down to the ornamental lake in the hope of persuading the Chiswick boatman to carve them more wooden ships.

Allowing themselves five minutes for digestion the two mothers then proceeded to walk the lawns; the Princess of Wales in her high collar of jewels and a garden bonnet, Princess Mary Adelaide ablaze in a gown of scarlet silk with no bonnet but, instead, a parasol as brightly coloured as the plumage of a bird of paradise. The smaller princess was trailed by a huge lolloping dog; the larger one carried a tiny snappy animal called Yes.

This was known by both families as a Chiswick afternoon, sometimes, though rarely, attended by the gentlemen, and on frightening occasions presided over by the Duchess of Cambridge, a rusty black figure with a not unkindly face but who muttered in guttural tones to Lady Geraldine, frightened the children, and made everyone feel nervous. Today she had failed to put in an appearance, and neither her daughter nor Alix was very sorry. They had much to talk about.

There were the lesser things: that is, lesser to most, though of major importance to the smooth working of the family. There had been changes in those vital advisers and communicators, the royal Private Secretaries. The Queen's General Grey had died, and in his place, to the amazement of the Waleses, she had appointed his nephew Sir Henry Ponsonby, a noted Liberal and supporter of Gladstone. Then the Prince's own Comptroller and Private Secretary had retired, and, to the Queen's displeasure, he had insisted on officially appointing Francis Knollys, his Comptroller's son, if for no other reason than that he had been unofficially doing most of the work for years. Then there had been a tiff between Mama and Bertie about racing, happily settled without rancour.

Alix and Mary Adelaide wheeled about, walking in the direction from which they had come, and talked warmly of Rumpenheim, and in chilly tones of what was going on in Prussia. Willy they

171

agreed was getting too big for his boots, and as for that atrocious Bismarck, from the way he was behaving it looked as if the French would have to teach him a sharp lesson in manners. Then they wheeled about a second time and discussed the Queen's anger at the way her son Arthur had been received in the United States. He had met with a chilling lack of cordiality and bad arrangements. Even Mr Gladstone had been shocked. But was it surprising, asked the practical Mary Adelaide, when there was a presidential election on and the Irish-Americans were in such a ferment against England?

After that the two friends sat down again, fanned themselves against the June heat, and talked of what to them were the really important matters.

Mary Adelaide's chief concern was her projected move into White Lodge. In defiance of her mother and brother and sister who considered the notion too foolhardy, she had wrung a reluctant consent from the Queen that the Tecks could take over White Lodge when the Waleses moved out. It had been conditional, of course, that they undertake to economize in other directions, otherwise the arrangement would prove to be impossible. The move was to be made in a month's time and Mary Adelaide was keen to learn what Alix would be leaving behind at White Lodge and what her dear friend thought of Franz's plans for redecoration, refurnishing and laying out a five-acre garden.

These plans scarcely seemed to be in accord with the Queen's known request for economies; but, explained Mary Adelaide, Franz had now been made Duke of Teck by the King of Würtemburg and, though he would have far preferred the Dukedom of Würtemburg or an English title, the honour demanded they maintain certain standards.

Alix, guessing at the height and cost of these standards, was simultaneously worried for her friend and amused by her exuberance. She tried to help as well as she could and then guided their talk to her own particular concern.

For a day or two she had wondered how far it would be wise to confide in Mary Adelaide who, though practical and kind, possessed hardly the stillest tongue in London. Yet she felt she had to tell someone in the family of her present predicament.

'Dear Mary,' she said. 'May I ask your advice?'

Mary Adelaide immediately said yes, and she put her head on

172

one side as she listened to what she already knew quite well: that Colonel Oliver Montagu, the Prince's great friend and Equerry and Colonel of the Blues, had entirely lost his heart to the Princess. The Colonel was paying her small attentions from the distance of a chivalrous knight, understanding quite well that theirs could be nothing more than a handkerchief flirtation. Alix wanted to know if she was wrong to accept his attentions and wrong too, to keep this a secret from her husband.

'Why, bless you,' retorted Mary Adelaide, twirling her parasol, 'he knows already. Of course he does. He has eyes in his head.'

Alix flushed. 'He knows and he does not object?' she said, amazed.

Such was Mary Adelaide's excitement that her parasol was by now whirling like a catherine wheel. 'Goose!' she cried. 'Goose! Bertie has absolute confidence in his Equerry and he would far rather that you were served by loving and devoted friends than by people who are indifferent to you. Charlotte Knollys also loves you. And so does Lady Macclesfield after her fashion. Of course you may accept Colonel Montagu's affection.'

Alix's face went pink with pleasure. 'You are sure, Mary dear? You are sure that you are not. . . . how is it put? . . . not being Hanoverian?'

Mary Adelaide's laugh brought two of the little princesses out from under the cedar boughs. She waved them back again. 'I am sure,' she said, and Alix realized that she meant it.

She was encouraged to confide her other anxiety: that under the pressure of public opinion Bertie was being dare-devil and carefree one day and intolerably moody the next. Perhaps, like Franz, he needed something to do. He seemed to be so busy. He was up early each day no matter at what hour he had gone to bed, and his routine was invariable and exacting, only broken by the little amount of public work he was permitted to do, and yet, for all his spent energy and time, he got nowhere. Being his father's son, he craved for more than a life of pleasure. And being frustrated was perhaps the reason for the increase in his eating. What poets did with words and composers with music, and painters with paint, her chefs were doing with food and drink, loving their creative work in catering for the Prince's growing appetite with the most delicious dishes, sauces, variations and surprises. He was eating tremendously – far too much for a fit man. . . .

173

Here Alix hesitated in embarrassment. It was hardly tactful to speak to the stoutest member of the royal family about eating.

But Mary Adelaide laid a hand on hers and again told her she was a goose. She thought, she said, that Alix was probably very right. She had always had a robust Hanoverian appetite but this had increased when Augusta had married and George had settled down with his actress. It had not been pleasant to be always in Mama's wake husband-hunting in the limited little sphere where they could be flushed out, and she had found her happiness in eating. And the more she had eaten, the fatter she had grown, and the slimmer her chances of finding a husband. 'But then,' she smiled, 'my adorable Franz came along, and here we are, so happy. Bertie's appetite will adjust itself when he has more responsibility.' She sighed. 'If only there was a way of letting the Queen know. She might, perhaps, be persuaded to help.'

'I doubt it,' said Alix in a thin voice which surprised Mary Adelaide.

They would have spoken further but Mac was at the Princess' elbow. Nurses and nursery maids were collecting their charges and shooing them across the lawns. Rag and porcelain dolls and crudely carved boats were bundled into children's barrows. The little dog Yes snapped disagreeably at the lolloping Great Dane. Another Chiswick afternoon was done.

12

No one for quite a time appreciated the fact that Otto von Bismarck had engineered the outbreak of the Franco–Prussian War in July 1870. He ballooned a political confrontation into a war crisis, then heightened the crisis by putting spice and vinegar into a telegram from the French before handing it on to his master. Naturally the King of Prussia was vexed. He replied in kind. This enraged the French who immediately demanded war.

Paris in the summer heat went mad with a martial frenzy. Flags waved by day and by night. The slightest suggestion of caution from anyone who doubted the wisdom of war with military

174

Prussia earned him the accusation of being a spy. Totally innocent people were jeered at, stoned, chased, thrown into the Seine, and one unfortunate was lynched. The *sans culottes* enjoyed themselves, but their frenzy was for the Empire, not jacobin. They seized a beer cart and ordered everyone who passed to drink to the Emperor. They stopped a horse tram and commanded an opera singer to stand on top and lead them in the *Marseillaise*. A foreign visitor to the city, unaware perhaps that this was unusual even in Paris, remarked that it was 'thrilling but quaint'.

The Prince of Wales was taken in by the newspapers like everyone else and he was entranced. His great friends the French were to march all the way to Berlin and then seize the hated Prussians by the throat.

A few days before war was actually declared Queen Victoria appeared in person at Aldershot for the first time since the death of her husband. Swelling with pride – vicarious, of course, for he could hardly fight with the French – Prince Albert Edward marched past at the head of his regiment. After the revue he took his Lieutenant-Colonel, Valentine Baker, on one side and discussed the possibilities of getting out there somehow to paste the Prussians with the French Emperor. His enthusiasm was infectious. Baker looked into it but discovered there was not the slightest chance. Strictly impartial neutrality with, if anything a slight bias towards the Prussians, because the English Princess Royal was Crown Princess, was the official English policy.

Fevered with enthusiasm the Prince toured the clubs to get the feelings of society. The men were with him entirely. They too would like to march with the French all the way to Berlin.

Authority forcibly damped down the anti-Prussian blaze the Prince was lighting. The Prime Minister requested, the Queen commanded him not to be so partisan in public. The family, for its own sake, begged him not to inflame people's opinions. Even Fritz, whose opinions he respected perhaps more than anyone alive, wrote to remonstrate with him. But he simply could not help it. He loved France and especially Paris. It was where he had been so delightfully entertained as a child. It was the shell of the enchanting Empress Marie-Eugénie Ignace Augustine de Montijo; shell of the delicious *cocottes*; shell of haute cuisine where master chefs competed to give 'Boulevard Wales' delectable surprises; shell of lively, amiable, clever and exquisite ladies of distinction,

175

and his dear, dear friends – Mouchy, Pourtalès and Greffuhle; and the shell of his adorable Princesse de Sagan and her beastly but obliging husband, *Fleur des Pois*. It was the home of everything that caught and held his admiration.

Alix was away in Copenhagen. Impulsively he decided to fetch her and the children home. She was not particularly pleased to have her holiday cut short. Nor was she pleased that she could not return to Marlborough House because builders and decorators made the place uninhabitable and, temporarily, they had to live in the Sutherlands' town house. But she was pleased with the change she saw in Bertie.

When she had left he had been morose and tetchy, hardly recognizable as the husband she knew and cared for. Now he was all smiles, all energy, bounding up and down the deck, describing with a fervour that would have done credit to the most ferocious *sans culotte* precisely what was to happen to their old enemies the Prussians.

In less than a fortnight he had changed again. Unexpected Prussian successes and the defeat of French arms cast him down into silent depression. His energy flagged. He stood by the telegraph machines in Marlborough House or at the Marlborough Club as the bad news came through. The Prussians' efficiency commanded his admiration, but he feared dreadfully for his beloved France.

Bismarck's plans were so thorough that Prussian army commanders were ordered to advance at a certain pace and in a certain method. Enemy towns which lay in the way of the advance were to be given formal warning that, on their arrival, the Prussians would expect certain supplies. Each Prussian soldier was to be provided with a kilo of bread, 400 grammes of meat, fifty grammes of coffee, five cigars and either a litre of wine or a litre of beer. Towns unable to make these supplies were to be razed. All proceeded with deadly accuracy according to Bismarck's plan.

Unable to speak his mind, the Prince of Wales watched the decimation of his friends' armies with a dull hopelessness. There was one moment of consolation when he heard that his sister, who crowed so shrilly about the superiority of Prussian arms, had been ordered back from the front by the King himself as her idea of organizing military hospitals were 'too English'. He could imagine Vicky's indignation. And then the Disraelis kindly tried to take his mind off things. He was invited to their country place at Hughenden where young Derby and his bride were staying; and there was a driven grouse shoot over the soft, undulating Buckinghamshire downs in which he and Derby bagged eighty brace.

Disraeli, out of office and not very well, tried to keep his royal guest distracted. So did Mary Anne, a spectral figure because cancer was eating her up and no amount of pearl-powder and paint and darkened eyebrows could hide her pallor or disguise the fact that she was in constant, brandy-suppressed pain. For the Prince's sake she had gone to immense trouble, arranging a dinner which she thought he would appreciate – good turtle soup – the turtles having been kept in clean straw in the Hughenden cellars and beheaded the night before – salmon, turbot in a rich sauce of shrimps, chicken breasts with asparagus points, and Boeuf a la Provençale. It was a beautifully cooked, perfectly balanced meal, presided over by the haggard Mary Anne whose wig was askew and whose smile was crooked, but whose heart was very affectionate to her admired Prince. And Disraeli and Derby kept the talk on exactly the right topics, flashing their wit from each other like sparks flying from flint and steel. And yet Bertie could not enjoy the dinner. It was too reminiscent of his beloved France, and the fashionable menu cards were in French and decorated with children playing at soldiers.

The French Emperor surrendered on September 2nd and was sent as a prisoner to Prussia. His Empress made a providential escape and reached England. Bertie cried with her and for her. Then the French declared themselves a Republic. . . . Paris was besieged. . . . His Parisian friends grew hungrier and hungrier. The only common commodities in the city were mustard and champagne. Reduced to elephants' trunks from the zoo and bits of camel and spaniel and ultimately to rats, the French suffered while Bismarck sat at headquarters eating delicacies and drinking their best wines.

Alix hardly knew how to calm Bertie when he heard that at the beginning of 1871 Vicky had sent Empress Eugénie a screen which had been looted from her own palace, a piece of gratuitous tactlessness he found difficult to forgive. And he lost control of his tongue and expressed in writing his regrets when the King of Prussia made himself German Emperor. He was not to be Emperor of Germany. Bismarck would not allow it because it was a

177

territorial title and German Emperor was more suitable to the age. But, whatever the title, its assumption caused great offence in England. Then came the capitulation; harsh terms by Prussia; enemy troops marching along the boulevards; crowing letters from Vicky who really was getting above herself; and then, as if Paris had not suffered enough, she was seized by the Communists who made another bloody jacobin reign of terror.

Bertie had never been so anti-republican and anti-democratic. His belligerence unnerved Gladstone who enjoyed visiting Sandringham and was disposed to be friendly on most accounts. And it angered and mystified the Queen, especially when he bitterly complained because she was permitting Louise to marry the Duke of Argyll's heir, the young Marquis of Lorne.

Bertie regarded his sister as an odd girl. In a late adolescent passion for Alix she had had a habit of sending her a series of china pugs with madly romantic letters and verses, and now she had taken to sculpture and the rights of modern women. Moreover, from someone or other in the family he had heard that a physical disability prevented her from ever having children, so there could hardly be any point in getting married anyway. But, though by no means his favourite sister, Louise was a Princess of the Blood, and Bertie thought it squalid and wrong for her to marry a mere subject.

Mama thought otherwise.

In March 1871 the Prince of Wales haughtily joined his mother in the bridal procession in St George's Chapel at Windsor.

Normally so genial, his sudden affliction of royal hauteur did not suit him in the least. He actually quarrelled with Alix, who took Mary Adelaide's side in a tiff between her and the Queen. Mama was right, he claimed, to check the Tecks and prevent them from using the royal livery and the same colour for their carriages as she did. But the strongest expression of his anti-republican feeling was in the great fuss he made of the Empress Eugénie and Prince Imperial and, when he was released from Germany and arrived in England, of the deposed Emperor himself.

Napoleon III had grown stouter in his imprisonment and his famous moustaches were no longed waxed and dyed. Grey-whiskered, with heavy eyes he had the heart but not the resources to try and recover his throne. Besides, as Gladstone forcefully told the Prince of Wales, there was not the least chance of England refusing to recognize the legitimate elected government of France. Without Britain at his back the Emperor stood no chance of ever ruling France again. Exile in Chislehurst, while remaining on the closest terms of friendship with the British royal family, was to be Napoleon's lot until his death, and when eventually the Communists' reign of terror finished, and, in an indescribable bloodbath, during which hostages like the Archbishop were shot to death, Paris was taken over by the official French government the Prince of Wales refused to send his congratulations or any message to the new republic.

Officially he had to accept it as the legitimate government of France, but he never accepted it in his heart. It was middle class, elitist, anti-Imperial, anti-aristocratic, anti-clerical, anti-everything he had cared for in the Paris of the Second Empire. For years he remained faithful to those of his friends who had suffered at the hands of Prussians, Communists and republicans, entertaining them in London and feeling for them in their misery. Moreover, with enormous tact, he maintained close contact with the other aspirants to power in France, the family of the King of the French, Louis Philippe. Exiled Bourbonists and Buonapartists joined in only three things, in their hatred of the republic, their love of France, and their love of the Prince of Wales.

It was at this time, when his spirits were already low, and his nerves were straying, that Alix was once more prematurely delivered of a child. As had happened with her first baby, nothing was ready, and although Alix herself was well enough, this time the child, her sixth, was a weakling. Hastily christened Alexander John, he died within twenty-four hours.

It was a loss suffered by many, many women at that time, but Alix was quite unprepared for it. Indeed, never in her long life was she to forget the baby who was always called John in the family. And nor could she ever forget her husband's extraordinarily intense emotion. He was inconsolable, he insisted on putting the little baby into its coffin himself. He arranged the pall and flowers. And, hand in hand with his sons Eddy and George, he walked to Sandringham Church for the burial.

Alix said she found his attitude peculiar and selfish. Her rights as a bereaved mother demanded that he give her the consolation she needed, but he was entirely wrapped up in his own grief. She wondered if secretly he was reproaching her. Irrationally, she started to reproach herself, and in her remorse she began to believe that if only she had taken better care of herself beforehand he might not have died.

The Queen agreed most cordially, but she transferred the responsibility to her son. If only Bertie had taken better care of his wife, and not allowed her to be such a gadabout as he was himself, they might not have lost their son. Through the medium of her majestic messenger, the Dean of Windsor, she told him so.

Very quietly the Prince accepted Dean Wellesley's gentle remonstrance. He undertook to be careful for the Princess in future. He also wrote to reassure his mother on the subject. But inwardly he was ablaze with indignation at being accused of neglecting his wife.

Looked at from every angle, he could not in conscience believe that the charge was true. He had never ceased to cherish Alix, even when she was as cold as ice itself and as distant as the stars, and he felt he had been done a grave injustice.

He was seldom critical of Alix even to himself. He tolerated her more obvious faults and tried to make light of them. But now he was disposed to make a more exact appraisal of their relationship. He realized that hardly once had she tried to help him in the strain and frustrations he had endured in the past few months. And this was not simply because of his infidelities. Clearly, long ago, knowing the difficulty he had in controlling his liking for women, she had decided to let him rip, but she still wanted to bind him to her by the strongest emotional ties. She made demands but she gave less and less; and, in future, he would be inclined to give less as well. She had her children, whom she adored in a hungry passionate fashion, and her incredibly boring relations in Denmark. And she had Mary Adelaide and Mac and Charlotte Knollys and now, thank God, Oliver Montagu. He was certain that Oliver would guard his honour because he saw Alix as a distant, divine, untouchable goddess, and because, though a lecher by nature, he was also disciplined and religious and a chivalrous knight. Bertie had often wondered if Alix loved Oliver. Certainly he did her. But it was of small moment. They were both spiritual creatures, not earthy like him. They enjoyed religious disputations and distant romantic adoration while he, to be frank, preferred fornication.

Bertie felt a little better after his re-appraisal. He continued to cherish his wife as a husband ought but at last he had faced her limitations as well as his own. It was perhaps significant that, although Alix was barely twenty-six, from that time she was to have no more children. Possibly the Prince had decided that only the devoted Montagu could warm himself at that ice or cover the distance which lay between Princess Alexandra and the world.

13

The Queen was invariably suspicious of what went on at Marlborough House, but far less critical of Sandringham. She had heard that decent people went there, though perforce they had to mix with more raffish guests. On one Sandringham week-end three of the guests were the Archbishop of Canterbury, the Commander-in-Chief and the Prime Minister, and the Prince of Wales marked the occasion by asking them to join him in planting a tree. To the Queen this sort of thing made her son's country place almost respectable, though she had not yet been there herself, and she would have been appalled had she known that it was at Sandringham that a plot had been hatched to prise her from her seclusion.

Gladstone broached the matter. At Sandringham he was a different man, no longer the grave statesman who found it difficult to smile. Probably the truth was that he, the People's William and son of a Scotch trader, relished the company of princes. He, who had such a careful eye on the powerful Temperance movement, enjoyed the Wales' brandy; and he, supposedly a life-long and fussy hater of tobacco, puffed at the Prince's cigars and cigarettes with nervous pleasure. It was Sandringham which gave him the confidence to be bold and say to his host that something had to be done about the Queen's seclusions. The country would not stand it any longer. The Republican Clubs were starting up again, and in the most unexpected places; and he was finding it next to impossible to suppress the radicals in his own party. Brown alone considered that his royal mistress, or 'Wumman' as he sometimes addressed her, ought not to be mithered.

Impressed by the Prime Minister's seriousness the Prince undertook to confer privately with some of those who were closest to the Queen's person. He would also sound out his brothers and sisters to see if any family pressure could be brought to bear.

His report at the end of a month was not cheering. Neither Lady Churchill nor Lady Ely nor even the Private Secretary had been at all hopeful that the Queen would alter her ways. But he promised that if pressure from the Ministry brought no results the family would present her with a form of protest. This had already been concocted by Princess Alice and signed by all senior members of the royal family, and put safely on one side against the day when it might have to be used.

Gladstone was sincerely grateful. He communicated secretly with Sir Henry Ponsonby, the Queen's Private Secretary, and they agreed that a good test of the strength of the Sovereign's feelings would be a government proposal that she postpone her proposed summer holiday in Balmoral for parliamentary reasons.

It was a sound test. Queen Victoria did not merely say no. She said very vociferously that any more ministerial bullying would force her to abdicate. She was feeling persecuted both by the gods and men. She considered Mr Gladstone was behaving atrociously, Arthur had upset her by falling out of a window at Buckingham Palace and landing on a policeman below, and the weather was unbearably hot.

She left for Balmoral on the date she had planned, and Alice went with her, the family protest hidden in her valise.

But the protest was never presented. No sooner did she reach her Scotch sanctuary than the Queen was taken severely ill. In her debility she suffered from an abscess on her side. It had to be lanced and it hurt abominably. She wept a great deal. Alice tore up the round-robin. No one, in decency, could wear Mama out further. Her nerves were stretched to breaking point. She was exceedingly sharp with Mr Gladstone, who had the misfortune to be Minister in Attendance. She bossed and bullied her children and grandchildren. She objected to Bertie's heartlessness. There she was, a miserable invalid in Scotland, and he and Alix had gone off on a jaunt to look at French battlefields and see the

Passion Play at Oberammergau. She objected even more when they separated: Alix to join her dreary family, Bertie to do something about his digestion and the size of his stomach by a cure at Homburg. He liked Homburg. The mineral springs there were especially valuable to overeaters, and a large international crowd of invalids and pleasure-lovers were there to keep him endlessly amused and occupied. He also liked a jaunty style of hat he found there and set a new fashion of wearing homburgs. But the Queen considered Homburg as bad for Bertie as Baden and wrote to say so. This time he took no notice. Recently he had picked up a useful habit from Alix – who had originally caught it from Mary Adelaide – of not answering difficult letters. But while Mama drummed her fingers impatiently in Scotland waiting for an explanation, Bertie found an unexpected bar to enjoying himself any further in Homburg. A *Reynolds' Newspaper* reporter sent off a biased, in fact totally untrue, paragraph to London:

The Heir Apparent to the British Throne is staking his gold upon the chances of a card or the roll of a ball – gold, be it remembered, that he obtained from the toil and sweat of the British working-man, without himself producing the value of a halfpenny.

Reading a copy in his own room at the spa, the Prince felt a sudden access of anger. It was infuriating that these scribblers wasted their time grubbing out gossip when there were important things to report. Why, in the United States alone the most extraordinary stories were breaking: The Tammany Ring which had corrupted the political life of New York was being exposed, a third of Chicago had gone up in flames, and a serious attempt was being made to stamp out bigamy in Utah. And *Reynolds' Newspaper*, with the largest guaranteed circulation of any newspaper in the world, was bothering itself about his private affairs in Homburg. Such slanted reports, added to the republican furore about the Queen's seclusion, could do a good deal of damage to the monarchy.

He crushed the paper in his powerful hands and threw it on the floor. Then he asked Francis Knollys to arrange for their departure to rejoin the Princess of Wales.

Not long afterwards he and Alix were back in England. His

short stay with her family had been excruciatingly boring to Bertie. But neither felt inclined to go to Abergeldie that year and suffer Mama's displeasure in person. Her letters and messages sent through third persons were bad enough. And so Alix went into the country while Bertie accepted an invitation to camp with his regiment in Hampshire, where Uncle George was copying foreign traditions and introducing European-style manoeuvres to England for the first time. Bertie's younger brother Arthur was there as well, learning to be a soldier, for he was destined for a full-time army career; and Alice on a journey to Balmoral managed to visit the camp, exclaim in wonder at the beauty of his 10th Hussar uniform and marvel at the complications of mimic warfare as directed by the Duke of Cambridge. The Prince enjoyed it thoroughly except for the mortification of being taken prisoner at the head of his detachment on the last day of manoeuvres.

After that he and Alix still kept away from Scotland. They accepted Lord Londesborough's invitation to stay at his house near Scarborough. It was on the sea, which they both loved. There was reasonable shooting in the area. Their fellow guests were carefully chosen. The Londesboroughs were civilized, friendly hosts.

At the end of October 1871 the Prince of Wales caught typhoid. He rambled as he lay on his bed.

In some ways it was pleasant. Time meant nothing any more, day mixed with night, two o'clock with three o'clock, Monday, for all he knew, might well have followed Wednesday. It was an amusing novelty to a man who lived to a strict routine and used every minute of every hour. It was pleasant, too, just to be. Being, someone had told him, is so much more worthwhile than doing. To lie with eyes closed, or open, or half open, exactly as he wished, and feel no sense of urgency to be doing things was another new sensation: no guns to seize from the hands of Peter Robinson and shoot at hoopoes and flamingoes; no clothes to take from Fuller's hands; no reins to hold; no diceboxes to shake; no cards to deal, fan out, and play; no counters to place; no orchids to pick; no race-glasses to focus; no treasures to handle; no knife and fork and spoon to use . . . nothing. And it was warm and cool in turn; exactly, it seemed, as he wished – like that American shower-bath at Cannes, the only, only one he had ever used and found sufficiently sensitive to touch.

184

It was a timeless, relaxing span of comfortable being. Part of it was, anyway.

The other part was different, and quite fearful to experience: the longing for tranquillity, for his thirst to be slaked, for the fires to be taken from his body, and then the freezing chills; the desperate hope that the shivering would cease, the shivering which made his tongue shake as it lolled outside his mouth; that they would not press food on him, not food, not food; that they would not lift him and roll him about and do things to him when he wished to be left in peace. All he wanted was to be untouched, unwashed, unshaved, abandoned. But when they had gone he was as lonely as the freak in a crowd, as cut off as the body sealed living in a coffin, as frightened as the boy locked up in the cellar. Gibbs had threatened it. Gibbs with his rod, his way of squeezing an ear lobe until it tingled into deadness, and coming back to life, seared with endless pain. Why was Gibbs there now? He heaved and struggled to rid himself of Gibbs; Gibbs Q.C., C.B., owner of a silver coffee pot presented by a grateful pupil Albert Edward, Prince of Wales; owner of a set of plate given by a grateful sovereign; Gibbs, author of *Once a Clergyman Always a Clergyman* . . . he must rid himself of Gibbs. He wanted Birch instead: pale-faced, kind Henry Mildred Birch whose whiskers had never quite met round his chin. And there was Birch, impaling a moth on a mounting pin, a moth they had caught with Papa out in the cobbled yard at Deeside. Papa. Where was Papa? . . .

Having no sense of time Bertie did not know exactly when he opened his eyes to find Mama at his side. Alix was there too. And Alice. And goodness knows how many more. Even Uncle George, tears running down his blown-out, crimson cheeks. They were all crying except Mama, and so he turned back to her. She took his hand. He realized he was in his own bed at home in Sandringham. And Mama was there.

'Thank you,' he began to whisper. Alice moistened his tongue with a dab of wet lint. It helped. He turned to Mama again. 'Thank you,' he said. 'For coming to see me. It is most kind. Most obliging.'

She blurred away. So did the others. And he was back in the timeless world where nothing happened and nothing was real until

185

the pains and vexations began again. Oh, God that he could have peace. Oh, God that he could be left alone. Oh, God that they would not keep him so alone. He wanted company and shouted for the seven Etonians: Gladstone, Carrington, Derby, Wood, Hinchingbrooke, Cadogan, and Van de Weyer. And his friends? his friends? his friends? his friends? They were legion: his Household and servants, his fellow officers, the fellow members of his club, the trainers and jockeys, the croupiers and gamesters, the loving, adorable women. He wanted them. He shouted for them by name. Nellie. Where was Nellie Clifden? and Skittles? and Long Nance Taylor and Poll Sellars? He stretched out for the heliotrope-scented Emilienne d'Alençon, for Hortense Schneider, for the jewel of them all Madame la Princesse de Sagan, Duchesse de Talleyrand-Périgord, Madame *Fleur des Pois*. . . .

His room at Sandringham came back to him on a December evening. He was enfeebled, worn out with his raging and the torment of his illness. Mama and Alix and Alice and all the family were there. They were crying with happiness. Quietly they told him he had been very ill. He and his groom and a fellow guest Lord Chesterfield had caught the insidious typhoid at Londesborough House, and he had been given up for lost on three occasions. The groom? Chesterfield? Mama and Alix exchanged glances; then Mama said firmly: 'Both, poor creatures, have died. But God has spared you, my own beloved child.' Her tears splashed on his forehead as she kissed him. 'The crisis has passed on today of all days.'

'Today?' repeated Bertie dully.

Alice explained. It was the 14th December. The tenth anniversary of Papa's death. Even in his weak state he realized what it must mean for his mother to be away from Windsor on that particular day. He tried to press her hand in gratitude.

'And now,' said Alice briskly, 'is there anything you especially want before you are tucked up.'

'Anything,' added Alix.

He looked at his wife and at his sister, sensing that there probably had been competition about who should nurse him. How best could he reconcile them? Then he caught sight of Uncle George's pink cheeks and white whiskers. The old man was

186

beaming amiably, for he had been terribly upset during the past few days.

'Uncle George,' said Bertie. 'I believe I should like a glass of beer. Bass' beer.'

The jellied-eel and cockle-swallowing mob were back on the Prince of Wales' side again. So were a good many of the middle-classes. Gladstone's royalty problem had been solved entirely fortuitously by the foul drains of Londesborough House. An upsurge of loyalty followed the Prince's typhoid which surprised everyone, even the Queen.

She herself was delighted. The family had dispersed from Sandringham. Alice had finished her nursing and, somewhat ungraciously, had been packed off to Darmstadt again. Uncle George, to his great delight, had been put in charge of replying to telegraphic inquiries. The two political parties strove to take the credit for the Prince of Wales' recovery entirely to themselves. The Church, quite correctly, claimed his unlooked-for recovery was a victory for prayer and a great Thanksgiving Service was arranged – a function so enormous and exhausting that it almost finished off the Prince of Wales, who drove with his wife and mother along a seven-mile route through thousands of cheering subjects to give thanks in London's cathedral. A special anthem was sung 'Thou hast not given me over to death' and was barely audible on account of the weeping of the Queen, her family and thirteen thousand other members of the congregation. It was an emotional, exhausting experience for the Prince who, quite naturally, staggered and had to lean on his wife's arm as the party left St Paul's. It was the high spot in a month or more of festivities, of poets and musicians competing with each other to supply odes and eulogies, of streets decorated with triumphal arches, buntings and venetian masts, of the presentation of scores of addresses of congratulations, of free concerts by German bands, bell ringing, artillery salutes, firework displays, and a liberal distribution of beer, beef and puddings to the indigent unemployed.

But there were spectres, naturally, at this feast of public thanksgiving. The republicans were silenced, the radicals intolerant of this praise of princes, and the Irish continued to pour seditious acid on to anything that was remotely English. A Fenian sympathizer

187 .

actually chose this time to make an attempt on the life of the Queen and, but for the vigilance of John Brown, he might well have hurt her badly. As it was, she was thoroughly frightened and, for the first time in her life, she showed it.

Bertie, remembering the beastly attack on her by the pensioned-off officer with a brass-headed can, was appalled at the shock she had received and gave her his warmest sympathy. She grasped his hand thankfully. One day she knew it would be his turn to be a target for lunatics and bigots.

'At least,' she said, trying to make light of it for his sake, because he was still in a very low state. 'At least it will have added a further fillip to the popularity of monarchy.'

She was quite right in this. Republicanism in England virtually disappeared in the extraordinary enthusiasm caused by the Prince's survival from typhoid, and the Queen's from an assassin's bullet.

In March when Bertie and Alix were leaving for a long convalescence in a royal yacht on the Mediterranean and went to say goodbye they found the Queen in a sunny mood. 'We must keep alive,' she said. 'Very much alive. Everything depends on our survival.'

14

Fuller, the Prince of Wales' valet, had a camera, or what was more usually called a photography machine: and despite the amount of waiting about this involved, and the limitations imposed on the practice of his hobby by regular attendance on his master, Fuller had a special talent for catching the mood of a subject. Scotch glen or little street in Baden came to life through Fuller's lens, as did such unlikely and difficult subjects as the young princes Eddy and George being taught arithmetic on the lawn at Sandringham, or the blue pigeon which was permitted to roam at will in the Princess' dressing-rooms, and which was persuaded to perch for long enough on the edge of a jade hand glass for Fuller to catch his likeness. His skill was such that he interested the Princess of Wales

188

in photography and she herself began to take it up as an agreeable pastime. But his skill was less in catching scenes and subjects with an opened lens than in recording away in his mind those which could never be photographed.

Occasionally, to selected intimates he would describe these subjects with a dash and vigour of expression that brought them at once to life, but only with one man, the Prince's second valet, could he bring himself to describe his masterpieces – the moods and manners of their own master. Neither of the Prince of Wales' valets would have concurred with the *mot* that no man is a hero to his valet. They admitted his faults. Few masters could be so explosive when he was upset. Things flew about, solid objects as well as words, but both held him in deep affection, enjoyed it when he enjoyed himself, felt his frustrations with him, and often suffered vicariously when he did.

Fuller's rich verbal daguerreotypes of H.R.H. in the arduously dull years which followed his typhoid were much appreciated by his assistant in the wardrobe. H.R.H. was described in every mood and state; most often sympathetically, though on occasions censoriously, but always accurately.

After their Mediterranean holiday, which the press rapidly described as a second honeymoon but which was no such thing – the Prince returned to find his mother and her Prime Minister bristling at each other like a pair of game birds, and all about himself.

His esteemed friend the Prime Minister was anxious to find him something to do, and, because of his previous success in Ireland and on account of the need to pacify that belligerent people, he had proposed to the Queen that a royal palace be established there where the Prince of Wales could rule as her Viceroy.

Back snapped the Queen: she already had a Viceroy who lived in a perfectly comfortable Viceregal Lodge. She was not having her prerogatives interfered with. Not on any account.

It had been unwise of Gladstone to use the word 'rule'. He returned to the attack several times and each time the Queen's snap was snappier and she liked her Prime Minister the less.

Fuller's picture of H.R.H.'s disillusionment was touching. Though thousands of Englishmen would have envied his position

189

and his leisure, the Prince wanted to do something. This was the despondent H.R.H.

Fuller's sympathetic picture of him as a puzzled father was no less astringent.

H.R.H. wanted his sons to get on. After the most careful consultation he had appointed a thirty-two-year-old clergyman, John Neale Dalton, to supervise their studies, but though the boys were happy, they appeared to be getting nowhere. Dalton was frank. They were being held back by their attachment to their mother. The *bonté* and childlikeness which won her such great popularity had affected her children. They were all strangely immature. Lacking any formal grounding in ordinary school subjects, and subjected to what H.R.H., in a frank moment, called 'damned nursery nonsense', they spoke always of 'Motherdear 'and called each other 'darling Eddy' and 'darling George' in the most unmanly, saccharine fashion.

Only Fuller – not even Mr Dalton – knew that his master had sought the advice of Princess Mary Adelaide of Teck. It was surprising, for H.R.H. did not altogether approve of his wife's close friendship with the Tecks; but, then, there was no denying that the Teck children, Princess May and her younger brothers, were bright little sparks. Under a steely application to normal studies they were doing very well. Princess May was already expert at languages and a great reader. The young Princes were destined for Eton.

Princess Mary Adelaide's advice was wise but not especially comforting to a puzzled father. To destroy the Princess' make-believe world by taking her children from her he thought would be both cruel and useless. Mr Dalton could be depended upon. Let him move the boys as quickly as he could from the nursery ambiency in which they had been living. School was out of the question. But why not the training-ship *Britannia*? As naval cadets they would soon mature. H.R.H. kept this in mind. Mr Dalton agreed. Naval cadetships were to be the present aim, with perhaps a career in the Navy for the younger boy, Prince George.

Of all H.R.H.'s greatest qualities the best perhaps was his tenderness. It was very obviously demonstrated when Napoleon III died in exile at Chislehurst and he was so good to the widowed Empress. But few people were sapient enough, or sufficiently close to him to see his tenderness of heart. Fuller's acuteness registered it all.

He saw his master's tenderness to Princess Alice when she lost one of her children, a favourite son. Like many in the royal family the child was an haemophiliac and had tumbled from a window on to a stone terrace twenty feet below. Princess Alice had herself picked up the unconscious little boy, and she had sat there until hours later her son died in her arms. H.R.H.'s tenderness for his favourite sister was as affecting as it was sincere.

He was as tender when his half-aunt Princess Feodore died and Mama lost a last important link with her own childhood and youth. It was a good and generous return to one who had shuddered in his presence at the time of his own father's death.

Another close relation was stricken, but with paralysis not death. The Duchess of Cambridge was partially paralysed while visiting her daughter out in Strelitz and after many months, in a shattering journey, she was brought back to be nursed by Uncle George and Princess Mary Adelaide. The Prince of Wales put himself out to be as helpful as possible. Sympathizing with Mary Adelaide, who he knew found the constant visits wearing, he bore with her chattering and complaining with a disciplined patience.

Considering how selfish he could be in some things, his care for others when they really needed help was touching. No one could have been more understanding and considerate when Disraeli lost his Mary Anne at Hughenden. He sensed the extremity of Dizzy's loss: his ache, his bewilderment, his feeling of helplessness. Great lovers had got hearts and understood the hearts of others. That was how Fuller put it when describing H.R.H.'s sadness for the wrinkled, lonely old Jew who had lost the love of his life.

This was H.R.H. at his most estimable.

Fuller saw, and admitted, that H.R.H. could be exactly the opposite of estimable – as unfeeling, vain and cruel as a small boy.

Maybe this was what he sometimes was. Playing happily with his sponge in the bath, giggling, shouting for soaps and loofahs, he was like a child with a floating toy duck or ship.

He was childish, too, in his vanity: petulant when for political

191

reasons the Queen would not permit him to accept the colonelcy of a Russian regiment, and he dearly wanted another uniform; then puffed out with vanity when she made him a field-marshal, looking at himself from each angle in the tall glass and snapping at poor Poole's fitter for being so slow with the additions to his uniform.

H.R.H. sitting in a chair, reading a scurrilous pamphlet against himself – trying to show a haughty indifference to what it said, but feeling it, feeling it very much all the same, and not able to stop his lower lip from trembling, was also the child.

And just as a child is, he could be cruel: mocking his Gentlemen who could not answer back; making them do undignified things. There was poor Mr Sykes, for example, whose special trick it was to crawl sycophantically on all fours as a bear while H.R.H. poured brandy on him.

And when some stood up to him, as a very few did – like the young widower Lord Rosebery, who was asked to place his London house at H.R.H.'s disposal for confidential assignations and most adamantly said no – he didn't in the least like it and was liable to sulk. These were photographs Fuller would have preferred to tear up in his memory; but they were indestructible, and made a whole picture of the master, who, even in his weakness, was deeply cared for.

There was an unusual photograph of H.R.H. being firm with his wife. Generally he was notably courteous to her, and allowed her to indulge her moods and fancies; but occasionally he found it necessary to be forceful and then he exercised a power which commanded her obedience and astonished both her Household and his, and certainly all the upper servants.

Only he could have made her visit Berlin in May, 1873 and there, at first by bonhomie, and then by shrewdly leading the whole family to abuse the common ogre, Chancellor Bismarck, he led his wife at last into agreement with her Prussian relations.

H.R.H. was stern, too, with the Princess when the Tsarevitch and Princess Dagmar, or Marie Feodorovona as she now had to be called, came to Marlborough House for an eight-week visit. He made it clear that it simply would not do to ride, drive, play loo and parchesi, and talk eternally over days in the Yellow Palace

192

schoolroom; and when she paid no attention and the beginning of the visit was as vapid and as aggravating to the Tsarevitch as he had feared, the Prince absolutely insisted that there had to be a good deal of entertaining and the ceremony which he knew she found distasteful but which, under the circumstances, was inevitable.

Fuller was less sure in his touch when describing the Princess of Wales, partly because, on the whole she treated her own servants inconsiderately, though, it was true, few ever left her service; but chiefly because Fuller believed that she treated his beloved master with unwarranted coldness. Malice, therefore, might have put a sparkle to some of his descriptions of her occasional rebellions against his authority, but there was nothing added to the story of her retort when she was reminded that she was already more than thirty minutes late for an important ceremony, and she said vindictively 'Let him wait. It will do him good.' Fuller, knowing H.R.H.'s punctiliousness and his close to obsession for punctuality, was aware of what he must have suffered without this additional piece of spite, and found his own respect for the Princess still further reduced.

Even when put out H.R.H. could still be grand. He had inherited from his mother a certain presence or grandeur which made him stand out from other people. It was not simply that he thrust himself forward like an Italian being photographed, which he undoubtedly did, but because he had an awareness of what was seemly in a ceremony.

He undertook the entertainment of the Shah of Persia and the Tsar of Russia with an aplomb that surprised everyone except his mother. He went to his brother's wedding in St Petersburg – for Affie despite many 'falls' had at last caught himself a Russian Grand-Duchess – and the Prince of Wales' demeanour was much approved of in a Court where protocol was starchy and any non-Russian royalty was regarded much as a poor and provincial relation. The Tsar was delighted with the Prince and said so.

Then, though it was much against his personal inclination, H.R.H. did as he was bidden and paid a formal call on the President in Paris. The President was flattered, delighted by the Prince's friendly courtesy, and much impressed by his grand manner

193

which he supposed sadly, being a mere elected head of state, he could never possibly achieve himself. And after that, despite Foreign Office anxieties that he might hurt republican susceptibilities in France, he undertook a tour of great houses – Esclimont, Serrant, Dompierre, Mello, Mouchy-le-Chatel, Chantilly, and back to the President again for a boar hunt at Marly, and the whole tour was a glittering success.

But, though grand in France, Fuller considered that H.R.H. was at his grandest out in India. He was sent there by Dizzy – for Dizzy was back at No. 10 Downing Street, solacing himself for the loss of dear Mary Anne by his deep attachment to the Queen, and long romantic correspondence with two other elderly ladies. He and Gladstone seemed to be taking turn and turn about like the carved figures in a Swiss barometer, and schoolboys had a new riddle: that Gladstone resembled a telescope because 'Disraeli drew him out, looked through him, and shut him up!' Dizzy had sublime ideas: to grant the Suez canal to the Queen as if it were a personal gift; to make her an empress, Empress of India; and to consolidate the good opinion of all Indians for the White Queen, he sent the Prince of Wales out there on a tour of splendour.

It was indeed splendid. His suite was magnificent and he took with him two of the greatest chefs in France. Thoughtful for his brother-in-law, King George, he also took a small herd of Improved Norfolks, plus a Sandringham pigman, to leave in Greece on the voyage out and, for his own special pleasure, he was accompanied by his poodle Bobêche. His reception in Bombay was tremendous. How grand he was, thought Fuller, as his master saluted the brown hordes from the back of a royal elephant, and received the native princes in marble, silk-draped halls with such relaxed grace that they were immediately put at their ease. How grand he was – even when déshabillé, so to speak, wearing a rough suit, leech-gaiters and puggareed hat to ride on the engine of the royal train and take over the controls; even when paddling in the soup-warm sea off Goa fish-netting with the natives. . . . Fuller was so proud of his master that involuntarily he began to imitate him. 'What the devil, Fuller,' asked the Prince, 'are you strutting like that for?' And his fellow servants teased it out of him in less than a week.

·   ·   ·   ·   ·

194

Another facet of H.R.H. was his explosive and powerful indignation. Rudeness or injustice or impertinence could bring it on and he became almost asthmatic, in danger of throttling himself with fury. And sometimes this deepened into a rumbling, long-lasting anger, entirely alien to the immature petulance he showed when he was thwarted.

There was his indignation, photographed and absolutely unfadeable in Fuller's mind, when the Lieutenant-Colonel of the Prince's own Regiment, Valentine Baker, was hounded out of the army. A tactical expert with a book to his credit, a rich wife, and a recent appointment to the assistant Quartermaster Generalship at Aldershot, and barely thirty, Baker had a full and useful life before him – but on 17 June, 1875, he entered a first-class compartment at Liphook on a train bound for London, and the only other occupant being a pretty young lady, he at first flirted mildly with her and then felt sufficiently encouraged to put an arm round her waist and kiss her cheek. At this the girl pulled the communication cord. It was broken and nothing happened, so she climbed out of the carriage, stood on the footboard and shrieked. When the train was eventually halted Baker was told he had committed an outrageous offence by kissing an unmarried lady. For the rest of the journey to London the insulted, unnamed lady travelled in the company of a clergyman while two self-appointed toughs stood guard over Lieutenant-Colonel Baker. For this, to the Prince's great indignation, he was brought to court, fined £500 and imprisoned for a year, cashiered and removed from the Army altogether. Again and again H.R.H. used his considerable influence in trying to find suitable employment for his unhappy friend, but it was a long time before he was successful, and all the time he smouldered with anger at the humbug of it all.

Then there was his rage at the behaviour of Lord Randolph Churchill in what came to be known as the Aylesford-Blandford scandal. On his way home from India the Prince heard that his friend Aylesford intended to divorce his wife, citing Blandford, Lord Randolph's brother as co-respondent. This was bad enough. Worse was that Randolph Churchill had somehow come into possession of a bundle of letters written by the Prince some time before to Lady Aylesford. Still worse he went to Marlborough House, tricked the Princess into receiving him, told her about the letters and said they would be published if the Prince did not do

195

all in his power to prevent the divorce. The Princess of Wales and
the Queen behaved perfectly – though the latter wished desperately
that her son would *not* write so many letters. Both supported the
Prince, showing they believed in his innocence, and Alix and the
children met him at Portsmouth and that evening they attended
the opera together to show society all was well. But H.R.H.'s contempt for the scoundrelly Churchill was biting. He challenged him
to a duel and received an insulting refusal. He insisted on an
apology, and an apology of a kind he got. Churchill's family, the
Marlboroughs, were packed off to the Lord Lieutenantship of
Ireland. Churchill himself thought it wise to visit his American
wife's relations in the States. The interdict went out from Marlborough House. Anyone in Society who in future received the
Randolph Churchills need not invite the Prince and Princess of
Wales to any entertainment whatsoever. Society obliged, except
Louisa Manchester who came out with her brave and famous
remark that she chose her own friends, but she was careful that
the hostile parties never met and because Louisa was Louisa, and
his friend Hartington's mistress, the Prince forgave her.

The Baker affair and the Aylesford-Blandford scandal were two
occasions when the Prince took no trouble to hide his feelings and
his indignation could be sensed not only by Fuller but by the
smallest boots in the deepest cellar at Marlborough House. Fuller
also registered and daguerreotyped less biting moods, but acrimonious ones for all that. For instance there was H.R.H.'s stern
reproach to the American who showed himself lacking in good
taste in election year. No one championed Americans in European
society more than the Prince of Wales, but there were some things
he could not tolerate. When this offending gentleman breezily
informed him that the successful candidate, Rutherford Hayes,
was widely known as 'Queen Victoria in Breeches', he was
instantly cold-shouldered by Queen Victoria's eldest son. Seething
beneath, it was difficult for the Prince to hide his feelings, but hide
them he did because he thought English–American good relations
were important. But Fuller heard of it later when he filled his
master's bath.

Fuller also learnt how impossible John Brown was becoming.
By now 'Brown Rows', as they were called, were commonplace.
Brown had quarrelled with almost all the Queen's children and
things had reached such a pitch that though he was blameworthy

in some respects, he was unjustly blamed for everything unlikeable in Mama's Scotch ménage. Prince Christian's 'opium den' as the Queen called it, a dim smoking room by the servants' quarters reached by crossing a cobbled yard and sparsely furnished with one table and one chair, was the only facility offered to smokers, an inadequacy for which Brown quite unjustly was blamed. He was blamed unjustly for the Queen's own parsimony in that she insisted on old newspaper squares being put in the lavatories so that nothing should be wasted. And he was even blamed for the colour of the paintwork – a dim marmalade colour for which no one in the family cared. But he was blameworthy when he failed to supervise the gillies' balls – which sometimes approached riots so liberal were the toasts. And he was blameworthy when he was too drunk himself to look after the Queen. And he was blameworthy, the Prince of Wales insisted, in that he had taken over the shooting and fishing facilities for his own amusement, and let the Queen's children feel they were enjoying her sport by his special kindness. In October 1874 the Prince let Mama know his feelings. He would not go to Abergeldie that autumn, he said, because Brown's interference in the sport had become intolerable. Very well, she replied starchily, let him stay away.

Fuller never actually caught the *ipsissima vera* of H.R.H.'s contretemps with H.M.; yet he was aware that there was a row between them when Princess Alice, by now Grand Duchess of Hesse-Darmstadt, came over for a visit to Balmoral and wished to stay two nights at Buckingham Palace on the way. To the Prince's dismay that simple request was refused. He expressed his indignation. But it made no difference. The Queen was busy plotting with Lady Ely against Gladstone. The old man had retired from the leadership of the Liberals and spent his time chopping down trees in Cheshire, but some sort of Bulgarian atrocities had worked him into such a fever that he had published a denunciating pamphlet. Dizzy, by now a belted earl, was worried although he hid it beneath an inscrutable exterior. So was the Queen worried. Alice had to do without her two-day stay in the Palace. Then came the stinging news that H.R.H.'s brother had been made an extra Private Secretary to his mother, and therefore was in possession of a despatch box key. There was little dignity in the Prince's complaint of unfairness, much hurtful commonsense in the Queen's reply.

．　　　．　　　．　　　．

But of all Fuller's photographs the most memorable was of H.R.H. in high spirits. His own personal enjoyment of a party was infectious and made the dullest gathering into something special. Something as ordinary as a picnic took on a new aspect if Albert Edwards was there. A ladies' archery contest, a croquet match, tennis and garden parties, even a children's afternoon of hide-and-seek was that much better if he was present. The Jockey Club vibrated when H.R.H. was announced at Ascot, and the Club at Newmarket bustled with gaiety when he went to occupy his apartments there for the races. At Cowes, where he regularly raced his yacht, they said the Solent glistened with champagne not spindrift because the Prince of Wales was there to organize the jollities. And at balls and great receptions he was magnificent.

The last Friday in July, three days before Goodwood, was the close of the London Season, and each year the Prince and Princess as King and Queen of Society tried to mark the occasion with some particular pleasure. The apogee of them all took place at the end of the season in '74: an elaborate *bal costumé*. Quadrilles had been arranged according to costume, and the Princess led off with the first 'Venetians' but, though the beauty of her jewelled dress made people catch their breath, her thunder was really stolen by the inimitable Princess Mary Adelaide, huge and imposing in silver, lace and vermilion, so vast and yet as graceful as a swan. 'Our double doge,' whispered Carrington into the Prince's ear, 'if not our triple.'

Then followed the quadrille of 'Vandykes', in which the Prince appeared as Charles the First, and complete, as he put it, with his head. His wig of shoulder-length cavalier curls was splendid with his beard, and the whole was topped with a black felt hat decorated with a single feather and pinned with an aigrette of diamonds.

Fuller with other peeping servants watched from vantage points on the lawns and the stairs. Never had he seen his master quite so ebullient – dancing till dawn, eating two suppers in scarlet tapestry-hung marquees, and then a breakfast before he was in Fuller's hands again – the hat, the sword, the Garter, the velvet cloak and cavalier wig all tumbled on the floor as he stepped sleepily into his nightshirt.

. . . . .

There are things which only a valet can know, or guess at; and two of Fuller's favourite photographs were sharp-cut pictures of H.R.H. being bashful.

The first he saw himself. It was snapped in India when the Prince shot his first elephant. It was an important sporting occasion and one of which he felt he could be proud. Moreover to succeed in sport so lavishly provided as it was in India showed an appreciation of his hosts' kindness. Told what custom demanded he marched to the elephant and to the clapping of his host and fellow guns, the huntsmen, beaters, and vast crowd of lookers on, he cut off the elephant's tail. Then Charlie Beresford, an irrepressible Irish naval officer and sharer in many of his escapades, added an informal touch by leaping on to the elephant's back where he danced a hornpipe. The clapping intensified. The hornpipe grew wilder. H.R.H. stood there with his trophy. And then suddenly Beresford was on the floor. The supposedly dead beast shook him off, stood up, and ambled off into the jungle, leaving a much embarrassed Prince of Wales holding his tail.

The second photograph of H.R.H.'s bashfulness was not actually seen by Fuller, but he had the business of clearing up afterwards and he could imagine it in every detail.

The setting for his embarrassment was the Château de Mello, south of Paris, one of the Princesse de Sagan's many homes and a favourite place for her assignations with H.R.H. She was his only acknowledged mistress amongst all his noble friends in France and she was determined to maintain her place as *maîtresse en titre*. At Mello, which she knew he loved, she distilled scents in her own laboratory to send his head a-whir with the essence of musk and orange flowers. For his pleasure she had the old château embellished and a colonnade of arches built to the cobbled stable-yard so that he could arrive in pomp, driven by four horses beneath the arches, round a huge fountain and up to the great front doors. Unfortunately though, Jeanne de Sagan's young son entertained the strongest feelings about his Mama's affair and and on one spring day, vexed by the sight of H.R.H.'s clothes neatly laid on a chair in his mother's boudoir, he seized the lot, ran outside and plunged them amongst the goldfish in the courtyard fountain.

Madame la Princesse was frenzied by her fifteen-year-old-son's behaviour, and le Prince de Galles, though outwardly composed,

199

was considerably bashful at having to drive home in a pair of borrowed and too-tight trousers.

Fuller, sorting out a valise of drenched clothes, green with waterweed and with here and there a snail and minute goldfish, kept his face as grave as a kirk elder, but underneath he was shaking with merriment – mentally photographing the unlikely scene for all posterity.

15

Some of his closest friends might have considered the five years after his attack of typhoid fever as the Albert Edward lotus years. Certainly he enjoyed them, or mostly so, but on 24 May in 1877 he realized that they had merely been his salad days.

His lotus years, he hoped, were just beginning.

On the 17th, a week before, while Mama was rapturously receiving Wagner at Windsor, the Prince had seen off his two boys and Mr Dalton to report aboard the training ship *Britannia*. Alix, staying with her brother in Athens, had been difficult. Understandably she would miss her sons. Less understandably she regarded her husband as a brute for sending them away from home. She telegraphed her feelings as a deprived mother. Bertie made no attempt to reason with her. Instead he simply ignored her complaints and wrote an affectionate letter describing the progress of the London season.

He did not, however, include an account of what took place on 24 May.

The photography machine had a strong social influence in the late '70s. In addition to formal engraved cards a few people had *carte de visite* photographs; not to demonstrate their glamour – for even ugly old Anthony Trollope had one done – but because they thought it was the thing. Certainly it was the thing to buy photographs of demi-mondaines and beautiful Society ladies who were all the rage.

The Prince of Wales, a connoisseur, saw most of the best-sellers, and amongst them the one that attracted him the most was a spiritual picture of a young lady, wearing her hair let down in a long white gown, as she sat at a desk writing with a quill by lamp-light. This, he declared to his friends Carrington and Charlie Beresford, was absolute perfection. He wished to meet the lady.

To hear, at Marlborough House, was very often to obey, but in this particular case, the Prince was advised to be prudent and contain his impatience until a discreet rendezvous could be arranged. The young lady was very well known and much talked about. In her picture she looked all innocence, very much the studious daughter of a clergyman which, oddly enough, happened to be true. Once she had been a Miss Le Breton, daughter of the Dean of Jersey, but she herself had traduced her father as 'a damned nuisance . . . couldn't be trusted with any woman anywhere', and she had married a ninny of an Irish widower named Langtry, come to London, and her beauty set a series of hearts on fire.

A rich American cattle puncher had taken her up and taught her to ride – an essential qualification for a beauty, as the captivating Skittles had known. Her first lesson had not been a success because no sooner had she been lifted into the saddle than she fainted, or so she said, and fell out again. But she had persevered and learnt to ride adequately if not with the skill of Skittles. Her fame spread. She was seen at certain parties. Millais painted her as the Jersey Lily. Lord Lonsdale, amongst others, was so much taken with her that, when riding with her in Rotten Row and another admirer Sir George Chetwyn complained that it was *his* day to ride with Mrs Langtry, Lonsdale jumped from his horse, leapt the railings, and assaulted Chetwyn with his bare fists.

Then Lillie moved still higher in the social scale. Prince Leopold, the Queen's special pet because of his haemophilia, bought a copy of Mrs Langtry's picture and hung it over his bed. No one, he ordered, was to touch it, and no one dared. But the Queen heard of it, marched to his bedroom, drew forth a chair, stood on it and took down the picture herself. Afterwards she and Jane Churchill admired the portrait before locking it away in a drawer. The Jersey Lily was certainly a beauty, but Leopold was an invalid and must learn not to burn his fingers. . . .

The new King of the Belgians – 'a *scamp*, so unlike his dear father !' wanted to burn his fingers, too. He took to calling on Mrs Langtry at the astounding hour of nine in the morning. Then the Crown Prince of Austria was lured over the Channel. He filled her room with flowers and invitations. Lillie could only take one step higher. . . .

Queen Victoria was for ever condemning her son's friends for leading him into wildness, but she did them an injustice. On some occasions, and this was one, they tried to restrain him. But Bertie's mind was made up. An obliging friend of a friend, an Arctic explorer, invited the Prince of Wales to supper after the opera, on 24 May, 1877, and there, with the potted Morcambe Bay shrimps, the devilled kidneys, the oysters and the whitebait which he loved so dearly, was Mrs Edward Langtry.

Lillie was twenty-three and despite her exciting life she was at the very peak of her loveliness. Albert Edward was rising thirty-six, to some extent already a victim of his gourmandizing, with barrel chest, thick neck and sausage fingers; and, although his beard was noble and vigorous, no matter what unguents and pomades Fuller applied, he could not be said to have had a good head of hair. But he had the advantage of being Prince of Wales and the still greater advantage of falling in love with Lillie. That he did so no one doubted.

Alix in tears told her brother the King of Greece that she had been humiliated. Bertie had publicly set up a mistress. From her small house in Mayfair Lillie had moved to a mansion in Hampstead. There she frequently received the Prince and the Prince made no pretence, using his own landau to call on her, and telling his intimates he was in love.

Possibly it was as well that Alix was with her brother at the time. He himself had a raffish reputation and the ability to gloss over the grosser aspects of what his brother-in-law was doing. He also adored his sister and therefore she listened to him, though at first with amazement, when he advised her to accept the situation.

'I am to behave as though nothing had happened?'

The King nodded.

'I am, if Bertie requires it, to receive this woman in my home.'

Another nod.

Alix gave a little shriek. She threw her arms round her brother. 'Willi you cannot be serious.'

'I am,' he said. 'Truly I am.'

She cried for a long time. Then dried her eyes. 'If you say so, and it is better for the children and for me; then I shall do it.'

'It is better for you all,' he returned.

The Queen learnt that her eldest son had lost his heart to Mrs Langtry. Convinced that he was too thoughtful to do anything which would humiliate Alix she trusted to his common sense and left it at that. She was afraid, she said to Jane Churchill, that the Prince Consort would not have liked it, but then such was his own personal purity he would not have understood such behaviour. Jane Churchill agreed. The Queen had travelled far from the days when she set herself obdurately against anything of which Albert might have disapproved. Though there was no doubting her eternal devotion to her husband and the sincerity of her continued mourning, she was no longer in thrall to his memory, and that was a good thing. Leopold's photograph of Mrs Langtry was taken out of the locked drawer and regarded by both ladies with great satisfaction. The Queen admitted again that she really possessed an almost ethereal beauty. Lady Churchill had a saucy anecdote to relate which the Queen pretended to find shocking but which really she rather enjoyed – that the bloodless Mr Langtry had at last raised an objection to his wife writing passionate love letters. Apparently he had held the blotting paper up to a looking glass to discover what she had written, but he soon had his tail between his legs again. He was told not to peek and pry, and his lady then stormed at the servants saying they had strict orders to change her blotting paper at least once a day. After a tut-tut, and a chuckle, the Queen then related something she had heard from Brown: that the crowds in the Park on a Sunday afternoon had so jostled Mrs Langtry, being anxious to see her beauty in the flesh, that she had been mobbed, rescued by the police and taken unconscious by ambulance to St George's hospital. Jane Churchill politely laughed, though she had already heard the story herself, in a slightly different version where the ambulance had been a cart, and the hospital had been St Mary's not St George's.

'Would it, dear Jane, be proper for Mrs Langtry to be invited to a Drawing Room?'

Lady Churchill thought it really would be very improper

indeed! but it would delight the Prince of Wales and do no real harm. She suggested that Sir Henry Ponsonby be asked to inquire from the Lord Chamberlain's office, and added with a smile: 'It would certainly satisfy your curiosity, Ma'am.'

Owing to the Queen's continued seclusion it was exceedingly rare for her to appear at Drawing Rooms; the Princess of Wales or another Princess deputizing for her. And when she did appear it never was for very long. Yet on the afternoon Mrs Langtry was presented – and her presentation was close to the end of the Drawing Room – the Queen received all her guests, staying for the full length of time. What she thought of Bertie's mistress she did not say. Perhaps only Lady Churchill ever knew.

16

Bertie felt properly balanced. The strains of his boyhood and youth were over. He was now a mature man with a gracious and beautiful wife, fine healthy children, a domineering but sometimes understanding mother, good friends, and a perfect mistress. Feeling properly balanced he was the better enabled to face the agonizing situation when his elder son caught typhoid. It seemed an endemic complaint to the royal house. The Queen herself had almost died of it in her girlhood, her husband had died of it, the life of the Prince of Wales had been despaired of twice because of it, and now Prince Eddy contracted the disease. He was assiduously cared for by Sir William Gull who had looked after the Prince of Wales, and no parents could have been more constant in visiting their child or sitting beside him. They shared a hopeless feeling that Eddy was doomed. When he actually survived to return to the *Britannia* they were truly surprised.

Having watched and waited and despaired together, their mutual joy joined them together again. Bertie showed his care in many affectionate ways. Alix did what under no other circumstance she felt she could have done and invited Mrs Langtry to Marlborough House.

It was a quiet afternoon affair, and, though nervous, Mrs

Langtry quickly recovered her poise and fell under the spell of the Princess' charm. Alix herself, possessive as she was, remembered all her brother had told her, and admired her rival's beauty. She had the consolation of knowing that because Bertie was polygamous by nature and easily bored, the Jersey Lily could not last for ever. Indeed she had heard from Charlotte Knollys that he was already making sheep's eyes at two other women: one, though it was hard to believe, an actress, and the other a girl from Ohio called Chamberlayne, whom Alix dismissed from her mind with a nursery giggle by nicknaming her 'Miss Chamberpots'.

It so happened she was right, that neither of these latest interests was to capture the Prince's heart as Lillie had done. The actress was, in fact, the great Bernhardt, but despite her artistry she did not have the entrée to Society until it was engineered by the Prince of Wales through his friends the Rothschilds. Obligingly they entertained Bernhardt and soon afterwards she was being received by a large number of people, though certainly not by everyone. Principal actresses in the Comédie Française were just a little too fast for the more conservative elements in the aristocracy. Nevertheless Bertie enjoyed his affair with Bernhardt, and he would, if he could, have enjoyed one with Miss Chamberpots despite her Middle-Western twang and her unladylike greed. Her appetite almost matched his own. Her regular breakfast was a fried sole followed by a beefsteak and two eggs liberally sprinkled with potatoes. This, though, he had to learn from the newspapers. He was seldom able to get any conversation out of the girl herself, and as she was an heiress as well as beautiful she was never out of sight of her parents, plus a bevy of inquisitive American newspapermen. Despite the fact that he followed her from Homburg to Cannes, Bertie never once got her on her own; and he gave up the chase. Later he was chagrined to hear that American newspapermen were writing up a romance which had never taken place, and that Mr Chamberlayne had told a reporter he, the Prince of Wales, was 'homely'. So back he went to Lillie, calling on her at the understood hour for love-making, tea-time; and supping with her frequently after balls and theatre parties.

The age was called Victorian, but the Sovereign herself disliked the dry-as-dust piety the word had come to suggest. She disapproved of extravagances, vulgarity and fastness, but she hated humbug most of all, and she was no spoilsport as many of her subjects made out. She irritated the sabbatarians by her enlightened views, liked her cigarette (to keep away the midges), her glass of whisky and appolinaris (to keep out the cold), and took an annual ticket in the Balmoral sweepstake. Nevertheless she found her family's goings-on far too much at times.

Bertie and Mrs Langtry and his flirtations with La Bernhardt and Miss Chamberlayne was one thing. His affair with Patsy Cornwallis-West was another, because Mrs Cornwallis-West was a lady in the terms the Queen understood whilst the others were not.

She screwed up her courage and mentioned that to Bertie himself. She chose a detour before approaching the main subject by remarking that she was astonished Bertie and Alix had been giving hospitality to the Prince of Orange, whose life was an open scandal throughout Europe. Bertie explained that 'dear old Citron' had only been down for the week-end at Sandringham, which ought to have done him good. Then boldly Mama brought up the matter of Mrs Cornwallis-West. She reminded her son that she was of a fine Irish family and her husband a Custos Rotulorum, that is, she added – as if explaining to a boy of ten, for it took her years and years to get out of her habit of being sarcastic with Bertie – the head justice of the country. Bertie knew all right. He also knew that the wicked Patsy called her oft cuckolded husband the High Cockolorum! But he gravely reassured his mother. His relationship with Mrs William Cornwallis-West was platonic – flirtatious, possibly, but platonic. At that time it was true. He thought it unnecessary to mention that he hoped to alter the nature of the relationship as soon as possible. Poor Mama, she would never have understood. . . .

Mama understood too much. She heard to her amazement that George of Cambridge – with a 'Mrs Fitzgeorge' in Queen Street, Mayfair, and his three fine Fitzgeorge sons over-spending and getting into trouble here and there and everywhere, had found himself another lady. Could it be true? In this case there was a direct way of finding out. Cousin Mary Adelaide of Teck was sent for. That convenient distance between White Lodge and Windsor, which had been one of Mary Adelaide's chief claims for the usefulness of the house she wanted, was covered in record time. And over tea the two cousins sat, the Queen on a hand-worked tapestry chair, Princess Mary Adelaide on the larger part of a substantial sofa – the one round and pert, as small as a hedgehog beside her hippopotamus of a relation. They talked of everything except George of Cambridge until tea had been taken away; then the handworked tapestry chair was moved a little closer to the substantial sofa, and Mary Alelaide admitted that George was being faithless to Mrs Fitzgeorge. He now was carrying on with a Mrs Beauclerk. A widow? Yes, thankfully, a widow. And what is she like? Well, Princess Mary Adelaide had not herself seen the lady, though on three occasions she had tried to engineer a meeting, but she gathered that she was petite and pretty and head over heels in love with dear George.

'Dear George!' echoed the Queen. 'Foolish George, I should say,' and she spoke anxiously about the Commander-in-Chief of her Army. 'Since Bertie's illness he has been growing odder and odder.'

Princess Mary Adelaide agreed. Because of what he called 'private sanitation' George had a different toothbrush for each day of the week. It was useful of course to a hostess who might not know how long he proposed to be her guest. A discreet investigation into the number of his toothbrushes would tell her. But it was odd all the same.

'Mary,' said the Queen severely. 'You are right it *is* odd. And now let me tell you something even odder....'

The sofa springs squeaked as Princess Mary Adelaide leant forward to hear that George had been reprimanding the troops for the habit of swearing; and before thousands of his men he had emphasized the point by bellowing 'I was talking it over with the Queen last night, and Her Majesty says she is damned if she will have it!'

17

On a beautiful May Day when riding down Rotten Row with Lillie at his side – she riding Redskin, a fine mare given her by a former admirer – Bertie was struck with the doubt, which must sometimes assail princes and those of exalted rank, as to the reality and sincerity of his friendships. With women he felt on fairly certain ground. In any case, as long as they were beautiful or clever or both he was quite satisfied with their company. But from men he demanded more and, in gloomy moments like these, he doubted if he had a real friend in the world. His following of society people called the Marlborough Set was a hybrid bunch. There were some of the old aristocracy. Hartington for example was very close to him, and too much of a Cavendish to be obsequious to a mere scion of Saxe-Coburg-Gotha. And with him he had brought Louisa and her cronies so that Smart Society was an amalgam of the Manchester Set and the Marlborough House Set. Carrington belonged there and Sutherland and the Beresfords, and Charley Wood and Sykes, of course, and Cadogan with scores of others. But there was a heavy vein in the Marlborough House Set of the new people – the new rich industrialists and nabobs of business, Jews and Americans, fast, raffish adventurers whom his mother and the older quieter patricians found detestable.

He confided in Lillie – which was a waste of time because, even if she had listened she would fail to understand, and in any case she was too busy enjoying the glamour of her situation. Gentlemen were raising their hats. Policemen and soldiers were saluting. Nursemaids were holding babies up to see them pass: the Prince murmuring distantly, she absorbing the admiration exactly like an electric cell taking in a charge.

The Prince went on thinking about his problem most of the day. There were the diversions of a heavy luncheon, a tricycle ride round the lawns at Marborough House, tea with Lillie – when, as custom demanded, he carried hat, cane and gloves into her drawing-room and laid them on the floor before eating a substantial meal; then a game of billiards at the Marlborough, a talk with Alix and a look at the children, a huge dinner, a concert, and supper at a little place where there was delicious food and private rooms of white and gold which he honestly believed Lillie knew nothing about – though of course she did, having been there often in the old days – with the Grand Duke Rudolph before Bertie came along and cut him out.

The same thoughts were at the back of his mind all day. How reliable were his friends? Could they be counted on?

Quite recently he had been let down. He recognized that he

was a bit more than a bully and could, on occasions, behave like a cad. But he generally tried to help friends who had fallen on hard times. Valentine Baker was a case in point. He was still pressing Dizzy to find something for him. And he had done the same for Charles Buller, who had been obliged to resign his commission in the Blues because of his debts. Buller had been found a job, or rather a job had been made for him, in looking after the Prince's collection of Indian treasures at that year's British stand at the Paris Exhibition. In full confidence that a grateful friend would have everything catalogued and arranged, Bertie had taken some important guests down for a preview, including the British Ambassador and *Fleur des Pois* himself, to find nothing done, crates everywhere, and the stand in charge of a *marc*-fired labourer who complained at being woken up and then grossly insulted the visitors. Despite this the job would have been kept open for Buller, had he not sent such a casual and insolent reply to the Prince's justifiable rebuke. And now he had heard Buller was off to gaol for writing a useless cheque.

It upset him a great deal. Could they all be the same? Could that charming Count Miecislas Jaraczewski, whom he had met on the Riviera and was such a social asset, be anything like Buller? His name was abominable, of course, and for the British had had to be changed to 'Sherry and Whiskers'. Could this fun-loving, amusing rip, really be humbugging him when he claimed to be his friend? Was even Hartington murmuring things against him into the white bosom of Louisa Manchester? Could Charley Wood, who was so religious, really be fond of a womanizer like himself? Were Carrington and Sutherland and the rest simply after the éclat of being known as the Prince's close friends?

Not for a long time had Bertie had such mistrust in himself and in other people; perhaps not since the day his father had told him that Mr Birch was to go. He got himself into such a state that he tugged at the bed bell.

Fuller appeared, as wide awake as if he had never been asleep. 'Sir?'

'I'm very thirsty, Fuller. A bottle of chilled hock would be very pleasant.'

'Of course, Sir.'

Fuller wondered what was the matter. Eventually he left his master sitting up in bed drinking hock, the tassel of his nightcap almost touching the long cigar he was smoking. He had insisted on the bed curtains being looped back.

Within twenty-four hours the Prince was reassured. Francis Knollys, his Private Secretary, had an unerring instinct in understanding his master's nerve crises and their causes. He knew that the Prince was not in the least a clever man, that is, not in the book-learning sense, but he had a great sensitivity. Knollys guessed at his problem and solved it in an uncharacteristic fashion. Not so solemn as his father, he was nevertheless a sober, quiet man and he astounded two of the Prince's more raffish friends Lord Marcus Beresford and his brother Lord Charles, by suggesting that they do something to raise his master's low spirits. He needed taking out of himself. . . .

Knollys could hardly have applied to a better quarter. All the Irish Beresfords led uproarious lives. Marcus, an elegant Regency figure, knew horseflesh up and down and inside out and trained the Prince's horses for him. Charles was that jovial sailor who had hornpiped on A. E.'s supposedly defunct elephant in India. Both were dashing. Both were tough because they had been brought up toughly and swore they would always wear the mark of the coronet from their mother's hairbrush on their backsides for the rest of their lives. Both were brave – each earned a V.C., as did another brother. And both kept a string of women as well as a string of hunters. Handing the Prince over to the Beresfords for a spell of spirit-raising was an inspiration. For a day or two all three behaved outrageously and certainly by the time the Beresfords had finished with Bertie he had lost all his doubts. There were such things as friends.

18

The Grand Duke Louis of Hesse saluted and took his brother-in-law's hand as he stepped from the train. Bertie was in mourning uniform and kissed Louis on both cheeks. He could not, he said, and he truly meant it, have come on a sadder occasion. Had his mother died, had Alix, even his children, he felt he could have borne it better than the loss of Alice. A little behind him stood his brother Prince Leopold, and handsome old Christian, Helena's husband. They too greeted the Grand Duke, offering their commiseration. Louis nodded dully. He led the way out to a closed carriage. They rode in silence to the Palace. Everything there was draped in black. There was a tang of sulphur. Fumigators had been at work. Because of infection Alice was already in her coffin and sealed. She could not be seen. Bertie considered this a dreadful deprivation. Leopold said nothing. Frankly Christian was relieved. Death chambers had no attraction for him. Diphtheria had decimated the Grand Ducal family. Alice's eldest child Victoria first caught the disease, then Alicky, then May, then her husband Louis, then their only son Ernest. With the exception of the smallest, May, who died, Alice herself nursed the family back to health. But in her exhaustion she too was infected and died on the 'dreadful anniversary', 14 December, when her father had died, and the date which had once almost claimed Bertie.

Waiting for the funeral was difficult. They filled it with smoking, talking quietly, nibbling at sweetmeats, denigrating the German Emperor who had forbidden his son and daughter-in-law to attend for fear of infection.

Then came the ceremony: as elaborate as only a small Court could make such a ceremony. It was touching that the coffin was draped with the Union Jack. It had been Alice's own particular request. It was touching, too, that an unknown countrywoman sent a wreath of rosemary for remembrance, and Bertie broke down and wept in the streets of Darmstadt when two girls pushed forward and laid on the hearse a crumpled bunch of flowers.

At the end of January 1879, when the Grand Duke Louis and his six children had fully regained their strength, the Prince of Wales went out in a royal yacht to meet the party at Flushing. He had gone on his own initiative, that is, he had thought of the idea a day or two before Mama had suggested it herself, and when he saw the pathetic group on the quayside he was glad that he had. He had always been family-minded, and somehow the loss of his favourite sister had strengthened the feeling still further. He told Louis that if things became too tedious at Windsor, where Mama

211

had planned he should be for two whole months, he was to propose himself and slip away to Sandringham or Marlborough House.

It would have been indelicate to mention it but both he and Mama hoped that perhaps he would look fondly on Alice's sister, Beatrice. There was an English law against marriage with a deceased wife's sister; but Dizzy, who had managed the bishops so cleverly about ritualism, could surely make them alter this peculiar prohibition.

Bertie accompanied the party all the way to Windsor and stayed in his apartments there. Louis, the Queen decided, needed cheering up – but not, she added hastily, noting the sudden eagerness in Bertie's eyes, not with a lot of chambering and wantonness. His eager smile died. He was not as familiar as his Mama with Holy Writ, and thought her way of putting things a little stark.

Sensibly Mama discussed all her plans for the Darmstadt children. They were to have an English governess who would send in detailed reports. Did Bertie approve? He did, with some reservations. The woman, he insisted, recalling his own past, would have to be ideal and chosen with particular care. And Louis must be given the reports first otherwise he would jump to the conclusion that there was a foreign spy at the centre of his own family life. Very good. Next the Queen proposed that the Darmstadt orphans should spend some of their holidays, certainly the summer ones, in England with their four cousins, Lenchen's children. Agreed. And Lenchen herself would go out once a year to Louis' court just to see that all was well. Bertie suggested that perhaps Alix might help in this? or Louise? Otherwise everything was being unloaded on to Lenchen. . . . Nonsense, said Mama. Alix with her increasing deafness could never get through to the children, and as for Louise, she knew nothing about children and did not want to, and, in any case, she was in Canada supposedly helping her husband Lorne who was Governor General. From this shrewd remark Bertie discovered that Mama already knew the rumours that Louise was not exactly misbehaving but certainly behaving indecorously out in Canada. The American press, with nothing to lose, actually stated that the Marquess of Lorne was a hen-pecked husband. Very well then, he agreed, Lenchen should go out once a year – but again he reminded his mother of Louis possibly misinterpreting this as interference

212

'Misinterpreting, rubbish!' snapped his mother. 'I as Alice's mother have the greatest right to interfere.'

Mama, thought Bertie, was getting very bossy. He did not envy Louis his two months at Windsor and later, when he had an opportunity, he repeated his invitation.

They did not meet again until March, for Arthur's wedding at Windsor; but, to begin with, there was not much chance to draw out Louis – who looked most dreadfully melancholy – because no less than twenty-six royalties had gathered for the wedding and Bertie had his special responsibilities to each. His primary duty was to be welcoming to his new sister-in-law, a task he found wearisome because she was a Prussian and a stately, flat-faced lady. He had met her at the same time as Arthur when both were in Berlin the previous February for a double family wedding, and had been surprised that his tall, good looking brother should have fallen so heavily for this odd princess. Perhaps he was merely using her as a means for getting away from Mama's hectoring, or possibly he was sorry for the girl? He'd every right to be, of course. Bertie was himself. Her parents were estranged and her beast of a father had punished his children by bending back their fingernails and sticking his own into the quicks. But being sorry for people doesn't bring them to life, nor make them amusing and clever, and Bertie, such was his nature, was soon bored by his duties to the Princess Louise Margherita.

Nor was Mama smitten by the thought of Arthur marrying a Prussian. She no longer cared for the Prussians – so grasping under Bismarck's iron hand, the sort of leaders of Germany Albert would never have countenanced. And the girl herself was so dull. She wrote in her journal:

Young, shy, not a beauty.

But she bore with Arthur's choice. Bertie and Affie had wrecked her nerves by their 'falls'. Leopold would 'fall' if he slipped her leash. Alone of her sons Arthur had never threatened to 'fall' and had dutifully persevered in his army career. She felt she owed him a free choice in this, and he appeared to be in love with his Louischen, as he called her; though right to the end of his bachelorhood, entirely overlooking the fact that he was twenty-eight years old and a regular officer in the Brigade of Guards, she kept the apron strings extremely tight. On the eve of his wedding she was still issuing edicts about him:

He must be looked after and dosed for he is yellow and green.

Considering the circumstances it was a less gloomy wedding than one might have expected. Arthur seemed to be so much in love. It was the thirteenth of the month and the superstitious, led by Mama's Scottish entourage, wrung their hands over the inauspicious date, but the day was brilliant, the marriage passed without anyone in the royal family making a fool of himself – which made it an almost unique event – and the breakfast was of such a quality that Bertie wondered if he dared to wean Mama's chief chef from Windsor into his own service. As the couple drove away from the Castle, young Prince George in his *Britannia* cadet's uniform hurled a shoe after them for luck. His uncle deftly caught it and returned it at a shattering speed, crying out: 'I hope you bat better than you bowl!'

Altogether a happy family event.

Afterwards there was time for Bertie to talk to his brother-in-law, Louis. The Grand Duke had livened up a little under the influence of the breakfast, but he was undeniably less brisk than he had been on arrival at Windsor. Mama he complained was so capable, which was his way of saying bossy; and she was for ever pushing Beatrice at him. He liked Beatrice as a sister-in-law. No one could have been kinder, but Mama was clearly bent on pushing them together. He was shown Beatrice's embroidery, her etchings, her own garden. He had eaten cakes cooked specially by Beatrice, read stories specially written by her, and admired her first attempts at photography. Mama had even remarked archly, as though these were recommendations, that Beatrice had had a boat named after her *and* a wing of the London Hospital. But Louis knew as well as Mama and Beatrice knew that marriage was out of the question. It would be illegal. . . .

Wretched Louis. Bertie consoled him as well as he could. Mama was Mama and though she might appear to have taken over Louis and his family, he could always give her the slip. Why, very soon she and Beatrice were off to Baveno in northern Italy.

Louis nodded. He knew. He had been invited to join the party.

'Then accept,' said Bertie, who knew his mother well. 'Accept,

214

but change your mind at the last moment, and come to us. Or, better still, take all your children back to Darmstadt. A ruler, you know,' he added 'ought to be in his own state.'

There was another moody, gloomy nod from Louis. Louis doubted, he said, if he dared. . . .

In the end he did summon up the courage. Events helped him. There was bad news from Vicky in Prussia. Her eleven-year old son had died of haemophilia. The Queen took the sad news very badly, fearful for her own beloved Leopold. And simultaneously Brown was making trouble about going off to a heathen land like Italy. He had to be petted, persuaded. Brown in a surly Scotch rage against foreigners was not a comfortable travelling-companion. And so the Queen barely noticed it when Louis and his brood quietly slipped away from Windsor. The children would be back soon – to stay with Aunt Lenchen and Uncle Christian, and Louis promised that all the Queen's arrangements for their upbringing were to be carried out. 'Very well, dear,' she murmured, abstractedly, kissing his cheek. 'If you feel you must go, you must. Poor, poor Alice.'

'Louis,' said the Prince of Wales when his brother-in-law was leaving. 'I dearly loved my sister Alice. Possibly she's the only woman who ever understood me. And I know how you two cared for one another. But marry again, Louis. Marry again. On no account permit Mama's choice of widowhood to keep you from choosing someone else. Leave a decent interval. Then do it. You've five orphaned children. Alice herself would have wished it.'

19

New Sandringham House was built of white stone and bright tawny brick, and sprawled over a large area.

Most people accepted it as an ordinary enough sort of country house of that particular period although a few who lived in more ancient and infinitely more comfortable houses, and a few who were discriminating but had no country houses of their own, considered it a fright. Lord Rosebery even said so, and rather hurt his friend the Prince until Bertie recalled that Rosebery's taste was eccentric, and maybe defective. After all, Rosebery had said he thought the drawing-room at Osborne the ugliest room in the world until he saw the drawing-room at Balmoral, and Bertie considered both were perfectly adequate. Moreover Bertie liked Sandringham because it was home, and he found it hard to conceal his irritation when the fastidious Rosebery said he supposed time and winds from the Wash would ultimately tone down the orange brickwork to a sandy colour, and meanwhile, perhaps, a creeper or two might serve. . . .

As most homes were at that time, Sandringham was crammed to capacity with heavy and light furniture, knick-knacks and decorations.

Here the Prince kept his collections: stuffed birds he had shot in the Holy Land and Egypt; likewise skins and stuffed heads, and mounted tusks, hoofs and horns from his Indian trip; cabinets of curios from India, Cairo, Jerusalem and Turkey, precious stones, intaglio work, puzzles and trick boxes, chessmen and mahjong tiles, Benares Buddhas, gongs, trays and incense burners; weapons of all kinds, from all over the world and from all ages, even a caseful of weapons personally collected by the Prince on the blasted battlefield of Sedan. And for a long time in the Saloon there were a pair of cannon named 'Eugénie' and 'Louis Napoleon', until, in the process of circumnavigating the two occasional tables, day bed, snail-ended sofa, white-wire jardiniere of hot-house plants, the photograph easel, the group of palms and the revolving bookcase which lay in a direct line between the two doors of the Saloon, the Prince twice barked his shins on 'Eugénie' and the cannon was relegated to a stuffy gunroom.

Drawing-rooms of varying sizes and colours ran along the west and afternoon side of the house, where there was also a fashionable conservatory, the traditional assignation place for Victorian lovers, furnished with oriental matting, cane and wrought-iron furniture, palms, ferns, exotics – including a mass of orchids – and two huge pictures: one of a white swan with a wicked violet eye; the other entitled 'Girls Bathing' which was far less prurient than it sounded. There were also *fumoirs* here and there – though the Prince smoked almost all the time and generally where he wanted; and, as might be expected from a modern go-ahead country gentleman, he had added to the usual attractions of his house an American bowling alley, a cycling track, a photography room, and a huge ballroom with a minstrels' gallery at one end and decorated with an armoury of deadly weapons on the walls.

Life at Sandringham passed as methodically as the beat of a pulse. Only the Princess herself was permitted, though never encouraged, to break the unvarying routine. The rules were stringent. Guests had to be up and about by a certain hour. They breakfasted and took luncheon together in the absence of the family at round tables holding from six to eight. Not until tea-time did they eat with their host and hostess, and then it was formally at a long table weighed down with food in the red and gold drawing-room, or, on fine days, in the Princess' tea-room, a garden house which made Rosebery wince because it was shaped like a Swiss chalet, equipped with a Scotch dairy and was decorated throughout with Indian tiles. Or even, when the wind was favourable, tea was eaten outside under awnings, near a creeper-covered cottage filled with monkeys and marmosets. Dinner was the occasion of the day. In the dining-room, after the Italian fashion, the Prince sat at the middle of one side of the long dining table, with the Princess opposite. The further a guest was moved towards the table ends the closer drew his day of departure. Though the Princess' High Church proclivities were well known, the Prince had not much interest in religion. Like his mother he had a sanguine belief that all would be all right in the end. Meanwhile sermons must be short and have a single point; and because he could not bear to sit through a whole church service, he and his Gentlemen would arrive at Sandringham Church just before the sermon – to a fresh peal of bells.

Here, in his Norfolk home, Albert Edward lost all feeling of that tension which sometimes assailed him at Court or in London. And he certainly found it more peaceful than his *en garcon* trips to France and to German watering-places. More sure of himself and at peace with himself, he felt secure at Sandringham, and in his locust years he would have admitted that he really enjoyed life in his country house far more than the Babylonish excesses he was supposed to indulge in elsewhere. It was here that he kept his own birthday celebrations, and Alix's birthday three weeks afterwards, and the great feast of Christmas. It was here that they had country balls for the local farmers and the local gentlefolk, and after the ball had been formally begun by the royal family dancing a quadrille, he would throw himself into the country dances which followed with his accustomed energy, and expect every one else to do the same. There were Highland dances as well as squares and rounds and jigs and 'Sir Roger' and 'The Triumph', and then huge suppers.

The Prince's younger brother, the Duke of Edinburgh, was the closest to him in age and they bore a striking physical resemblance to each other. Their tastes, too were the same except that Affie preferred the company of musical Jews and would have travelled a hundred miles to hear Mrs Ronalds sing the works of Arthur Sullivan, and Bertie preferred the Haute Juiverie and would sooner have travelled a hundred miles to enjoy the company of a Rothschild or a Sassoon. But since they had been forcibly separated in the nursery, 'for their own good', they had never been intimate friends and on occasions they had quarrelled quite seriously: once at the time when Affie was showing too much attention to Alix and once when Affie's wife demanded precedence over Alix because she was a Russian Grand-Duchess – a piece of nonsense which Mama had very quickly settled. And Affie, with his undoubtedly successful Naval career, always managed to make his unoccupied elder brother feel small about his lack of occupation.

Therefore it came as rather a surprise when Affie on shore leave and his Grand-Duchess Marie proposed themselves for a week or two at Sandringham in the hard winter of 1879–1880. There were sharp frosts, skating on the lake with everyone drinking hot chocolate or negus, and gaming in the evenings. And there was naturally a ball – led off by four couples of the royalties in a quadrille. After that Affie stood or sat and watched his elder brother hurl himself as vigorously as a schoolboy into all the country dances. At supper he chaffed Bertie, who was tucking into cold beef and horseradish. 'One day, dear Bertie, you will have a seizure. A thirteen-course dinner, an evening's jumping about, and now a heavy supper.' He wagged an admonitory finger.

Bertie refused to be teased. 'After this,' he said through beef and horseradish, 'You and I are off to the bowling alley. I want to see if you still play badly.'

But Affie did not want to play bowls and said so. He took the guest's right to choose to go to the conservatory instead. He wanted, he said, to talk.

'Oh, very well.'

Bertie finished his supper and unenthusiastically went off with his brother to the conservatory. It was dimly lighted and, being a fair man, he stood in the doorway and said loudly. 'If anyone is tucked away behind a palm or an orchid pot he had better come out now. Or' he warned, raising his voice, 'I shall regard him as an eavesdropper.'

To his surprise and then to his amusement Lady Macclesfield appeared. Her face flushed. Obviously she had slipped off from the festivities to snatch a few minutes sleep. The Prince bowed. 'I presume Ma'am,' he said, 'that you are alone?'

She swept him a curtsey. 'Entirely, Sir. Entirely.'

He stood on one side to let her pass which she did with a sigh at the thought of continuing her duties in waiting far into the night.

The two princes sat on a white wrought-iron garden seat which swung from pivots. It needed oiling and squeaked. Both had brought glasses of brandy. Bertie sipped at his, waiting. He expected to be touched for a loan and steeled himself to say no. Affie's extravagances were always leading him into debt, but they could not match his own. Or perhaps Marie was being difficult. Obviously she was a proud, unlikeable little piece and when she could catch her husband, which was not often, she had him very much under her unsavoury thumb. But it was neither of these problems which held Affie's attention at that moment. He wanted to know if it was true than Langtry was suing for a divorce. No, said his brother shortly, it was a rumour published in a scandal-mongering weekly *Town Talk*, and as he had been named as co-respondent, together with Londesborough and Lonsdale, the editor was to be sued for criminal libel.

Prince Alfred clicked the glass against his teeth. 'Oh,' he said reflectively, and then again 'Oh!'

'Well?'

'You see. . . .' After a pause, Prince Alfred went on: 'I was wondering if you and Lillie were finished? I mean, now that La Bernhardt has caught you, you can hardly have the time. . . .'

219

His brother interrupted him with a laugh. Really it was a guffaw. 'So you want her yourself, Affie? Is that it?'

'I should not,' replied his brother, 'be averse to the idea.'

'Nor, I assume, would Lillie. She adores Princes of the Blood Royal.'

'And you would not mind?'

'Not in the least.'

It was true. Bertie was no longer in love with Lillie. She had killed it herself with her airs and her sulks. Who could love such a woman for long? Bernhardt, now, was different. She gave a distinct impression of caring deeply for her new protector, and he loved her dearly – while he was wise enough to recognize that so talented a tragedienne could simulate any sort of feeling if she wished.

The two princes sat comfortably sipping their brandy and talking with an intimacy that was unusual for them. Inevitably they spoke about Mama: her indomitable spirit, her grief when that June the Prince Imperial had been killed whilst fighting in South Africa in the British Army, a tragedy that had chilled her for weeks. They spoke of her sweet romance with Dizzy who was more like an Egyptian mummy than ever; of her rages at Gladstone whom by now she had come to hate.

'And he deserves it,' smiled Bertie. 'He really does. I have told him so. He is dreadfully, needlessly tactless.'

Affie whistled. He was impressed – to him Gladstone was a great figure on the political stage, and being away at sea so often he was not aware of his brother's friendship with the Gladstones. 'You told him so?' he repeated.

Bertie nodded. 'But it will make no difference. Only a month ago in his campaign he called Mama's assumption of the title of Empress of India theatrical bombast and folly. You can imagine how she received that piece of news. . . .'

Both brothers laughed. Then Affie said seriously: 'I hope she is well guarded? Has Dizzy made sure of it? We all know how stubborn she can be, but there are some very dangerous people about besides the Fenians.'

Bertie reassured him. Dizzy and his Home Secretary had also been worried by recent attempts of anarchists. The Tsar was always under the threat of assassination, and a crazy waiter had recently shot at the King and Queen of Spain. Plain clothes men were guarding the Queen of England with the strict instructions that they were to be unobtrusive.

'If she finds them,' remarked Bertie, 'she will be in a volcanic rage even though Dizzy gave the order.' He reflected for a moment, wondering whether or not to confide in a brother who generally did not have his confidence. He decided on this occasion to do so. 'Two things worry me at present, and I should like your advice.'

Affie was surprised. 'Certainly,' he said quickly. 'If I can help, I shall.'

'The first is Mama's determination that my friends are bad for the children. She says they ought not to meet. And I have told her they will be kept apart. With the boys it is not difficult, but less easy with the girls, who can't be shut away in a convent sort of life in their own home.'

'They'll come to no harm,' advised his brother. 'Not so long as Alix brings them up sensibly.'

'That,' admitted Bertie unhappily, 'is just the trouble. I'm afraid she's reined them in too tightly and unless she is careful they will never reach proper maturity. Even the boys are younger than their years. They are soft, compared to what we were at their age, they are soft. Innocent, yes, which is a great thing. But I worry greatly about their immaturity.'

Having admitted so much to Affie he told him the rest; that Dalton seriously feared Prince Eddy could not make the grade, even as a naval cadet; that he was behind, far behind George, who himself was not all that bright. Neither had any languages. Mathematics were closed books to them. Writing letters was difficult enough and their immaturity showed through and through. 'Why Affie,' he concluded, 'they are cadets aboard the *Bacchante* having the adventure of their lives, and all they can do is giggle because the papers report there's been a mutiny aboard, and that they've had their noses tatooed in Jamaica because they were photographed in the Botanic Gardens with orchid pollen on their noses.' He threw his hands in the air. 'At their age you and I weren't exactly rips but we weren't soft.'

'Nor, I expect, are they,' said Affie to the other's surprise. 'Their naïve letters to Motherdear don't say much because they can't express themselves yet, but I've been a naval cadet myself. I know what sort of life they'll be leading. I know Dalton's there

221

to keep an eye on them, but wasn't it your particular wish that they should mess with their mates and have a bit of sense knocked into them that way?'

Bertie nodded. 'Yes.' His cigar had gone out. He tried to relight it.

Affie smiled. 'I don't want to distress you, Bertie; nor have you railing at the Senior Service, but perhaps you ought to know that your dear boys aren't, and can't be, as innocent as you suppose.'

The match burnt down and was thrown away. Bertie's cigar still remained unlighted.

Affie explained. Messmates would have made sure the young princes heard all about their father's goings-on. By now they would have heard of the Mordaunt affair, almost certainly about Schneider and the Princesse de Sagan, and absolutely certainly about his affairs with Langtry and Miss Chamberpots, Patsy Cornwallis-West and La Bernhardt. . . .

'Impossible!' cut in Bertie angrily. 'Quite impossible!'

His brother shook his head. 'Not at all impossible. In case you have forgotten, boys can be exceedingly cruel.' He paused. 'I don't think in this case that your boys will have heard the scandal about Alix's knee, but they might.'

Bertie whitened. Rumour in its muck-raking had attributed the Princess of Wales' permanently stiff knee not to her rheumatic fever but to a gonorrhoeal synovitis, a disease he was said to have passed on to her himself. 'It is monstrous,' he said quietly.

'I agree, monstrous. And no one believes it. But rumours like that persist. Cadets hear these things and pass them on. As I say, they'll probably not have been so devilish as to pass on that particular story to Eddy and George, but there are plenty of others. Cadets read newspaper reports. . . .'

'Calumnies!'

Maybe, but do cadets have the grown-up *savoir faire* to separate a report from a calumny? Furthermore,' continued Affie, beckoning with the palm of his hand for Bertie to remain seated a moment because Bertie looked as if he was about to spring to his feet. 'Furthermore, cadets when they go to their first ship have to undergo certain initiations. Even on a specially commissioned warship they will have had to go through the customs.'

'Initiations?' exclaimed Bertie in a dazed voice. 'Customs?'

'Precisely,' said Affie. He grinned. Then he described them.

222

When he had finished his brother gazed at him unbelievingly. Then, in a rage he jumped to his feet. 'Impossible. Impossible. Dalton is there. He would not permit it. He would not permit such a degrading, disgusting . . .'

Affie calmed him with difficulty. 'Dalton would know nothing about it. He cannot possibly know what goes on all the time on the orlop deck. The boys are princes but also naval cadets. They will not wish to be different. You should not wish them to be different from everyone else. The initiation is as old as the Navy. It was actually forbidden in 1863, but it certainly still goes on.'

'Good God Almighty!' exclaimed the Prince of Wales. 'You went through all that too?'

'I did,' replied his brother. 'And very strange it was. Your cigar's gone out, Bertie.'

On 3 May in 1880 the Prince of Wales met his sons off Spithead when the *Bacchante,* dressed overall, dropped anchor. To a trilling of bosun's pipes and the thud of the saluting gun he stepped aboard, saluted the quarter deck, and greeted the Captain and Dalton. Then he turned to his sons; now aged sixteen and fifteen respectively.

With a rush of affection he kissed them both. The heart stirrings and wonderings and feelings of regret, even of remorse, which had been engendered by Affie's frank conversation in the Sandringham conservatory, were all forgotten. What did it matter if the boys had lost their innocence? It had to be one day. And what did it matter that they must be aware of his wayward life? That, too, could not be kept secret for ever. What mattered was that they were his sons and he dearly loved them and he could see from their eyes that they dearly loved him too.

'Come boys,' he said gruffly. 'We must take my barge to Osborne House. Grandmama will be waiting.'

More trilling of bosun's pipes, salutes, presentations of arms, and the royal party was over the side: a father proud of his sons, and, in fact, two sons very proud of their father.

PART THREE

PART THREE

1

The years slipped by, and the most frequently heard complaint from one of the most occupied men in the kingdom was that he had nothing to do.

The Prince of Wales' energies were burnt up with ruling Society, race meetings, yachting, shooting, gaming, travelling, and a succession of discreet affairs. He was circumspect and not only for fear of becoming prey again to the moral outrage of the British middle classes but also because, unlike the Sun King, Charles the Second and George the Fourth, he had no taste for flaunting his mistresses and the demi-mondaines who pleased him.

His routine now included visits to country houses where accommodating hostesses would select their guest lists with the greatest care. It was said that one or two even went so far as to have estate carpenters and builders in, swear them to secrecy, and afterwards order the construction of slip-rooms and routes through wainscoting and thick walls for their august guest's convenience.

Yet, however successfully his peccadilloes might be hidden from the masses, Albert Edward's micawberism was an open secret. Ends never met with him. Being fond of gaming and extravagant, and married to an extravagant wife, his money troubles multiplied. Borrowing from moneylenders at absurb percentages against his expectations was hardly any help, and though he took advice from the Rothschilds and other financiers and bankers on his affairs, Knollys could never get them straight, and both the Prince and his Comptroller worried constantly about them.

But the Prince's primary concern was the perennial one – how to get hold of that enviable key so that he could have an approximate idea of what, one day, his work and his position would be. Naturally he already had a very good idea. Francis Knollys made certain of that. But the ultimate goal, to possess a despatch box key as his young brother Leopold did, was denied him.

He felt as embarrassed as a schoolboy when Knollys caught him idly practising the royal signature he might one day use on a scrap of paper. Hastily he blotted it and threw the paper away. He was not eager to be king, he told himself, not eager to sit on the English throne because the throne was Mama's; nevertheless in his secret heart he knew he longed to be in the first place – with all its riches, and influence, and patronage, and splendour – and not stay for ever in a very meagre second place.

A bad conscience about this, or genuine concern, made him particularly careful for his mother as the years went by. She was as strong and as resolute as ever; but her props, one by one, were giving way.

To begin with, her favourite Lord Beaconsfield unexpectedly lost an election. Having to do without Dizzy had appalled the Queen.

'*The downfall of Beaconsfieldism,*' the new Prime Minister had thundered, '*is like the vanishing of some vast magnificent castle*'

He was right. But to the Queen's further chagrin the new Prime Minister was not Lord Hartington as everyone had expected, but the exceedingly old – and, to her, odious – W. E. Gladstone. Overlooking the fact that he had resigned the leadership of the Liberals some time before, Gladstone left his Cheshire retirement to lead the country and reverse Dizzy's pro-Turkish policy to a pro-Greek one. The change was acceptable to Marlborough House, but hateful to Windsor, and the Prince tried very hard to conciliate his mother and his wife.

Then, most distressing of all, a year later Dizzy died.

The Prince went himself to see Dizzy sealed in a vault at Hughenden beside his Mary Anne, and he felt, as the Queen most deeply felt, that they had not only lost a devoted friend but also a conjurer at overcoming political difficulties and smoothing rough family surfaces. Mama was hardly herself for a considerable time after her dear friend's death.

After that Leopold insisted on marrying and leading an independent life. It would be a short life, inevitably so, because of

228

his haemophilia, but the Queen no longer felt she could deny him what he really wanted. With a sadness she found difficult to conceal, she gave her permission.

Then George Cambridge began to behave badly and vex the Queen. He would not allow a single reform in her Army and was behaving more peculiarly than ever. When Colonel Barnaby flew right across the Channel in a balloon the Commander-in-Chief wanted to do the same. His cousin put her royal foot down. George arriving in France by balloon! It was preposterous!

Then the Queen was shot at again – but this time in Eton, where the boys gave the villain a drubbing with their umbrellas.

Then the Irish went mad. There was no other word for it. They had been seditious for years but in 1883 they reached unparalleled heights of lunacy; and their pretensions were as mad as their reckless bombing.

Then, when she needed him most, Brown died. . . .

Looking after Mama became one of the Prince of Wales' chief occupations. Not that he was for ever arriving at Osborne or Balmoral or Windsor and interfering with arrangements. That would have suited neither and done no good at all. But he was careful after Brown's death to be especially patient with her and try to appreciate her problems.

Lady Churchill was his invaluable emissary at Court; and he asked the help, too, of a young clergyman named Randall Davidson who had been appointed to the Deanery at Windsor, and who – after a brave brush with the Queen about her proposal to publish a life of Brown – became her closest adviser. The Prince liked Davidson, and the liking was reciprocated.

When she was cross-patchy the Queen was inclined to think and say that her heir's life was an endless quest for pleasure. Jane Churchill and Randall Davidson knew better.

They were aware how much the Prince controlled his temper when his mother complained.

They were aware of his calming influence in Princess Mary Adelaide's crisis when, owing to her wild extravagances, the Tecks were forced into exile abroad, there to pass their time very expensively in Florence and Switzerland and as the guests of the mannish, gluttonous, violet-gowned Princess Catherine of Württemberg, 'who never did anyone any good', said Mama crossly. Whether or not this was true, the Princess possibly regretted her hospitality because the Duke of Teck arranged *Ombres Chinoises* in her coach-house and burnt the whole place to the ground. The Prince of Wales soothed his mother, agreeing – though maybe with his tongue in his cheek – when the Duke of Teck's nerves began to go astray and she spoke of 'divine wrath and providence'.

He went to great trouble when, as everyone had known would happen, his brother Leopold died out in Cannes. The Prince was at Aintree, watching his own horse fail to get a place in the Grand National, when he heard the news, and at once he set out for Cannes to fetch his brother's body home and escort his young widow who was already carrying a child. Even though he did not get Leopold's despatch box key, as he now expected, he concealed from his grief-stricken mother that her youngest son, in defiance of the rule of a lifetime, had been dancing energetically, and had collapsed and died as a result.

Lady Churchill and Dean Davidson also knew of the Prince's good influence when Louis of Hesse-Darmstadt at last re-married – though unfortunately this time to an impossible woman named Kalomine and the wedding had to be annulled almost at once; and they were aware of his good influence in attempting to reason with the Queen when Khartoum fell and she felt that the execrable Gladstone had killed beloved General Gordon. He had heard the news himself while taking a vigorous part in the Cannes battle of flowers and, realizing how it would affect his mother, he had immediately telegraphed, and afterwards written and visited her personally to explain that Gladstone was really much less of an ogre than he seemed.

Then again he did his best to soothe her when Beatrice announced that she wished to marry Prince Henry of Battenberg. Believing this meant she would lose her last prop and stay, Mama had the vapours and put Beatrice into coventry for three months. She would only communicate with her by letter or through third parties. Eventually she was persuaded to relent, and chiefly by the Prince of Wales. He made her understand that Prince Henry, or Liko as everyone called him, was an exceptionally fine man, and moreover that the royal routine need hardly be disturbed because he and Beatrice had offered to make their home with Mama and live with her permanently. Reluctantly she forced herself to accept

230

the idea, and within a few months of the wedding she became devoted to Liko and grateful for his presence. When children arrived she declared they would keep her young. As a token of her gratitude for this new happiness and because Bertie had been so persuasive on behalf of Beatrice and Liko, she at last gave her son the longed-for key to despatch boxes. Momentarily she hesitated, simply because Mr Gladstone thought it such an excellent plan, but she would not go back on her word. Despite Bertie's shortcomings, and despite the fact that he and she had quite often been at loggerheads, he had been a dear boy since Brown died and at times most helpful. He should have his key.

The Prince of Wales was enormously pleased. In fact he made little use of the key, and Francis Knollys positively regretted the change as he had to make précis of all documents which might interest his master, but it was a symbol of something he had aspired to for years.

Once Beatrice was married the Queen changed her mind about the blessedness of the single state. She was frequently heard to say that all young women ought to be married and enthusiastically agreed with Bertie that suitable husbands would soon have to be found for his three daughters. She said as much to Alix. But it made not the slightest difference to Alix's determination to hold on to her children.

Bertie reflected gloomily that most of his life had been spent in pleading with forceful personalities to change their mind: with Papa and Gibbs about the regimen of his education; with Mama about a hundred and one things and most of all to prise her from her seclusion – which at last had been partially effected; and now with his wife who, though her appearance made her seem fragile, was adamantine about her children. She wanted her girls with her and they wanted to be with their Motherdear. Her boys had been torn from her: Eddy to go to Cambridge and thence into the Army, while George was to keep to his career in the Navy. Without her girls, what would she do? It was a childish claim; self-pitying and inconsiderate to the children; but Alix was immovable.

It annoyed her mother-in-law a great deal. She was already vexed with Alix for being so open in her approval of Gladstone's

231

Greek policy. It had come to her ears that Alix had send the detestable man a jewelled pencil-case shaped like an axe and mawkishly inscribed:

From the Princess of Wales to the great People's William,
because of the many trees he has axed, and of the many
questions he has 'axed', and in the hope that he will not
cut down the Greek frontier by another yard.

Alix's politics, puns, and partiality for Gladstone revolted the Queen, and now it appeared she was determined to fly in the face of her expressed wishes and Bertie's, and keep her daughters in leading-strings, and stupid ones at that. It was perverse of her, positively disloyal.

Mama's wrath boiled. Her grandchildren, she declared, were not live dolls existing for the sole delectation of their mother. They were Princesses of the Blood Royal, negotiable in foreign marriage markets, and – which was far more important – they were growing women who needed to be women and not kept retarded as playthings.

But the Queen's anger and her forthrightness were no more persuasive with Alix than Bertie's pleadings had been. He knew that one might as well try to melt a glacier with a packet of lucifers. Louise, Victoria and Maud were frosted to Motherdear and that was that.

The Prince minded it very much indeed. It was worse for him, perhaps, because of the three only Louise showed any liveliness. The others were torpid, shy and pathetic little things compared with their beautiful and majestic mother. To his chagrin they did not even stand comparison with their contemporaries and close friends the Teck children.

Despite the handicaps of having a colossal, spendthrift mother and a dotty father, the Tecks were a bright sparkling quartet. They did not even appear to mind that at Court their mother had to sit on two gilt chairs, not one, that sometimes she ate all the buttered toast intended for their school-room tea before they could get at it, that occasionally in the highest spirits she took part in their dancing lessons; and it seemed a matter of affection or pride to them rather than an embarrassment when their mama's alpenstock – alone of all alpenstocks – broke with a crack on a mountain road in Switzerland. Nor did they mind the oddities of their father, who chain-smoked pipe after pipe and yelled at people. Nor did they even appear to mind that the Queen and the Cambridges had driven them all abroad. They lived happily in exile, and the children loved their fat mother when she sang *Studentlieder* with marvellous verve in public, and went in for such impractical schemes as a Society for Promoting Kindness to Animals amongst the Peasant Children of Tuscany. . . .

Ahab gazing into Naboth's vineyard hardly did so more enviously than Prince Albert Edward gazing at the delectable children of Fat Mary and poor, mad Franz of Teck. He made up his mind that as soon as they returned from Europe, May Teck and her brothers Dolly, Frank and Alge, should often be invited to Marlborough House – in the hope that a little of their liveliness and acumen might brush off, as it were, on his own sluggish girls and boys.

Quite soon afterwards the Duchess of Cambridge sent word to her daughter that she might return to England. Characteristically Mary Adelaide replied that it was not yet quite convenient for her to do so. When she did, it was to be confronted by certain stringent family conditions, accept them, forget them, and live as extravagantly as before.

For the second time the Prince of Wales went to Princess Mary Adelaide for help and advice. He explained how worried he and the Queen were about his daughters. Could Mary Adelaide persuade Alix to be less obdurate and loosen the reins on her poor girls? Mary Adelaide was not sanguine. Better than most she knew the steely determination which lay beneath the sweet and delicate face Alix invariably showed to the world. However, she undertook to try.

To Bertie's consternation she failed, and she and her children could hardly bring a spark of life into his shy and dreary daughters. It was heart-breaking. With a bad conscience about abandoning them to their fate he busied himself trying to do all that he could for his sons.

George presented few difficulties. He might be a little stodgy and prudish and, when in his mother's company, unattractively infantile, but he was straightforward, hardworking, and keen on the Navy. After careful study the Prince found there wasn't a trace of badness in him.

Eddy, on the other hand, posed serious problems. He had his mother's vagueness and his father's passionate nature, and he was absurdly immature; but what he was really capable of defied even Mr Dalton's penetrating analysis. The Tutor, in fact, had a secret fear that the Heir-but-One was not quite up to the mark. He showed no enthusiasm for anything save cats and *Treasure Island*, which could hardly be considered a qualification for kingship. Dalton urged the Prince that it was essential for the boy to be carefully trained by the right man amongst companions of his own age. The Prince agreed. Cambridge was decided on – largely because the Prince had enjoyed it more than Oxford – and, re-calling his own experiences as an undergraduate, he made up his mind that Eddy should not live in his own house apart from everyone else, but in an ordinary set of rooms in Trinity. Dalton observed that selecting the right Cambridge tutor was of para-mount importance. He and the Prince of Wales took advice in many quarters and they went to great pains to find the right man. Eventually they chose a young don who appeared to have every possible qualification. James Kenneth Stephen was the son of one of the most exceptional judges on the Queen's Bench, a young man of elegant taste and great scholarship, but his strongest re-commendation – so far as the Prince and Dalton were concerned – was his likeability and his talent at inspiring young men with his own love of learning.

Eddy took to him at once. He also took to a carefully selected group of young men who were to go up to Trinity at the same time. A reading party was arranged at Sandringham.

Dalton was full of praise for the way young Stephen handled his charges. He was Jim already to most of them. The Prince of Wales beamed genially because something at last was being done for poor Eddy. The Princess of Wales could not have been more hospitable. Somehow the reading party reminded her of family holidays in Denmark long ago. Stephen thoroughly enjoyed him-self, though he admitted it was hard work striving to put more into his royal pupil's head than the adventures of Jim Hawkins, Long John Silver and Ben Gunn.

2

The Prince of Wales strongly disliked his nephew Willy. He was sorry, as everyone was, for the boy's physical deformity, but he saw that as no reason why he should be sycophantic to his grandfather the German Emperor, rude to his parents, and insufferable to everyone else.

Willy was not untalented; that had to be allowed; but his bombast and his obsessions were maddening, and everything about him seemed to have been theatrical from the moment of his birth. His arrival had actually been announced to the waiting troops by an elderly marshal who, too excited to open a window, had put his fist through the glass and bawled: 'Children, it's a braw recruit!' The braw recruit had done little since that time to endear himself to his uncle, and, unfortunately, the dislike was reciprocated.

As a child Willy had been impossible. Then, as a young man, he added the sin of impertinence. It had been war between 'the young cub' and 'the old peacock' from the moment Willy behaved badly on a visit to Sandringham. He was invited there to keep his uncle's birthday – for the English royal family was the most anniversary-minded in Europe – and straightaway he refused to fall in with the Sandringham routine. In his uncle's eyes this was almost the equivalent of questioning the liturgy of the Church. He was deeply affronted, but Willy paid no attention, and simply strutted and chattered. Then, two days before the birthday, he pointedly left for Windsor. Albert Edward was deeply hurt; his wife extremely angry.

When Willy married in the following February his uncle was there for Vicky's sake. But the Princess of Wales refused to attend and told everyone why. She much enjoyed relating the spiteful story of how Willy's bride's welcome to Berlin had gone awry because an enterprising American had insinuated a float extolling Singer sewing machines into the royal procession.

Ever since, uncle and nephew had glared at each other across the German Ocean, meeting when family duties obliged them to, but not otherwise. Willy's censorious cracks about his uncle's mistresses were as faithfully repeated to the Prince of Wales as Bertie's cracks about Prince William of Prussia's fantastic egotism were repeated in Berlin.

Uncle and nephew shared an unashamed love of clothes, but whereas the Prince of Wales was an authority on uniforms and always correct to the point of fussiness when wearing Court and plain clothes, Willy's love for dressing-up was farcical. He might appear at an informal tea party in an evening shirt and a gold-frogged coat of green, and even at an informal dinner he seldom wore less than four Orders. Partly to tease his nephew, and partly out of curiosity – for heaven alone knew what Willy would do with it – the Prince sent him a costume of the Royal Stuart tartan with all the accoutrements of Highland dress. Willy at once had himself photographed as a Highland chieftain and distributed copies to all the family with the enigmatic note below: 'I bide my time!' 'What *can* the young idiot mean?' asked his irritated uncle.

But these, and many more like them, were but pinpricks. What alienated Willy from so many of his English relations was his pact with his grandfather and the terrible Bismarck, and his persistent rudeness to his own parents. He allowed himself to be led by the nose by those politicians who did not care for his father's liberal ideas. It was even rumoured that a general called Waldersee, nicknamed 'the Badger' because of his habit of sniffing out hidden secrets, had told Willy the Army would support him in the event of a contretemps between father and son. And Mrs Badger, an American hot-gospeller who temporarily cured Willy's known fondness for swearing, strong cigars and dirty stories, was reported as actually saying to her neophyte: 'If ever there is a question of a *coup d'état* against your mother, you can count on me.' It really was too much.

Vicky wrote sadly from Berlin to her mother:

We must trust to later years and changed circumstances
to cure him. Fritz takes it profoundly au tragique *whilst*
I try to be patient and do not lose courage.

Understandably Fritz took his son's behaviour very badly. It was a tragic situation, as he and only a very few intimates understood. At the opening of the Suez Canal the hospitality had been too

236

lavish, and in a weak moment he had contracted a mild infection of syphilis. As a result he had an increasingly serious throat condition which affected his speech, gave him considerable pain, and worked terribly on his nerves. Intuitively he knew that he was doomed; worse, that he would never have the time to implement his ideas for making Germany into a democratic, cultured empire. His father was so reactionary that they called him 'Grapeshot', and he appeared to be immortal. His own time on the throne would be short. Very short. And after that his strutting, Bismarck-befouled son Willy would lord it as the autocrat of Germany.

When Queen Victoria's Golden Jubilee celebrations took place it seemed as if no one recalled her long years of stubborn seclusion. A socialist or an Irishman might boo or hiss, but he took his life in his hands if he did. London was packed to honour the Queen Empress, and she – a diminutive figure wearing a bonnet not a crown – made the crowds give her a Trafalgar and Waterloo welcome. She was stunned by the noise they made, by their enthusiasm, by their obvious affection for her.

Almost matching her in popularity was the Duchess of Teck in violet and dark-green silk the size of a bell tent; and the tall, golden-bearded Crown Prince of Germany clothed in white and silver and with the German eagle on his helmet. He drew an enormous amount of applause because of his magnificence. He was Charlemagne again, personified.

His son, the obstreperous Prince William, did nothing but grumble. He complained that in precedence his wife, Dona, was being received after the Queen of Hawaii – who was a black. His uncle and his grandmother, both of whom had enlightened ideas on the polite treatment of natives, and esoteric views about royalty of whatever colour, each attempted the impossibility of trying to make Willy feel small. They might have saved their breath. He was far too inflated. Once indeed he had stiffly remarked to a courtier who sympathized with him on having a cold: 'It is *not* an ordinary cold either. But a *big* cold. Everything about me is *big*!' Such an individual was not going to have his wife giving precedence to a black. He grumbled to his uncle about imaginary or unintended slights to his dignity, and because the Prince of Wales had had something to do with the arrangements,

237

he impolitely complained of the appalling lack of efficiency in the organization.

Because the arrangements had indeed been a little casual, the Prince of Wales good-naturedly admitted the charge. But then, golden jubilees being such rarities, the authorities had had no precedents. . . .

Maybe, interrupted Willy sourly, but even the most feeble-minded authority might have thought to ventilate the marquees in the grounds of Buckingham Palace. The ladies – some of them Prussian ladies, too – had suffered severely. Some had actually swooned. . . .

'Until,' put in his vexed uncle, 'until British ingenuity solved the problem and the gentlemen ripped holes in the canvas. . . .'

'And one of your friends –' carried on Willy sharply, because he never could leave anything alone – 'one of *your* most particular friends disgraced himself in the process.'

For the first time the Prince's face relaxed in a smile. Determined to make some use at last of his ceremonial rapier, his friend had decided to cut windows in the marquee and had pinked a house-maid on the other side of the canvas, causing a hideous squawking.

But Willy saw nothing amusing in it. Nothing at all. Could he lack all traces of humour? Only he in all the family scowled at the affront to his grandmother's dignity when the story was told at family dinner that a huge balloon had been released from Hyde Park at a Jubilee tea party for children, and one little girl had shrieked: 'Look! look! look! There's the Queen going up to Heaven!' The rest of the family, led by his grandmother, thought it exceedingly funny. Willy did not.

No one was sorry when Willy and Dona left.

Fritz and Vicky stayed on. They had taken a house in North London for the Jubilee and afterwards went down to Osborne with Mama and then on to Scotland. Everyone understood by now that Fritz was seriously ill. He rallied well at times but never for long. Speech was painful to him. On occasions he found it impossible to talk at all.

Only the Prince of Wales was aware that a Scottish doctor had diagnosed syphilis of the larynx because Fritz had told him so.

238

He also knew that he could not be permanently cured and grieved for him and for Vicky and for Germany. Then came worse news. The Crown Prince and Princess had gone directly to San Remo, hoping that the mild climate might be beneficial. Fritz wrote from there to say that his trouble had erupted again, though this time in a different part of the throat. Mackenzie, the Scotch doctor sent out by Queen Victoria, added a fresh diagnosis. His patient now had cancer in addition to syphilis. An Austrian physician and two Germans agreed with him. They wished to operate. But Fritz refused. He knew that his condition was incurable.

The Prince of Wales was at Cannes with the Princesse de Sagan when he received his brother-in-law's confidential letter. Immediately he travelled to San Remo to see him. He found both Fritz and Vicky distraught. Fritz could no longer speak at all and had to communicate by writing. And Willy, characteristically, at this terrible time for his parents, had been behaving abominably.

He had arrived without previous notice at San Remo, been rude to his mother, callously indifferent to his father's wretchedness, and told them he had instructions from his grandfather to write a candid report on everything the doctors said and did. For this reason he had refused to walk out with his mother, inferring that she was trying to keep him away from the doctors, and had gone so far as to half-turn his back on her. . . .

'On you !' exclaimed Bertie.

Vicky nodded. 'I told him,' she cried, 'that he was ill-mannered and a disgrace, and I should ask his father to forbid him the house.'

Bertie did his best to soothe them both. But by now they had great bitterness in their hearts. They absolutely refused to be reconciled to their son, and Bertie could understand it when he heard that Willy had said in public it would have been far better if his papa had died gloriously in the 1879 campaign. His great friend, the Count of Eulenburg, also reported Willy as saying: 'It is very questionable if a man who cannot speak has any right whatever to become King of Prussia and German Emperor.'

Such extraordinary heartlessness shocked Bertie more than anything in his life before. Willingly he would have stayed with Fritz and Vicky but, in a few days, he and Alix were to celebrate their Silver Wedding in London. Mama was to dine for the first time

239

at Marlborough House and the arrangements had been made weeks beforehand. He was obliged to leave San Remo.

Vicky and her dying husband understood his position. Both wept as he kissed them goodbye. In his special train to Paris and the Channel ports, the Prince of Wales could not catch a moment's sleep. . . .

Within ten days the Prince was back on the Continent.

The German Emperor died on 7 March 1888 – three days before the Waleses' Silver Wedding, and cast a long shadow on what otherwise would have been a brilliant occasion. The Marlborough House Ball had to be cancelled, but the family dinner took place, with Mama there in person, and Alix looking absurdly young in white and silver, and Bertie as agreeable and attentive as ever, despite his deep anxieties for Vicky and Fritz. One thing he noticed at the dinner was something of a consolation: that his daughter Maud was not indifferent to the charms of young Frank of Teck. If she could be cut from Alix's apron-strings, Frank would make a very jolly son-in-law. He had his father's good looks and his mother's cleverness and sense of humour. And he was undoubtedly high-spirited. Quite recently he had been expelled from Wellington for throwing his headmaster (Gladstone's son-in-law) over a hedge. . . .

Four days after his Silver Wedding the Prince and Eddy set off for the old Emperor's funeral. The speechless Fritz had moved painfully to Charlottenburg, but he was too ill to be at his father's funeral. Willy, the new Crown Prince, represented him. The young cub and the old peacock walked side by side in the ceremonies. Neither exchanged a word.

Two months later the Prince of Wales was again in Berlin; this time for a wedding between cousins, his sister Alice's daughter Irene and his sister Vicky's son Henry. By sheer will power Fritz got himself to the ceremony, and afterwards collapsed.

Bertie heard from Vicky what young Willy had been up to; plotting with Bismarck against his own father; greedily, openly counting the days before he himself would assume power.

For the first time in his life Bertie found it really distasteful to don a uniform. He had to because he was Colonel of the Blücher Hussars and was required to inspect them, but Germany was

240

behaving so badly to the new Emperor and to his own sister that he was reluctant to wear the heavy red regimental coat. He let this be known.

Only a month later the new Emperor died.

Bertie was at Ascot when he heard of Fritz's death. He at once left the racecourse, summoned his elder son, and left for Berlin.

It was his third visit within three months, and undoubtedly the worst. Vicky's love for Fritz had been very like that of Mama for Papa, but – unlike her mother – she had lost not only a beloved husband but also power and place. As the Empress Frederick her sphere of influence was small. She was not even her own mistress. Her son, now William the Second, was fully in charge, and some extraordinary force was making him behave as unpleasantly as possible to his English relations.

He did not check the rumour that his own mother had caused her husband's death by insisting on a Scotch doctor.

He renamed his mother's house without her permission.

He surrounded it with soldiers, and ordered that no papers or documents were to be allowed out without his permission.

He was barely civil to his uncles and aunts and cousins who came to his father's funeral.

For Vicky's sake the Prince of Wales was forbearing and polite to his nephew. For Vicky's sake he held his tongue when Bismarck's son offensively referred to the dead Emperor as an 'incubus'. For her sake he wore the by now hated Prussian uniform. For her sake he made no fuss when, a little later, he visited Vienna and a much-embarrassed Franz-Josef had to ask him to leave the Austrian capital. It appeared that the new German Emperor had announced his intention of honouring Vienna and had stipulated that no other foreign royalty should be in the city at the same time. A crowing nephew had driven out a righteously indignant uncle.

Like Bertie, the Queen had put up with a great deal of nonsense from Willy for her daughter's sake, but this slight to the Prince of Wales was going too far. She was glacial with the German Imperial representatives who came to announce her grandson's formal accession to the throne. She wrote him a grandmother-to-grandson letter about the need to find his mother suitable accommodation, not the place he had chosen:

241

An Empress, she emphasized, *could not well live in a little villa* !

At the same time she deprecated his token observance of mourning, wondering why he was moving about so soon after his dear father's death.

To her amazement, Willy's reply was not of the grandson-to-grandmother variety. To the contrary, it was notably bombastic:

I deem it necessary that monarchs should meet often and confer together to look out for dangers which threaten the monarchical principle from democratical and republican parties in all parts of the world.

Then came a piece of magniloquence which made his grand-mother say more than 'Stuff and nonsense!' and she lost her temper. Willy complained through his ambassador in London that the Prince of Wales was treating him as a nephew and not as a reigning sovereign. This made the Queen of England blaze with anger. She called her grandson's complaint vulgar, absurd and untrue, told Lord Salisbury neither she nor the Prince would put up with such an affront, and made it abundantly clear to the ambassador that His Imperial Majesty the German Emperor would not be welcome in her kingdom for a very long time.

Yet Willy continued strutting and striking attitudes and exercising his recently acquired powers in the maddest way. Being anti-French he ordered that in future imperial menus should be in German, and *Canapé d'anchois* appeared as *Kleine Fische zur divan*, or little fishes on divans. This was nothing compared with putting a niece under house arrest because he saw her riding a bicycle; and, in a jocular mood, he almost started an international incident by pinching the King of Bulgaria's behind. The stories which circulated round the courts of Europe made people wonder if Willy was really quite right in the head. Evidently he was obsessed with hating his uncle, the Prince of Wales, compiling and distributing a list of grievances about him.

His first complaint was that Albert Edward was a fair-weather friend, and that he was idle and fickle. It hurt his uncle because just at that time his old boyhood friend William Henry Gladstone had died, and he was feeling conscience-stricken for not having visited him more often during his long illness. Only just did he manage to prevent himself from remarking on Willy's almost total lack of friends except for his violet-scented relationship with Count Philipp zu Eulenburg, a writer and singer of ballads, whom he called his Phili.

Next Willy accused his uncle of being a philistine. He himself was continuously occupied with what he called 'cultural pursuits' – which included conducting cavalry bands in the proper playing of *'Funiculi funicula'* 'as it was done in Italy'; judging innumerable choirs at the Bavarian equivalent of an eisteddfod from ten in the morning until six at night; and redesigning the perfectly adequate architect's plans for the post office at Memel and the railway station at Altona; and he considered himself far more of an intellectual than his uncle. This was too close to the mark to bear a reply from England, but it wounded Albert Edward all the same.

After that Willy, apparently unaware of his own megalomania, said his uncle had an exaggerated sense of his own importance, and quoted as an example, the Sandringham 'rule' of all males staying up until their host had gone to bed. Albert Edward merely laughed at such absurdity from the martinet of all martinets.

Then Willy made his uncle really angry by charging him with gluttony, lechery and extravagance, and by saying that far from being the great international diplomat he thought he was, he was merely a common spy. Willy actually wrote this to his fellow sovereign, the Tsar, fairly certain that as the Tsar was the Princess of Wales' brother-in-law, his view would get back to England. It did, and Albert Edward who prided himself on the help he was able to give in foreign affairs was furious. At least, he remarked, he was discreet – unlike his nephew who was once overheard confiding the most secret state matters to a pilot taken on board to guide his yacht out of Bari; and he was tactful – again unlike Willy who consistently referred to the little King of Italy as 'that dwarf', and the Queen of Italy, whose father was the Prince of Montenegro, as 'that daughter of a cattle thief'. As for the charge of being a glutton and a satyr and extravagant – Willy was presumably kept content by his bovine Dona, but he could not manage for an hour without feminine sympathy and understanding and flattery; and there was talk in England of guests actually being kept hungry at the Imperial table unless there were mince pies, for which the Emperor had a passion. Furthermore, no one in the family could match him for extravagance. In his excess of joy at succeeding to the throne he ordered a brand-new yacht, and a new imperial train of twelve gold, blue and cream coaches to carry him about Europe; and the newspapers rashly listed the treasure he carried with him on his tour of capitals soon after his father's death: three gold photograph frames, thirty gold watches and chains, a hundred caskets, twenty gem-set Orders of the Eagle, fifty valuable breastpins and eighty diamond rings. . . .

Back and forth, back and forth went the ball of dislike between English uncle and German nephew.

Eventually Willy stopped being spiteful. His ministers advised him that it was unwise to chafe England's future sovereign too far. Germany was in no sense prepared to fall out with the British Empire. Because his mother was the English Princess Royal far more than because she was the Empress Frederick and his mother, Willy permitted her to buy a site at the foot of the Taunus Mountains near Kronberg, and there she built herself a long house in a hotch-potch style which contained Gothic German turrets, an Italianate campanile, and the best features of an Elizabethan manor house. Then he pleased his grandmother – even his mother – by getting rid of Bismarck. The old Chancellor had once remarked that his new master was like a balloon and if the string were released one never knew where he'd be off to. Unhappily for him he forgot his own aphorism, let go of the string, and found himself packed off to his country estate with 300 packing cases of documents and 13,000 bottles of wine. Offered a pension, he refused. It was like a Christmas tip to the postman, he complained. And, while he accepted the Dukedom of Lauenburg, he said he preferred to be called Prince Bismarck all the same, and would only use the new title when travelling incognito. . . .

Antennae of family feeling, certainly not family friendship, were extended across the German Ocean. For her daughter's sake, so that Vicky should not be pestered by her cad of a son, the Queen at last invited him to Osborne. She made him an English admiral. Willy was intoxicated, ecstatic, quite giddy at the thought of wearing the same uniform as Nelson. He begged Grandmama to accept the Colonelcy of his own Dragoon Guards in exchange. She accepted, but she showed no enthusiasm.

The old peacock and the young cub still growled about one another to their intimates, but for the present they no longer growled at each other in public.

3

In the same year as Mama became Colonel of the Prussian Dragoon Guards Alix finally acknowledged that she could not hold on to all her daughters for ever. Her own family in Denmark, Bertie, Mama, Mary Adelaide and anyone at all who had any influence on her made her change her mind. And maybe the realization that her swans were really geese after all had something to do with it. It was painful for a beautiful mother to accept that her daughters were singularly plain and dull; and, as a result, natural to try to please them.

None of the princesses was ugly and they did not deserve the family nickname of the Hags, but they were still undistinguished-looking and an uneducated lot, and lethargic and childish. Louise's nineteenth birthday was actually celebrated with a children's party which had been a painful embarrassment to her sophisticated father and cousins. And one or other of the princesses was always ailing. The Queen was quite definite in her opinion as to the cause, writing to her widowed daughter Vicky:

The health of those girls is not enough looked after.

Victoria, the least plain, was the most melancholy and the most often ill; but her elder sister, Louise – long-faced and dull – came a close second; and Maud, the youngest, was not far behind.

The Prince's hopes that Maud might marry Frank of Teck had had to be abandoned on discovering that the young man's reputation was scarcely edifying. Now to his surprise – for she was a mousy girl – he discovered that his eldest daughter Louise wanted to marry one of his own personal cronies, the elderly Earl of Fife.

He gave the credit to Mary Adelaide, who had insisted on taking Louise to the Italian Lakes on a family holiday – a ruse for the Tecks to get there themselves which did not escape the cynical old Duchess of Cambridge. The old lady said it was 'bosh and humbug' to claim the holiday was for Louise's sake, and taking Louise merely added to the expense. It was one of the last forceful utterances of this remarkable lady who, at the age of ninety-one – when her son George was with his troops in Ireland, her daughter Augusta with her family in Strelitz, and her daughter Mary Adelaide, unaware of her mother's condition, singing arias in her bath at White Lodge – abruptly died.

Frankly, the Prince of Wales had doubted if anyone, even the resourceful Mary Adelaide, could do anything to enliven his torpid Louise, but there was no doubt that, after her holiday with the Tecks, Louise did brighten up. She had been brought on wonderfully by Mary Adelaide and her daughter May. Therefore the Prince supposed he ought to be grateful and consent immediately when Fife came to him and said he and the princess had come to some sort of mutual understanding. This was how the nervous Fife put it himself, and the Prince was not surprised. As a connoisseur of women's beauty and a frank man, he put Louise in a fairly low category. Poor girl. She was twenty-two and so tongue-tied that conversation with a stranger was agony for her. But he temporized; neither encouraging Fife nor putting him off. He would have to consult with the Queen, he said, and of course with Louise's mother. . . .

Privately the Prince was not best pleased. Fife was a good friend, but he was forty. And, recalling his own strong objections when his sister Louise married a subject, he was reluctant to ask Mama's permission for his daughter to do the same. Then there was Alix. This was not the sort of match for which he was prepared to do great battle with Alix.

To his great surprise Alix consented.

Having changed her mind about keeping all her daughters at home, Louise, as the eldest, should naturally be the first to marry, and Alix thought her wish to marry Fife, a mere subject, sweetly romantic. It so happened that Bertie had found her in an unusually romantic mood, recollecting her son George's beautiful but impossible affection for the lovely Julie Stonor who, as the orphan daughter of one of her favourite Ladies in Waiting, lived permanently with the Waleses. George's love was impossible because she was a commoner and a Roman Catholic, but it was just the sort of superb, idealistic romance which she herself valued so highly – and which, incidentally, seemed to help him avoid the apparently inevitable Hanoverian 'fall'. It was a platonic love affair on a plane with her great friendship for Oliver Montagu, and the Galahad devotion she was now being given by Sir Dighton Probyn, a chivalrous old soldier, who had been appointed her Comptroller. So romantic were her feelings just at that time that she showed real keenness for her eldest daughter to marry.

'But of course,' she cried to her astonished husband. 'Of course she must marry Fife. And you press Mama to make him a duke. Do, Bertie dear. An earl will hardly do.'

Scratching his head over the volte-face the Prince quickly got in touch with the Queen. Kindly she did not remind him of the fuss he had made when his sister married Lorne, and she at once gave her consent. She was delighted, she said, that at last one of his daughters was to marry, and for Alix's sake – as she had particularly asked for it – Fife should be given a dukedom. She also warmly approved Louise's own decision: to drop her title of Royal Highness and live quietly as the Duchess of Fife at East Sheen Lodge in Richmond Park and at Mar Lodge near Balmoral.

After Bertie had left her, the Queen sat at her desk and wrote a long letter to her eldest daughter:

> *It is a vy brilliant Marriage in a worldly point of*
> *view as he is* immensely *rich.*

Two days before the Wales wedding the Gladstones celebrated their Golden Wedding. The Queen sent an appropriate telegram. The Prince of Wales sent a colossal silver-gilt inkstand which, remarked the old statesman, was far too impressive to hold mere ink. Then, on the last Saturday in July – and the last day of the Season – he and Mrs Gladstone went to the Private Chapel in Buckingham Palace for Princess Louise's wedding.

The Prince received them warmly. He was the perfect host as ever, though Gladstone's eye was yet sharp enough to detect that he seemed a little distracted.

Was he unwell? wondered Gladstone. Undoubtedly the Prince had been feeling the constant chivvying of his exasperating

German nephew; and he had been perturbed by the shocking news from Austria that the Crown Prince had shot his mistress and then himself in a forest hunting lodge. Then, Gladstone recalled, an old, old connection of the Prince's had recently died; the widow of his friend and Governor, General Bruce – and Mrs Bruce had not died gracefully in her bed, as old ladies and especially Bedchamber Women in Ordinary to the Queen ought to die, but on number 3 platform on Victoria Station. Gladstone knew that things of this kind could upset the Prince a great deal, and it was obvious to everyone that he was getting older and feeling his age. Albert Edward was much balder, and, despite his energetic pursuits and his annual cure at German spas, he was thickening out badly, and Gladstone had heard that the Season had been particularly trying for him. In addition to his dozens of engagements he had had to receive and entertain the Shah on his second visit to England, restrain the old gentleman's oriental grossness, and assure him that he absolutely could *not* buy Nellie, Countess of Londonderry, because, though not altogether virtuous, the Countess was not for sale.

Poor Prince. Gladstone often found himself sympathizing with Albert Edward. He never managed to see him as Dizzy had done – as an unredeemed Prince Hal always on the search for Falstaff. Nevertheless he saw that the Prince was not quite himself at his daughter's wedding. Evidently he had something on his mind.

Many, many years before, as a young princess, Victoria had gone home from a ball given at St James's by Queen Adelaide, her head in a spin because for the first time she had fallen in love. The object of her passion had been the fifteen-year old Guy, Lord Brook, heir to the Earldom of Warwick. The passion had passed, but not without pain, and she always kept a small place in her heart for the memory of that ball.

Nowadays she occasionally received his son at Court, and his son's wife, herself a great heiress who had once caught the Queen's eye as a possible wife for her dearest Leopold. And quite recently, from an undisclosed source, she heard that same lady had caught her eldest son's eye; more than this, that, at the age of forty-eight, he had quite absurdly fallen in love with her.

It was as disgraceful as his long-lived, hothouse affair with

248

Patsy Cornwallis-West because both were 'ladies' in the correct sense: and here was the twenty-nine-year-old, fabulously rich Daisy Brook, with a husband, a son and a daughter, admitting with not the least sense of shame that she was Bertie's mistress, constructing a special railway line so that he could get down to her country place with the maximum of speed and comfort, and entertaining him in Essex as though she were Pompadour at Bellevue.

All this was precisely true. The Queen's informants, as usual, were accurate. And it was one reason why – as Gladstone's sharp eye detected – the Prince appeared distracted at his daughter's wedding. He was in love again, marvellously, wildly in love; and this time with the most intriguing, mischievous and lively woman he had ever met. She rode to hounds with light hands but a lion's heart in courage. She amused. She pleased. She satisfied. She was his adorable Daisy.

There was another reason, and a far less happy one, for his distraction – and perhaps the Queen knew nothing of it although little was hidden from her. In fact, while heartened enormously by Daisy, the Prince was cast down and deeply concerned about his elder son.

Tales from Cambridge had caused him to go there and see for himself what Eddy was up to. He realized afterwards he might have saved himself the trouble. What had it benefited his own father to go up to Cambridge about Nellie Clifden? Sons at a certain stage in their growth are incapable of communicating with their fathers. He should have remembered it. But he was so disturbed by what he had heard that, after a discreet interval, he caused private inquiries to be made. It appeared from these reports that Eddy was including amongst his associates some birds of exotic and peculiar plumage. They had a common denominator in that most of them in their time appeared to have stayed at Fryston, home of Richard Monkton Milnes, Lord Houghton, and Fryston was considered very *outré*.

The Prince had sent for an intimate and knowledgeable friend. Was there any harm, he asked, in his son being friendly with such people? From his own experience he knew that a growing prince required freedom like everyone else. A boy needed to spread his wings. . . .

With infinite tact and patience his intimate friend enlightened him: old Richard Monkton Milnes was a famous philanthropist,

249

yes; and once he had been the apple of Florence Nightingale's eye – though she refused to marry him when asked – and socially he was quite acceptable, being a great breakfaster of lions of all kinds (Carlyle, with Scottish acidity, had remarked that if the Almighty returned to earth He would at once be invited to a Monkton Milnes breakfast); but there was another, veiled side to the man. He had, for example, introduced the works of the Marquis de Sade to that disgraceful poet, Swinburne, and he had so great a collection of erotica that Fryston was nicknamed 'Aphrodisiopolis'. His friends, who had had influence on Prince Albert Victor at Cambridge, had included Simeon Solomon, a perverted painter, and Oscar Browning, a Fellow of King's who had been dismissed from a lucrative housemastership at Eton for having an overheated relationship with the cleverest and most beautiful boy in the school – George Nathaniel Curzon.

'Curzon !' repeated the astounded Prince.

He was hurriedly assured that the proud, good-looking Member of Parliament who had such a grasp of Indian affairs, had simply been the *object* of Mr Browning's perfervid attentions.

But the Prince of Wales remained stunned. He knew that Eddy had gone sometimes to Mr Browning's famous 'Sunday Evenings' – which meant that the Heir-but-One had hobnobbed with blue-jackets and stableboys as well as with scholars and epicene literati.

And then he learnt that at Cambridge Eddy had also dined and kept company with the extraordinary Lord Ronald Sutherland-Gower.

This confirmed what he had suspected but would have preferred not to know because Lord Ronald was uncle to his own great friend, the Duke of Sutherland, and he knew all about Lord Ronald. Though harmless and gentle he would have been described as a Greek or a Uranist by the exquisites of Cambridge, or as a Nancy Dawson by everyone else. It followed that, very probably, Eddy was the same.

It was a fact no father wished to learn, but the Prince was not the sort of man to wring his hands and do nothing. He had sent for Sir William Gull and demanded a cure. His physician was sympathetic but not hopeful. Though quacks promised cures, he himself was in no position to do so. In fact, he said he believed that intersexuality was no more curable than the common cold. Possibly Sir William was in advance of his time. He thought it

250

probable that Prince Albert Victor's retarded development was the cause of his ability to enjoy sexual relations with men and boys as well as with women.

The Prince thanked him for his advice. Later he brooded a little on those words 'retarded development'. He was a man who liked to search out reasons. Unlike the Queen, the Prince of Wales was a fault-finder. Was Eddy's misfortune due to his poor upbringing – which, at base, was his responsibility? or had it been caused by the cocoon of infantilism in which Alix had wrapped all her children? In either case they appeared to have failed the boy as parents. The reflection caused him to brood on his own upbringing. Until then he had considered it over-strict, too inhuman. Now he was no longer sure.

Then the Prince cheered himself up. Even if he was a bit of a Nancy Dawson, Eddy still liked the girls. He'd been proving it with a glaring lack of discretion ever since he began his military training. But now, at the time of his sister's wedding, he had startled the family – and especially his father – by declaring a sudden passion for his own first cousin, Alicky of Hesse-Darmstadt.

Alix, who had indulged Eddy all his life, was enthusiastic. Bertie was not. It was not simply because he, alone of all the family, was aware of Eddy's secret, but because quite frankly he did not think him good enough for Alicky.

Notwithstanding all Dalton's efforts, and those of Jim Stephen at Cambridge and his Commanding Officer's tireless attempt to turn him into a good soldier, Eddy was as lethargic as his sisters and, in intellectual matters, a mere glowing coal. Nothing, ever, would blow him into flame, and that, in his father's opinion, made him unfit to marry one of Alice's beautiful and clever daughters. Alice had been a very favourite, irreplaceable sister, and he was not having her children threatened with unsatisfactory marriages if he could help it. Moreover, repeated marriages between first cousins – and his own father and mother had been first cousins – was sound enough in the racing stable and pigeon loft, but it carried an element of risk in royal circles.

Even while marrying off Louise to Fife, the Prince was praying that a miracle would happen and that Alice's daughter would not accept the suit of his unstable problem of a son.

. . . . .

251

The miracle took place.

To everyone's amazement the princess of so small a German state refused the grand offer from England. She said, in the kindest way, that it simply wasn't possible. She loved Eddy as a cousin, but she was not in love with him.

The Prince was relieved beyond measure, Alix was mortified. Eddy seemed quite unconcerned. The Queen, who had seen a great deal of Alicky in her upbringing at Windsor and Darmstadt, was mildly disappointed. Yet at the same time she was proud of her granddaughter.

> *She shows great strength of character,* she wrote to Vicky in Kronberg, *all her family and all of us wish it, and she refuses the greatest position there is.*

Eddy's cousin Mossy was proposed as a substitute. But Mossy was Willy's youngest sister and Eddy cared no more for the strutting German Emperor than his father did. He made up some sort of polite reason for not even considering the idea.

Then, unhappily, discretion flew from him. When not with his regiment he was slyly enjoying himself in London. He was not bad looking, but with his long neck and long arms he had earned the nickname 'Collar and Cuffs'. They were features which were bound to be recognized. Quite often they were.

4

On the Prince of Wales' birthday in 1888 the Queen sent a cypher telegram to her Prime Minister, the Marquis of Salisbury:

THIS NEW MOST GHASTLY MURDER
SHOWS THE ABSOLUTE NECESSITY
FOR SOME DECIDED ACTION

She was referring to the seventh in a series of murders of London prostitutes by a maniac already known as Jack the Ripper.

Salisbury was as concerned as his sovereign, but the Ripper was mad and clever. Only twelve days later – actually on the birthday of the Empress Frederick, the Prince of Wales' eldest sister – he struck again. Poor Annie Farmer was added to Mary Kelly and the others. In the next few months he killed four more. Because of his supposed ineptitude the Commissioner of Police for the Metropolitan area was obliged to resign.

In fact, when the murders stopped, it was supposed that the Ripper had died, but myths were seeded, and they grew and enlarged for years. There were always people ready to suggest that the Ripper's identity had been concealed by those in high places, and the Police Commissioner pensioned off as a contented scapegoat. No one paid much attention to them. But the very, very few who were aware of the facts believed that what had been done had been done for the best: J. K. Stephen, Cambridge tutor and close friend to the Prince of Wales' son, was put away as criminally insane.

The Prince was vastly relieved when the mess was finally tidied up. Had it been widely known that Stephen was the Ripper it must have reflected badly on his old friend Prince Albert Victor, and on the Queen and the Prince of Wales and their advisers, in fact on the monarchy as a whole. The truth had had to be suppressed. And there had been moments in the past months – terrible moments which the Prince would hardly admit even to himself – when he had wondered if in any way his son Eddy had been implicated. Now that the truth had been established his doubts had gone. He could sleep easily once more.

But it was not to be for long. On top of the Stephen incident came the Cleveland Street scandal – and this, far from being suppressed, was at first widely publicized.

Sir Francis Knollys broke it to his master. The Metropolitan Police had discovered a rendezvous club in Cleveland Street where boy professionals met men by assignation. The Earl of Euston, heir to the Duke of Grafton, was named as an *habitué* of this male brothel; and so, unhappily, was Lord Arthur Somerset, one of the Prince's extra equerries. 'Podge' Somerset was more than an extra equerry, and, as it happened, Superintendent of the Prince's Stables. He was also a close friend; and never once had Albert Edward suspected this particular failing.

'I won't believe it,' he exclaimed.

253

But in face of the evidence he was forced to do so.

He recalled poor Arthur Clinton's suicide in 1870. Now Euston and Podge Somerset. All duke's sons, too.

The Queen was distraught at the terrible disgrace, though Bertie guessed she was not absolutely sure what the aristocracy had been up to. Indeed, although she had accepted the 1885 Amendment against homosexuality, she had only done so 'on trust' as she put it to Lord Rosebery – and even then women had had to be left out for the simple reason that no one could or dared to explain to the Queen what lesbians were. But she knew that these dukes' sons had been disgracing the aristocracy, and letting down their Queen. . . .

The Prince of Wales was puzzled, and frightened for his friends as he read about curly-headed telegraph boys with the unlikely names of Algernon Alley and Thickbloom in a press campaign against Nancy Dawsons and the aristocracy run by the ambitious, radical editor of a weekly.

Warrants were issued and, while Euston stood his ground and won his case for criminal libel against the ambitious, radical editor, Podge Somerset fled to Turkey.

'Turkey,' said the Prince to Knollys, 'is much better than suicide.' And then he wrote to the Prime Minister to say how pleased he was that his Extra Equerry had slipped from the law and asking, as a matter of charity, that if he did slip back again from time to time to see his parents, he should be allowed to do so without fear of being apprehended.

It was the best he could do for his erstwhile friend, but even as he was doing it, he was given an official warning that his elder son's name was also being mentioned in connection with the Cleveland Street scandal.

When he had got over the shock the Prince bore it well. He sensed rather than knew that if it was being bandied about London the Queen would also be aware of the scandal. So, very probably, would Alix.

He was incapable of saying anything about it to either. But neither said a word of protest when he bundled Eddy off to India while the Cleveland Street scandal died and its bits were brushed under the carpet.

254

5

As if it was not bad enough to have such an heir, and to have his beloved family at the very centre of what was described by the Member for Stockport as a 'hideous and foetid gangrene', Albert Edward suddenly found himself in a feud with one of his oldest and best friends, the lively Charlie Beresford.

Through his influence Lord Charles had been made Fourth Lord of the Admiralty and ever since he had fought the more reactionary of the admirals in an effort to improve the service. Since he was his protégé, the Prince had attempted to excuse Beresford's ruthless use of his position as a private member of Parliament to attack his own government, but he had condemned his use of outside help in his crusade for reform at the Admiralty. Manipulating public opinion by the press was particularly repugnant to him and he told Beresford so, advising him to resign his post, cool off, and go to sea. To his surprise Beresford stayed in office. For a further year the two wrangled, until their former friendship stood in danger of cracking and then, at last, Lord Charles went back into active service.

Against this quarrelsome background, another and far more personal squabble developed.

Before succumbing to the charms of the Prince of Wales, Daisy Brook had enjoyed a long affair with Charlie Beresford. Indeed at one time the two friends had competed for her favours and a story had circulated in the Marlborough House set that the wild Lord Charles, believing he had an assignation with the adorable Daisy at a country house, had leapt into her bed in the dark long after midnight crying 'cock-a-doodle-do' to discover – much like Mr Pickwick in the Great White House at Ipswich – that he was in the wrong bed. Instead of Daisy, he found himself between an alarmed Bishop of Chester and his wife.

All that was in the past, but, Daisy now belonging solely to Albert Edward, and, being on his side, wrote a long extravagant letter to her former lover, reproaching him for his behaviour, and telling him – as only darling Daisy could – exactly what she thought of him.

Beresford was too good-natured to be much offended, though as Daisy told the Prince, 'I shouldn't like to be his valet the day he gets the letter'; but, being Irish, he was careless and he left the letter about.

His wife found it, dreaded that he might once more fall victim to Daisy Brook's charms – for she was still enticing even when writing a furious letter – and took it along to her solicitor and gave him strict instructions. With the aid of the letter he was to make sure that Lady Brook played no further part in the affairs of the house of Beresford.

Bertie dined with Daisy that evening. She had already heard from the solicitors and deeply regretted writing the letter. From what she recalled, and it was not all that easy to remember every word she had written, it had been compromising to say the least.

The Prince cocked an eyebrow. 'Compromising to whom?'

Daisy waved a bejewelled hand. 'Why, everyone,' she exclaimed. 'Everyone.'

Bertie's heart sank. He foresaw trouble.

The next day he interviewed Lady Charles' solicitor and asked if he might read the letter. Afterwards, with great feeling, he declared that really it was only worth burning. Hysterics showed in every line. Women as excitable as Lady Brook invariably had runaway pens. It would be better for everyone that the letter should be burnt.

The solicitor, with surprising bravery, refused to do this without instructions from Lady Charles. And so the Prince swallowed his pride and called on Lady Charles. She said no. She would not agree. Under no circumstances. The next day he called again. She felt unable to refuse him admittance, but she point blank refused his earnest request.

He then did what he felt chivalry demanded. He had to protect his Daisy even if she was silly. He put Lady Charles under a social boycott.

She was mortified beyond belief, and the boycott being effective she had next to nothing to do and became bored. She wrote hysterical letters to her family and friends. She wrote dozens to her husband at sea. When he came ashore he was to defend and protect her, do something to put her back into Society. Battered by her pleadings Charles Beresford forgot all that he owed to his old friend the Prince of Wales. When he came ashore from his command he worked himself into a fury of righteous indignation, arrived at Marlborough House in a great rage, shouted at the Prince, threatened to expose him to the press in revenge for the social boycotting of his wife, and grew so uncontrolled that he raised his fist to strike the Prince.

'Beresford,' the Prince warned him quietly, 'You have gone too far.'

Indeed his one-time friend had been close to committing *lèse majesté*. That was quite unpardonable.

Beresford stormed out of Marlborough House and went back to sea; realizing that far from softening the Prince's attitude he had only hardened it. Lady Charles was now completely and absolutely beyond the social pale.

There was a strong streak of sentimentality in the Prince of Wales and he was proverbially loyal to his friends – especially when they got into scrapes. But he felt quite unable to forgive Beresford and this made him miserable.

His depression was deepened when Eddy returned from India. The Khedive had evidently given the boy the time of his life in Cairo on the way home, for he arrived looking green, worn out, and wretchedly ill.

Eddy's grandmother reproved him, not only for worrying her and his parents, but for destroying his health by overdoing things. In her heart she was appalled at the thought that this ill-looking, long-necked, stringy, far from intelligent prince might one day be King of England; but, for Bertie's sake – because he particularly asked it – she made Eddy Duke of Clarence and Avondale. When this didn't suit and everyone asked why two dukedoms, why not simply the Duke of Clarence? she snappily replied that Garter King-of-Arms had advised it because the Earldom of Clarence was already a subsidiary title of Leopold's posthumous son, the little Duke of Albany, and the Dukedom of Avondale was a perfectly respectable Scottish title held by George the Second before he became Prince of Wales. In any case, she wrote to Vicky:

> *. . . I am very sorry Eddie should be lowered to a Duke like any one of the nobility wh. a Prince can never be. Nothing is so fine and grand as a Royal Prince.*

257

It was fortunate that neither she nor his mother were aware that the brand new Duke of Clarence and Avondale was picking up old contacts in London.

There was the accommodating W. Jones who kept a male brothel at 12, Little College Street.

There was the famous Mrs Truman who kept a similar establishment next to the Albany barracks.

There were the pick-up pubs – *The Crown, The Windsor Castle, The Packenham*; and Nancy Dawson clubs where Collar and Cuffs was always welcome.

At one, the exclusive *Hundred Guineas Club,* members and their guests assumed girl's names, and the Queen would have been outraged if she had known that in this insalubrious establishment, the Heir-but-One was known simply as 'Victoria'.

The Prince of Wales heard a little and guessed a lot. He was worried to death, and enormously relieved when Eddy fell in love again – though, typically, the boy chose entirely the wrong sort of girl. She was the daughter of the Comte de Paris, Bourbon Pretender to the throne of France, and a Roman Catholic.

But in this affair Eddy was luckier and his devotion was returned. Princess Hélène of Orleans genuinely fell in love with him.

Eddy's sister Louise of Fife helped the romance along. She invited Eddy and the Orleans family to stay at Mar Lodge. When she discovered that Eddy in his stupidity and fickleness was also showing an interest in a third party, Lady Sybil St Clair Erskine, Louise abruptly lost her phlegm and shyness and gave him a terrific piece of her mind. Chastened, he concentrated on one lady, and in Scotland he and Hélène became engaged. She had been persuaded to change her religion and they supposed that no one, not even Grandmama, could possibly object. Nevertheless when they went to announce the engagement, their courage lessened with each of the twelve miles which separated Mar Lodge and Balmoral. By the time they reached the Queen, both were in a dithering state of nerves. But Victoria who knew far more about love than most people gave her credit for, saw at once how much Princess Hélène adored her unsatisfactory grandson. Perhaps she would be able to wake him up and make him a presentable monarch when the time came. She embraced both and astounded them by giving her permission.

The Prince and Princess of Wales were startled but overjoyed. So was the Comtesse de Paris, a remarkable woman who shot and went deer stalking, and smoked a pipe and the Prince's best cigars. But the Comte de Paris himself stepped into the arrangements and insisted that under no circumstances could his daughter be allowed to change her religion.

Long and complicated negotiations opened between the Queen, the Comte, the Prince of Wales, Lord Salisbury and afterwards Lord Rosebery and the Vatican while Princess Hélène ate her heart out. Eventually she went herself to Rome to plead for a special dispensation from the Pope, although she knew it was useless.

Eddy professed himself to be still in love with her, though his feckless eyes were straying back to Lady Sybil St Clair Erskine. Simultaneously, as soon as he returned to London, 'Victoria' was given a warm welcome home by the *habitués* of *The Hundred Guineas*.

His hopes dashed that his problem son could be so well married off, the Prince of Wales became even more despondent.

He was worried, too, because Mama had got herself into the hands of a rascally Indian. Ever since the Jubilee she had liked to be attended by Indians, regarding them, no doubt, as a romantic symbol of her authority in the East, but one whom she brought on and named her Munshi had turned out to be as domineering as Brown.

In fact, as his brother Arthur put it, this brown Brown was a thoroughly bad lot.

At the Braemar games he had ordered Arthur about as though he were a minor official and not Duke of Connaught and a Prince of the Blood. And doubts had been expressed in diplomatic circles as to the Munshi's trustworthiness with official secrets.

Trying to persuade Mama, through Knollys and Ponsonby, that she ought to be a little more discreet, was to invite nothing more than a stubborn refusal and trouble for himself. Nevertheless, the Prince felt he ought to do it. And, as he had expected, he got small thanks.

He was also worried about his fatness and his shortness of breath. He hated the cures at German watering places because his

259

diet was so rigorously reduced, and he tended to cheat. Fatness prevented him from taking the exercise he had once enjoyed. He would dance an occasional quadrille and waltz, but no more. And he no longer walked up game. The little shooting he did was at birds driven to him. His energies had seriously flagged. At race meetings he tended to sit still, a thing which was almost unheard of.

An added burden was the threat of financial disaster. Despite the care of his Comptroller, Sir Dighton Probyn, and despite loans and excellent advice from the millionaire Bavarian Jew, Baron Maurice de Hirsch, the Prince's financial difficulties were considerable. He hoped and trusted that Hirsch would be able to adjust them, and meanwhile he found his greatest relaxation in gaming for high stakes.

Probyn had confidence in Hirsch but his mane of hair and huge spreading whiskers perceptibly whitened as his royal master's gambling got him deeper and deeper into debt. Baccarat, said Probyn, would be his undoing. It was an illegal game which provided the simplest way to lose fortunes. Amongst the Marlborough House set it was termed 'baccy'. And the Prince played it night after night, losing, recouping, losing, recouping. It was the only thing which appeared to give him any pleasure at all for it took his mind off all his worries – worries about money, about Mama's brown Brown, about Charlie Beresford, about his health, about Eddy. . . .

6

It had become an exhausting as well as expensive business entertaining the Prince of Wales. He expected and must have the best of everything and the long-suffering Christopher Sykes who had always entertained him for the St Leger Stakes found that in 1890 he was spent out and quite unable to do so. But others were willing to spend almost anything in order to scrape an acquaintance with the heir to the throne, and the Prince, soured by his anxieties that year and by his lack of physical tone, was self-centred enough to ignore Sykes' plight, and go where he would be more comfortable and where there would be 'baccy'. This was the house of the socially aspiring Arthur Wilson, a rich shipowner, at his house near Doncaster named Tranby Croft.

At Tranby Croft the Prince was spoilt with the best of everything, except possibly the company. Daisy was prevented from being there by the unexpected death of an uncle, and on the very first evening a guest was caught cheating at 'baccy'.

Only the son of the house noticed it. And for the sake of his parents' social aspirations he would have been wise to have ignored it. As it was, he informed one of his father's guests that he had seen Sir William Gordon-Cumming manipulating his counters so that in effect he was placing his bet after he had the advantage of seeing his cards. It was crude cheating, but common enough to have a name of its own in French gambling circles, *la poussette*. The fellow guest watched on the second night and he agreed with young Wilson. They consulted a third guest, Lord Edward Somerset, a brother to the unhappy exiled Podge, and he also saw Gordon-Cumming cheating.

It all ended by the cheater being required to sign a declaration that he would never play cards again while everyone then undertook to keep silent about the matter. Then Gordon-Cumming left, and so – to the great mortification of the Wilsons – did the Prince of Wales. For the last day of the races he moved from the house which he now found distasteful to the mess of his own regiment, the 10th Hussars, in York.

The very next morning he saw the Brooks as they travelled through York on their way to Daisy's uncle's funeral, and foolishly he mentioned the upsetting contretemps which had occurred in the house of those pretentious Wilson people at Tranby Croft. Daisy was not called 'the babbling brook' for nothing. But the fault was not all the Prince of Wales'. Other guests told their wives that Gordon-Cumming had been caught cheating. Quite naturally, as soon as he heard the matter was public knowledge, and because at no time had he admitted the allegation, Gordon-Cumming told his solicitor to bring an action against his five original accusers.

The paper which he had signed had been witnessed by others in the house party.

Amongst the signatures was the scrawl 'Albert Edward'.

·   ·   ·   ·   ·

261

In the following five months the Prince and his advisers did everything they could to avoid the scandal which they knew must explode if the case was brought to open court. As a serving officer Gordon-Cumming could have been tried by the Army and dismissed; but his solicitors appealed to the Judge Advocate-General that such a case would prejudice the civil action and therefore was out of the question. This satisfied the Judge Advocate-General, though it did not satisfy the Prince of Wales.

Bertie was most desperately unhappy.

He knew that he would be subpoena'd as a witness, that his failure of duty in not reporting a fellow officer for dishonourable conduct to his commanding officer was contrary to Article 41 of Queen's Regulations for the Army. He knew that all he had had to put up with after the Mordaunt case was a flea-bite compared with the moral outrage of the public when they discovered he had been keeping such company and playing an illegal game for high stakes. The non-conformists, the anti-any-sort-of-fun bigots were far more numerous and powerful and far more vocal than they had been twenty-one years before.....

And meanwhile there was the awful problem of his debts, and his Nancy Dawson of a son, and poor George's hopeless love for pretty Julie Stonor, and the tongue-licking that was going on in Grub Street in anticipation of spearing him through and through and through in the reports of the trial; and Daisy was being demanding; and Lady Charles Beresford still creating a rumpus about her exclusion from society; and Alix, for some reason or other, had retired into a world of her own where he could not penetrate and where she could not help. Only Mama was at his right hand, which was odd really, considering how starchy and unfeeling, in fact, how thoroughly unpleasant she had been to him at times. . . .

The case was heard in public between the 1st and 9th June in 1891.

Feeling frightened, fat and old, His Royal Highness the Prince of Wales sat in open court for the whole hearing and gave evidence. He had expected some degree of hostility and unpleasantness, but nowhere near as much as he actually received. Gordon-Cummings' counsel was waspish. He mentioned there had often

262

been cases in which honourable men had been willing 'to sacrifice themselves to support a tottering throne and prop a falling dynasty'. The Prince whitened, but counsel had not finished with him. He claimed the plaintiff had been victimized to save the honour of a Prince who was notorious for playing an illegal game, a Prince who on bad evidence had jumped stupidly to a false conclusion, and a Prince who, quite improperly for a field-marshal, had offended against Article 41 of the Queen's Regulations.

It was an appalling experience for the Prince of Wales, and there was barely a crumb of comfort in the fact that the jury returned a verdict against Gordon-Cumming, who was promptly cashiered, expelled from his clubs, and socially ostracized.

The Prince sat at his desk after reading précis of the newspaper accounts of the trial. He was stunned to discover that the guilty man, the blackguard who had cheated, was being treated like a hero in his native Scotland. Gordon-Cumming had been received with cheers and a band, and an address of welcome from the Provost of Forres, and had done himself very well indeed by immediately marrying a very beautiful and very rich American girl.

But over Bertie's own royal head there burst a thunderstorm of execration which he found impossible to comprehend. The press went out of its way to be offensive. *The Times* actually suggested that he ought to sign a public declaration never to play cards again. . . .

The Court and the Ministry and the Church combined to find a method of placating the outraged middle classes. But none was successful and all were acutely embarrassing to the Prince.

Noble ladies of Low Church Evangelical views begged the Archbishop of Canterbury to remonstrate with the heir to the throne and hold penitential services in his private chapel for the cleansing of the monarchy. Willy, not missing such an excellent chance to anger his uncle, wrote a formal letter to the Queen to say how much he regretted that an Honorary Colonel of Prussian Hussars had got himself into so unsavoury a mess. Alix, when he turned to her for comfort, did what she could but expressed her sympathy in a peculiar way by choosing that moment to invite Lady Brook to Marlborough House. Daisy arrived and fascinated everyone. But even she could not cheer Albert Edward. She actually embarrassed him by posturing in his own home. He far preferred her at her own place in Essex, or at a country house party, or at an intimate supper after the theatre. She did not belong to Marlborough House.

In the obloquy which raged over the Prince of Wales he had only two real consolations.

Mama was still on his side. She thought it all very sad, but she would not hear a word against him in her presence.

And the masses, the jellied-eel and cockle-swallowing race-goers who had deserted him at the time of the Mordaunt Case, were mostly loyal. On this occasion, although middle-class propriety was outraged, the masses saw no harm in their Prince having a bet with his friends. This time they didn't say: 'That's a cough lozenge for the Prince, that is.' It was a scrap of comfort for the unhappy Prince of Wales. Already he was referring to 1891 as 'this hateful year'.

It was to be prophetic.

7

Lady Charles Beresford was a calmer person than her husband. Nevertheless she had spirit. She disliked, positively hated Daisy Brook, who was peacocking that summer at Marlborough House and although she did not dislike him as a man, she took exquisite pleasure in the public outcry against the Prince of Wales simply because he belonged to Daisy. It was Daisy's fault that she was denied the social life she so much valued and depended on.

Suddenly she announced that, exasperated beyond endurance, she would tolerate her ostracism no longer. She would sell up and live abroad where people were polite.

Her timing was superb. She chose exactly the right moment to make her announcement – when the Prince was feeling jaded and her husband was feeling bored. After life at the Admiralty as Fourth Sea Lord, wild Lord Charles found life at sea very tame. His wife's announcement that she was having to leave England because she was so wretched reignited his fury with the

Prince, and his Irish temper burst like a shower of sparks from a Roman Candle.

He gave his command naval hell and hades for a fortnight after he heard the news. Then he apologized to his officers. In his spacious cabin he sat at a desk and wrote out his hate for the man who had once been his friend.

> *I consider that from the beginning by your unasked for interference and subsequent action you have deliberately used your high position to insult a humbler. ... The days of duelling are past, but there is a more just way of getting right done than can duelling, and that is — publicity.*

Knowing the Prince's present difficulties and aware of his fear of the press because it owed no responsibility to anyone at all, Lord Charles threatened to reveal the exact truth about England's future king and in such detail that all previous attacks on him, including the shocking Tranby Croft affair, would look like religious tracts.

He was flying his flag aboard the *Undaunted*. Happily for him the Commander was a sympathetic and wise man who did not mind risking the admiral's displeasure by giving unwelcome advice when he was asked for his opinion. He read the letter very carefully and recommended that it should not be sent direct to the Prince. It would be more prudent, he suggested, perhaps in the end more effective, if the letter was shown by Lady Charles to the Prime Minister before the Prince saw it.

Lord Charles saw the point. His wife had already been badgering Lord Salisbury about her ostracism, to which, cautious man, he had made some very non-committal replies. But Salisbury would be obliged to do something about this letter.

He sent it to his wife instructing her to show it to the Prime Minister, but not to forward it to the Prince unless and until she received a cable of instructions from the *Undaunted*.

Salisbury with his massive brow and beard and his special power in Conservative policies as a Cecil, was appalled by the letter. He strongly counselled restraint. At the same time he acquainted the Prince with a much watered-down version of Lord Charles' threat. Simultaneously Albert Edward learnt that

Lady Charles was consulting the very barrister who had been so unnecessarily insulting to him in open court only a few weeks before. And he learnt as well that Lady Charles' sister had circulated an anonymous pamphlet entitled *Lady River* which was violently anti-Daisy and contained a full copy of her original letter for all London to read. With pursed lips the Prince asked Fuller to go out and buy a copy. It exceeded his worst expectations.

Never had the Prince felt so desolate and alone.

Eddy, had he been brighter, might have made an understanding confidant, but he was hardly up to the mark. It had recently been decided by the family that the only way to keep him out of serious trouble was to marry him off without delay, and after exploring every possibility, May, Princess Mary Adelaide's only daughter had been chosen on the grounds that she was not unattractive and had plenty of common sense. In any other European court her morganatic blood would have been a bar, but Victoria was more enlightened than her fellow sovereigns and she thought May clever and adaptable enough to manage Eddy. Poor May. The Prince was sorry for her. Eddy was no glamorous knight – although Hélène of Orleans appeared to have thought him one. To his father he was simply a problem and could be no help in this crisis.

His younger son was busy paying off his first command, the little gunboat *Thrush*, and getting himself gazetted commander; and, in any case, George was possibly too naïf to confide in. He had developed a passion for naval affairs and stamp-collecting and, in the complications of the Beresford–Daisy Brook affair, would have been quite out of his depth.

Nor could he even go for comfort to his married daughter for Louise's unique method of dealing with the scandals which touched on her father appeared to be to ignore them. To her they simply did not exist.

Alix ought to have been his standby, especially at such a time, but she had written to say that she did not intend to return from her annual visit to her parents in Denmark on the date she had arranged. Instead she and her unmarried daughters planned to go to see her sister the Tsaritsa in the Crimea and afterwards her brother in Greece, and she was not sure when she would return home. Evidently she had heard all the rumours. Evidently she was very hurt. Evidently she was going to make him pay.

266

On 9 November, that miserable year, the Prince of Wales celebrated his fiftieth birthday at Sandringham. He was in cramped, uncomfortable conditions, as a great part of the house had been burnt out eight days before. Both his sons were there: Eddy staring pop-eyed at nothing and talking about May Teck, George busy with his stamps. But Alix was not there; not there on his fiftieth birthday. His house party was small as it had to be and they quickly caught his own wretchedness which made them a despondent lot. A chilly wind blew round the house and penetrated the tarpaulins over cracks in the masonry and fallen-in-roofs. Occasionally with this wind, which came uninterrupted from the Arctic Circle, there was a thin freezing rain – far worse than sleet or hail.

On the day after his birthday – why they could not arrive on the proper day the Prince never discovered – a deputation arrived from the actors and actor managers of the English stage. As Prince of Wales he had done much to make acting a more respectable profession, and he was touched that, unlike so many people, they had remembered his birthday and brought him a present. It was a very expensive cigar box, a little gaudy perhaps as it was of gold and studded with diamonds, but Albert Edward appreciated the sentiments it expressed. And he enjoyed entertaining the deputation. It was led by the eccentric Herbert Beerbohm Tree, whose magnificent oddities had recently been topped by his entering a post office to buy a penny stamp and, on being given one, asked 'But have you no others?' Then, when the patient postal clerk offered him a sheet, he pointed at a stamp right in the middle, saying: 'I will take that one.' The Prince liked Tree. But when Tree and the other bright actors and actor–managers had gone, he relapsed into his former gloom.

Two days later George complained of a headache. Eyestrain, decided his father. Peering at postage stamps through a glass and wielding tweezers was bound to be bad for him. But it was not eyestrain. Suddenly, frighteningly, his temperature soared. His father had him out of the half burnt-out house immediately and on a special train to London. Marlborough House was the only fit place to be ill in. And Gull, when he met the train, announced that Prince George was indeed very ill. He had typhoid.

The Prince begged Knollys to telegraph for the Princess. She

267

was located at Livadia, whence she dashed across Europe with her daughters in a series of special trains. She was met by the Prince on the 22nd. He rushed her to Marlborough House where George still lay mortally ill. They were together when the crisis was reached two days later.

Like his father and his grandmother George was in excellent condition when he contracted the disease and he had the force to withstand it. He lived, but both parents realized it had been a very close thing.

The year's scandals seemed very insignificant against what might have happened if George had died. His typhoid joined them together in a closer understanding than they had had for years. And Alix was there, at Bertie's elbow, when the Beresford scandal blew up again and this time, it really looked as if the mad Lord Charles would carry out his threat and publish a stark and intimate account of the Prince's failings for all the world to read.

Lord Salisbury had been trained in diplomacy by Disraeli. He was by blood a Cecil. For long periods he was a Minister of the Crown and three times he formed administrations of his own, but in all his career no problem demanded so much of his skill as the settlement between the Prince of Wales and Lord Charles Beresford. The Queen herself was much involved, and conspicuously on her son's side. The Beresfords as a family were split down the middle; Lord Marcus staying loyal to the Prince rather than to his feckless brother. The Princess of Wales maintained a dignified forbearance throughout. Only Salisbury and the Queen could have made the Prince do as Lord Charles demanded. He had to agree to the temporary exclusion of Lady Brook from Court as she was the originator of the brawl, and he himself had to write a letter of apology to his former friend. On Christmas Eve and at Marlborough House, not at Sandringham where Christmas had been spent all his married life, he steeled himself to write the necessary apology.

It had, indeed, been a hateful year.

8

All her married life Princess Mary Adelaide had been obliged to be careful and quite seriously she believed that she had been. It had always gone much against the grain with her to re-use parcel paper and unknot string, and these with all her other small economies were nuisances and therefore took on the character of real sacrifices. One included keeping biscuits – for she was a considerable between-meal nibbler – in any sort of container other than a proper biscuit barrel because it gave her a virtuous feeling of having to do without, and this had given rise to one of the more famous Mary Adelaide remarks. Her children's governess had objected to keeping biscuits in a hair box and earned herself a withering reproof: 'If a Princess of Great Britain and Ireland can eat biscuits out of a hair box, so I presume can the daughter of a Dresden dentist!' But however large and stringent her sacrifices appeared to her, she was incapable of economizing. In her financial exile to Florence she gave the most brilliant parties, appearing in the royal box at the opera in her tiara and diamonds; and all through the worst winter months her room was packed with tuberoses and violets. She was a chronic spendthrift and perpetually in financial difficulties but (a rare thing in the royal family) an eternal optimist. It was as well because like the Prince of Wales she was beginning to feel her weight and years, and her husband had suffered some sort of seizure out in Florence and though no longer physically paralysed, Franz was partially off his head. This bore heavily on Mary Adelaide, who took an unusual way out of the difficulty by pretending that he was perfectly all right.

When she heard the first intimations that her own beloved May might be chosen to marry the Heir-but-One she behaved characteristically. Franz and May herself said the whole idea was quite out of the question and impossible. Mary Adelaide simply planned and plotted to make sure it came about.

May was sent for to Balmoral to be looked over by the Queen.

Her approval and consent was essential and so Mary Adelaide chose the most charming of her attractive sons, Prince Dolly, to chaperone his sister. She emphasized to him, though not to May, that it was important for Princess Beatrice to approve as well because of her influence.

Bearing all this in mind Dolly cleverly made up to Aunt Beatrice, as he called her. When May was not out driving with the Queen, she was with her brother and Aunt Beatrice, relaxing and smoking furtive cigarettes, in the Battenberg apartments.

Aunt Beatrice said yes. So did the Queen.

After that it was up to the Duke of Clarence himself. Though his father warned him it would be more delicate to hold his hand until after Christmas, by which time Princess Hélène of Orleans would be out of the country, Eddy found himself with the Tecks at a country house party at Luton Hoo in December. Princess Mary Adelaide was jolly and very encouraging. He was clay in her hands and without fuss he did what he regarded as his duty. May did hers. They were betrothed.

No one, least of all Mary Adelaide, who had been allowed to marry for love, believed that it was a love match; but Eddy was not too unpresentable and her three sons were considerate enough not to tell her of his appalling reputation.

She knew a few things about him naturally. No one savoured a little gossip more than the Duchess of Teck. But she was totally unaware that she was handing her only and beloved daughter to one of Jack the Ripper's closest friends, and 'Victoria' of *The Hundred Guineas*. Her brother George might say confidentially that he was a deplorable soldier, but he could get on with people, and he could shoot snipe and play hockey. . . . On the whole Princess Mary Adelaide was very satisfied with the match and barely could stop herself rubbing her hands at the thought that her appalling money difficulties might at last be over.

On 4 January, 1892 the Duke and Duchess of Teck with their daughter May and George, the Duke of Cambridge travelled with Albert Edward and Prince Eddy on the Prince of Wales' Special down to Sandringham.

Eddy and his father had been to the funeral of the Queen's half-sister's son, Prince Victor of Hohenlohe, and part of the

270

journey was taken up in discussing their precise relationship by law. But Eddy barely joined in, being totally uninterested in such a puzzle and having a cold in the head.

He looked morose, thought Mary Adelaide, peeping at him from beneath her bonnet rim. Poor May. She would not like it if her husband was a brooder and it looked as if he might be. Nevertheless there was little doubt as to who was to be *unter dem Pantoffel* in this case. May might be shy and reserved – no doubt, reflected her astute mother, because she herself was the exact opposite – but both shared the same sense of humour and quick perception, and both, without any difficulty at all, could manage the Duke of Teck, and very probably both could manage the Duke of Clarence and Avondale.

With another peep she regarded her daughter.

May was not a classical beauty, but a girl any mother might be proud of – undoubtedly attractive, tall, and well-proportioned. Her face was as serious as Queen Victoria's but like hers it could light up in a radiant smile and twinkling eyes of china-blue. No, May's eyes were a deeper blue than the Queen's. An Irish painter friend in Florence had described them as the blue of riebeckite. Her main defect was her hair which she wore dressed tightly according to the fashion of the middle 'seventies, with a braid round the back of her head and a bang on her forehead. It was not really suitable for a tall serious girl, but she was imprisoned by fashion like everyone else.

Mary Adelaide's quicksilver mind went off at a tangent. When May was Duchess of Clarence and Avondale she would be in a position to set not follow fashions, and if she could be persuaded that a bang of artificial hair did not suit her, she might break the mode. The Queen, she knew, would be on her side. The bang and fringe style of hair dressing had caused a snort of derision from Balmoral. It made pretty girls, said the Queen, look like poodles. . . .

The Prince of Wales' Special arrived at Wolverton Station exactly on time, but less smoothly than the Prince could have wished. As the train stopped his hat was jerked a half-inch forwards. As he descended on to the carpeted platform he told the stationmaster to warn the driver that it must not happen again.

His son George was there to welcome the party. He kissed his father and Aunt Mary Adelaide.

271

The others would have come too, he explained, to welcome May as Eddy's fiancée, but Victoria had one of her worst colds and had been packed off to bed. It looked as if she might have influenza.

Less than a fortnight later another special train took the Teck family back to London. No one spoke. Dressed in full mourning each had his thoughts.

Those of Franz, Duke of Teck were confused. His nerves had been badly upset by the events at Sandringham, badly upset, badly upset. He clutched the top of his cane tightly and clenched his teeth.

His wife, Princess Mary Adelaide, sat as though she were stunned. Perhaps nothing in her life, no experience had been so ghastly as their stay at Sandringham. All her dreams, all her plans, all her hopes were broken.

Princess May sat stiff-backed, worried about her beloved mother and father. She knew it was useless trying to cheer them. They had been there with her and all Eddy's family in his little bedroom for the terrible, stuffy, agonizing death struggle which had kept them on their feet and in a constant agony of apprehension for six long hours.

Already they were singing a new, sad ballad in the pubs and clubs of frozen Norfolk. Where the words came from, no one knew, but they were sung to the tune of *God Bless the Prince of Wales*.

> *With love and true devotion,*
> *They watched by his bedside*
> *But all was gloom and sadness,*
> *The moment that he died*
> *He closed his eyes for ever,*
> *They kissed his pallid cheek,*
> *In breathless tones his mother said,*
> *O speak, my darling, speak!*
>
> *A nation wrapped in mourning,*
> *Shed bitter tears today,*
> *For the noble Duke of Clarence,*
> *And fair young Princess May.*

272

9

The Prince of Wales broke down three times after his son's death.

The first occasion was when Oliver Montagu, hearing the news, drove straight over to comfort the grieving couple. Then he let his tears flow freely, and felt the better for it.

The second time was at Windsor. Alix had wished Eddy to lie beside their little son John at Sandringham, and had asked Mama for her permission. But though, surprisingly, Mama gave it, Bertie himself insisted that Windsor was the proper burying-place for a Prince of the Blood, and to deaden his feelings he had busily made most of the arrangements himself, But his feelings had broken through at the funeral and he wept bitterly.

> *Forasmuch as it hath pleased Almighty God of his great mercy to take unto himself the soul of our dear brother here departed . . .*

Bertie knew that, contrary to the Queen's expressed wishes, Alix was there at the funeral, privately watching from Catherine of Aragon's Closet, whence Mama had watched their own brilliant wedding twenty-nine years before. He wiped away his tears. After the Committal, Franz of Teck handed him what would have been May's bridal-wreath of orange blossom, and he placed it lightly upon the coffin.

And that night, alone in his apartments at Windsor, he kept his feelings in check by planning a funeral monument for his son. Then Knollys knocked at his door and came in. He believed, he said, that the Prince would wish to know that a further wreath had been added to those which already decorated Prince Albert Victor's tomb: a wreath of immortelles bearing a card with the simple inscription, *Hélène*. Was it to be left in position? Yes, said the Prince immediately. Hélène of Orleans had loved his son in a way no other woman had ever done. Her small wreath deserved its place. When Knollys had left he pushed aside the papers on his desk, put his head in his hands, and burst into tears. . . .

Unknown to him, another who had loved Eddy and was now in

273

a criminal lunatic asylum, was also expressing his devotion. On the very day he heard of the Prince's death Jim Stephen pushed his plate aside and said he would speak, eat and drink no more. The authorities did not force-feed him. Stephen, the Ripper, was to be allowed to go in his own way, and twenty days later he died.

The Prince took Alix and his family to Osborne.

Mama, who knew herself the keenest cutting-edge of grief, was frankly surprised to see them so broken up. George, now Heir-but-One, was thin and pale from his typhoid, and he had been so extraordinarily fond of his brother that he simply could not control his tears. Neither Alix nor her two unmarried daughters attempted to do so. Even Bertie was in a constant state of depression. Osborne had never been a particularly inspiriting place since the death of the Prince Consort but that February it was distressingly joyless.

To begin with, the Queen bore with it because she was grieved herself that Eddy had died. He had not been especially lovable but he had been her grandson and she had seen him at his better moments. But later she insisted on talking privately to her son about practical matters: and to her amazement and horror he began to weep.

In a moment she had risen from her chair and found herself consoling him. He was in her arms as he had not been for many years and it touched both of them deeply.

'Well,' she said ruefully, wiping a tear from her eyes. 'No one would think we were two old things of seventy-four and fifty-one.'

He wiped his own eyes, helped her back into her seat and mumbled an apology.

'No need,' she cried. 'No need. My governess told me that a good cry is sovereign, and no doubt Laddle told you the same.'

'She did,' he agreed. He managed to smile. 'Not that I often enjoy it.'

'Perhaps you should,' suggested Mama. Then she bade him sit down and talk. 'For talk we must. The family, the dynasty, everything depends on us being level-headed.'

Relieved by his tears he found himself able to talk sensibly and practically about what was to be done.

It was unspoken between them, but understood all the same, that Eddy's death had really been a merciful providence for the

274

British monarchy. He must surely have failed as king. Now if anything happened to George – and he looked peaky enough – Louise would be heir; and with all respect to her granddaughter, said the Queen firmly, there would not long be a monarchy if Louise sat on the throne. Bertie agreed.

'Therefore,' hurried on Mama, 'we must have George out of the Navy and brought on a little in languages and history and law, so that he will not disgrace our house.'

His eyes fell.

She laid a hand on his arm. 'That was not intended, dearest Bertie, as a slight upon yourself. Truly. We have not always been in accord because – well, because I doubted your ability to manage affairs. But recently you have proved me wrong. Being mischievous, and this is how I shall put it, you have had misfortunes and you have been dreadfully uncircumspect. But I am aware,' she went on to his surprise, 'how you have had to pay for it. And none of us –' here she tapped his arm again – 'none of us is perfect.'

'Dearest Mama,' he murmured.

She kissed him. 'And when we have brought George on we must find him a wife so that he may give England heirs.' She put her head slightly on one side. 'Poor May, to be widowed, so to speak, before she was married. Do you think she might be persuaded to transfer her affections?'

Bertie had had the same idea. Having been really a perfect partner for poor Eddy, May would be perfect for George.

'But George,' he reminded his mother, 'has been rather keen on Affie's daughter.'

It was true. As a naval officer Prince George had served under his uncle at Malta and seen much of his cousins. Riding beside them on his horse Real Jam, or being in their company at Carnival time and pelted with sugar plums by the exuberant citizens of Valetta, he had at last stilled his impossible longing for Julie Stonor and lost his heart to his cousin Marie.

The Queen looked over her son's head at the ceiling. 'Marie, I happen to know, will not have him. In her own words, she regards him as "a beloved chum", but nothing else.'

Bertie started. He himself had already guessed the embarrassing truth, but how *did* Mama find out about such things?

'And,' she continued, 'George has not shown any partiality for Lenchen's girl.'

275

This was also true. Lenchen had been pushing her younger daughter, Princess Helena Victoria, at George since the previous autumn, but without success. The poor girl had a kind heart but such a long nose that she was nicknamed the Snipe.

'I feel sure,' said the Queen quietly, still looking over her son's head, 'I feel sure that George knows his duty.'

'You may count on that, Mama. But such an arrangement would require extremely delicate handling. . . .'

She interrupted him. 'I think,' she said, 'that you may leave that to me.'

'You, Mama?'

She nodded. 'I shall write to Mary Adelaide and propose that the Tecks come here. Afterwards perhaps you and Alix and your family could take May away with you so that you are all together for the 27th.'

This was the day on which the wedding should have taken place.

He agreed. 'But where, Mama? Our house is out of the question, the memories would be too painful. White Lodge is too small –'

'Hartington!' said the Queen suddenly. 'I mean Devonshire. He has properties everywhere. And he is one of your friends.'

The Prince considered. Harty-Tarty had recently succeeded to the dukedom and though carrying on his liaison with Louisa Manchester he was high in the Queen's favour as a bolster between her and the odious Gladstone. It was true he had properties all over the place.

'Compton Place,' he suggested at length. 'It is at Eastbourne and could accommodate us well.'

'Then do, please, arrange it, dearest Bertie.' After a moment, she added. 'The Duke is one of your nicer friends, though I do hope you will urge him to marry the Duchess of Manchester now that she is widowed and he is in a position to do so.'

Bertie smiled. 'He needs to be looked after,' he said jokingly.

But his mother did not see it as a joke. 'Indeed you are right,' she said seriously; 'He is becoming so dreadfully vague. Do you know that, when I went down to see Mr Ferdinand Rothschild's place at Waddesdon, Lord Hartington happened to be there and when I held out my hand he actually shook it instead of kissing it.' She forced a smile. 'He shook it.'

.   .   .   .   .

276

Vague or no, the new Duke of Devonshire was very happy to place Compton Place at the Prince's disposal, and it was there that the Waleses took May for the mournful 27th. She and George went shopping in Eastbourne and played bézique in the evenings. He liked to talk to her about his dead brother. She noted how ill and thin he looked himself and how little he was sleeping.

Grieving and anxious and trying not to show it, the Prince of Wales wrote from Eastbourne to ask his mother to make George a duke.

Confessing again that she could not see the point, she nevertheless complied to please her son. George was created Duke of York and took his seat in the House of Lords.

After a nine-day visit to Compton Place Princess May returned home. She sensed that her mother was intriguing but, for the time being, she remained ignorant of the web that was being spun. Then it became obvious.

Mary Adelaide proposed to a rich friend that she should take her and the Duke of Teck and their grieving daughter to Cannes, and on 9 March they left, trusting that there May would recuperate from her sorrow. It could be no coincidence that on the same date the Prince and Princess of Wales with their unmarried children arrived at Cap Martin, a discreet distance from Cannes.

George and May realized they were being manoeuvred into a position which both found embarrassing and from which neither could escape. From playing bézique together at Eastbourne to giving and returning visits with their parents on the Riviera might seem to be a natural step, but the purpose was painfully clear. To her mother's dismay May showed a stubbornly independent spirit, pointing out that she was, after all, in the deepest mourning and had three huge signed photographs of Eddy in her room. . . .

More than anyone else the Prince of Wales was sensitive to May's dilemma, and decided something should be done to end it. In any case he was becoming bored with this slow and coy game played out on a coast he knew so well and where the Princesse de Sagan had a charming villa. The result was that Alix and her children were packed off back to England. George left to spend his last few weeks in the Navy, commanding H.M.S. *Melampus* in summer manoeuvres, and the Tecks went on to Stuttgart.

At Stuttgart they met the King and Queen of Württemberg and Aunt Vera who suffered from terrible St Vitus's dance and had to be constantly attended by an army sergeant who cushioned her from bruising herself against the furniture. They also saw the mannish, violet-faced Princess Catherine, who appeared to have forgiven the Duke of Teck for burning down her stables with his *ombres chinoises*, although clearly he attracted fires because, during their short stay, a fire broke out in the sitting-room shared by Princess Mary Adelaide and her daughter. Very little was destroyed but amongst the burnt items were the three huge signed photographs of Prince Eddy – which everyone save May considered a very significant event. She, with her feet on the ground, merely deprecated having muslin curtains within dangerous reach of reading lamps.

By now she was certain that her destiny and George's were inescapable. There was a family precedent for it in Dagmar's decision to marry the Tsarevitch's brother after he had died; and she now ruled as Empress of All the Russias and was very happy indeed with her Alexander. There ought to be no reason why May should not do the same and change from Eddy to George. But she would not permit the process to be hurried. Pressing dynastic reasons urged haste, but she thought decency mattered more, and shyly she would not commit herself.

As it turned out she was right to do this because, as they saw more and more of each other, she and George developed a genuine fondness for each other. She sensed that he would be easy to love and hold her affections. To him May was a most acceptable replacement for Julie Stonor, whom he could never marry, and his cousin Marie of Edinburgh who had been rapidly married off to the Crown Prince of Romania, and she was infinitely more attractive to him than his cousin the Snipe. But he was still nervous about 'the switch' as he called it.

Quite naturally, to begin with, Motherdear shared his nervous apprehension. His father quietly encouraged him. His sister, Louise of Fife, was positive that it was the right thing to do. But the most powerful and obvious force was, of course, Grandmama, whose views she made clear. George bravely made a stand on one matter. At Eddy's death the Queen had asked him to change his name to Albert, and, taking private advice from Sir Henry Ponsonby, he had consistently refused. But there was no denying Grandmama's wish that he should marry May. In fact only George of Cambridge, urged on by his devoted admirer the romantic Lady Geraldine

Somerset, was hostile to 'the switch'. Considering his own philandering career with Mrs Fitzgeorge, Mrs Beauclerk, and a Mrs Vyner amongst others, he was not in the strongest position to remonstrate with the Queen, but, egged on by Lady Geraldine, he did. The Queen stood none of his nonsense. Nor did his sister Augusta who was over in London from Strelitz and whom he had hoped to get on his side. On 11 July Lady Geraldine confided in shocked tones to her diary that the Grand Duchess had told her:

May has never been in love and is most *unlikely ever to be so!*

There really was nothing that anyone could do as May was pushed at George and George was pushed at May.

10

Queen Victoria was delighted to see the satisfactory unfolding of her plot. She and Mary Adelaide were quite frequently in communication and the romance helped to soothe her grief at the death that spring of her son-in-law, Louis of Hesse, and her intense annoyance when, at the impossible age of eighty-two-and-a-half, Gladstone was re-elected and formed his fourth Ministry. She consoled herself with the reflection that Gladstone could not possibly last long, either because of his great age or because of his notion to let the seditious Irish rule themselves – a programme which must inevitably bring him down.

And there were other soothing consolations that summer. Things turned out very well indeed. Bertie used all his persuasive power to press Lord Rosebery to join Gladstone's government as Foreign Minister, which was a relief because the Queen had a special fondness for Lord Rosebery. And then George was sent off to learn German at Heidelberg; the Duke of Devonshire at last married Louisa Manchester – giving her the doubtful honour of being called 'the double duchess'; and Gladstone was trampled by a cow in Cheshire. She expressed her sympathy, of course, to Mrs

Gladstone. One had to. But she was much amused to hear from Jane Churchill that an ostentatious wreath had arrived at Gladstone's house intended for the cow (which had been shot). Attached was a label which read: *'To the memory of the patriotic Cow which sacrificed its life to save Ireland from Home Rule'*. Finally her hopes were fulfilled as Gladstone was proved incapable of carrying on. The official story – which she heard – was that his eyesight was failing and he could manage no longer. The true story, which the Prince of Wales knew but which was kept from her was that, already outraged because he had shattered the Liberals over Home Rule, his colleagues in the Cabinet had driven him out of office. Overstrained and partially senile he had gone off in a temper to Biarritz, confident that his absence would force the Cabinet to its knees. Instead he was sent an emissary to demand not only that he resign the premiership but also his seat in Parliament. And so the last audience took place when the old man of eighty-three handed in his seals. The Queen accepted them with her accustomed politeness, but did not thank him for his services. In her heart she thought he had served her and the country badly. To thank him for that would be humbug. That handsome and thoroughly dependable Lord Rosebery was put in Gladstone's place and Victoria turned her attention once more to the urgent necessity of marrying George and May.

On being created Duke of York, George had been given the Duchess of Cambridge's apartments in St James's which he and his father and his sister Louise had done up with a man from Maple's. Thenceforth it was called York House. He was also given a grim little villa on the Sandringham estate, which up to that time had been used to house extra bachelor guests. It was poky, inconvenient, made gloomy by surrounding shrubberies, and if it had not had a garden pool with a lead pelican amongst bamboos, it would have looked exactly like a minor railway station on the Great Eastern Railway. Father and son and daughter had again been busy with the man from Maple's – furnishing and decorating this unsatisfactory place, known now as York Cottage.

Princess May, who could narrow her lips into the thinnest of thin lines of disapproval, was distressed. She had inherited excellent taste from her mother and father, and it irked her that her

280

future homes were being done over by a man from Maple's simply because amongst the Prince of Wales' flashier parvenu friends was Maple himself. But she could say nothing. Although an understanding was in the air, there was not as yet an official betrothal. In any case politeness would have obliged her to hold her tongue. Maple might be pre-arranging what were to be *her* houses in a modern style which was not to her taste, yet she knew that the Prince of Wales and George were trying to do their best for her. So she gritted her teeth and said nothing except to her mother and father. All three exclaimed in horror when they heard that George's sitting-room, as glum as a cell because of high laurels outside the north window, had been rendered 'cheerful' by covering the walls with the red cloth then being used for the trousers of French private soldiers. But exclamations of horror made in private at the White Lodge in Richmond did not stay the hand of the Maple's man.

Something else intervened to slow down the destined engagement. This was a real tragedy for the Princess of Wales who, in the January of 1892, a year after Eddy's death, lost her Galahad, Oliver Montagu.

He had been unwell for some time, only just managed to show the Princess how to cast a salmon fly at Mar Lodge the autumn before, and had been sent to Egypt for the winter. Then, in Cairo, he died.

For a quarter of a century he and the Princess had been platonic lovers, idealizing their romance by the quality of its purity, and Alix at first felt unable to face life. Charlotte Knollys and George between them made her pull herself together. Wisely the Prince did not interfere in this most intimate matter, but he made his sincere feelings of sympathy clear. Alix paid a private visit to Hinchingbrooke, where Montagu was to be buried in the family vault, and begged his brother to place a cross which she highly valued in his coffin overnight. On the day of the funeral she stayed at home on her knees with this cross in her hands while her husband and son went over for the service. Afterwards both did all they could to soothe her grief.

To Princess Mary Adelaide's alarm she heard that Alix was to take George off on a cruise in the Mediterranean. Ostensibly they were to visit their Greek relations. In fact, as Mary Adelaide well knew, Alix was hoping to recover her own poise after the death of her beloved friend, and she wanted to indulge herself in the company of her remaining son. With Eddy and Oliver Montagu gone, George was now doubly precious to her. For weeks she would have him again in her coils, prolonging his childhood, sapping his resolution.

So worried was she that Mary Adelaide confided her alarm to her cousin the Queen. Victoria comforted her. It was true that Alix had disgracefully kept her children in a state bordering on infantilism, giving them childish presents, and even indulging in childish horseplay. It was an open secret of which the family as a whole were thoroughly ashamed that a few years before the stately and beautiful Princess of Wales and her heavily bearded son of twenty-two, then a Lieutenant in the Royal Navy, had scandalized the Sandringham servants by fighting a duel with soda water syphons and a hunting crop. But, though George was undoubtedly immature, fifteen years' service in the Royal Navy must have instilled in him a reverence for duty, and he knew his duty as heir presumptive. Moreover, seeing some of Alix's more mundane relations ought to be a help. In fact she was sure it would be. Far from the young man being sapped of all resolution he would probably return home steeled to make a definite proposal.

The Queen was right. Stiffened by long and intimate talks with his Aunt Olga, the Queen of Greece, who knew May Teck and loved her dearly, George returned to London ready to do his duty.

It was done at his sister Louise's place at Sheen. The Tecks had diplomatically gone out driving and May was taking tea with the Fifes when Prince George arrived. But he tugged at his beard, and kept flattening his already flat hair with the palm of his hand, and would have no bread and butter or anything else.

To the last he had to be pushed.

His sister firmly took him in hand: 'Now George,' she said, 'don't you think you ought to take May into the garden to look at the frogs in the pond?'

Two months later the Duke of York and Princess May of Teck were married in the Chapel Royal. The day was perfect. The crowds were frantic with excitement and good wishes. Royalties were there from all over Europe. The bride and bridegroom were composed and evidently very happy. Only one thing marred what would otherwise have been a perfect day. Poor Duke Franz of Teck persuaded himself that he would never see his beloved daughter again and howled like a child, but at once the Queen stepped in and put things to rights. She took the Duke's hand and pressed it and kept holding it and cheered him up and stopped him crying.

<h1 style="text-align:center">11</h1>

In 1894 Willy arrived uninvited for the Cowes regatta and won the Queen's Cup.

The Prince of Wales was mortified. True he himself had beaten an American favourite in another race, but all the pleasure he had taken in his new and splendid sloop *Britannia* was dimmed both by Willy's crowing and by the necessity to be polite to his officious nephew.

Then there was the affair of the private race between the Prince and a friend, in which – totally uninvited and unwanted – Willy joined in his own yacht. Off Sandown they were partially becalmed and the Prince signalled a proposal that, as the Queen was giving a full-dress dinner in honour of her nephew that evening, they should abandon the race and go ashore. But Willy would not hear of it. The race was fought out and both arrived long after the Queen had left the dining-room.

Willy had to be forgiven, for reasons of protocol. The Prince was not. For a day or two, he felt the full sting of Mama's displeasure. But for this, rightly, he blamed his nephew not his mother, and bore with it patiently.

Even when she was reproving him the Prince found himself much more at ease with Mama. The way she had stood by him during that awful year of 1891; the way she had managed the engagement and marriage of May and George to ensure a continuance of heirs for England; the way she indulged him in understanding both his Hanoverian appetite for high living and his considerable difficulties with Alix, had altered his whole attitude to

Mama. It had made him far less critical of her prickliness, far less inclined to carp at what he had once called her damned interference in his private affairs, and far more able to appreciate her whims and fancies. He could appreciate at last how progressive she was, far more so than most of her fellow monarchs. She received divorced women at Drawing-rooms, and Jews and Americans were given the entrée as well. She even made his old friend Natty Rothschild a peer, allowing him to make his oath on the Jewish scriptures, and she had been persuaded to accept that atheistical, pro-contraceptionist, radical *enfant terrible*, Bradlaugh, as a member of her House of Commons. Moreover – good for her – she refused absolutely to associate herself with any of the puritan societies which seemed to have been formed for the exclusive purpose of cutting down fun, and vexed Evangelicals everywhere by refusing to consent to the appointment of a famous teetotaller to a Canonry of Westminster unless he promised never to preach on total abstinence there.

Some of the Prince's acquaintances who had long before fallen into the habit of regarding the Queen as stuffy were astounded by his changed views. Evidently he was proud of her. He made it plain to everyone that there was no one quite like his mother, not only because she was the doyenne of all European sovereigns and so old and so wise, but also because her people both in Great Britain and the Empire appeared to have raised her to a state of semi-deification. Her figure was appearing not only in carved statuary in every principal city in the Empire but in stained-glass church windows too; and her foibles were respected as the foibles of a goddess. For example, knowing her insistence on not being recognized when out driving privately, people climbed trees and went to endless trouble to hide themselves when she appeared – though this was a display of loyalty which had its ridiculous side when one of her ministers, six feet four inches high, found himself with only a small shrub to hide in as the Queen's pony chair approached.

Bertie collected these stories of his mother's slow deification, and he was exceptionally proud of them. He now thought it improbable that he would ever rule himself. Mama would outlive him. Apart from her unconquerable aversion for Gladstone and anyone who criticized her Munshi, she was as level-headed as ever. Moreover she was as tough as ever: driving out in Scotland through mists, seas of mud, sheeting rain and blizzards, and although, as she remarked, she was often 'soaked to the undergarments', she took no harm. She slept and ate as well as ever and worked exceedingly hard, much harder, in fact, than he did and he doubted if he would ever have the strength to fill a day as she could.

He mentioned this to Knollys – unconsciously hoping, perhaps, that his Private Secretary would chaff him and tell him he was imagining things. But Knollys did no such thing. He simply wagged his head in agreement. This cemented Albert Edward's own inner conviction that he had not long to last, that his stoutness and wheezing and lack of tone made it imperative to train George as quickly as possible to succeed his grandmother. He begged Knollys to do all in his power to help the Duke of York to prepare himself against the day.

Again Knollys surprised and rather dismayed him by at once undertaking to do everything he could. Momentarily a shadow fell over the Prince, but he was not the sort of man to allow considerations of mortality to spoil the present for very long. Knollys opened serious discussions with the Duke of York's Comptroller, while the Duke of York's father jovially returned to five square meals a day, what his set loved to call 'roguey-poguery', and *les girls*.

The Prince's *vie orageuse* had given way principally to a liking for lively female company and little more.

The Earl of Warwick, who had once stirred the Queen's heart at a ball of Queen Adelaide's, was dead, and Darling Daisy was now a Countess. She had also become a tiresome social reformer, and rode more madly to hounds than ever. Albert Edward begged her to give up hunting but she could not promise, she said. Their affair was slipping into that less passionate, more easy state known at the time as being 'great chums'. But there was never a shortage of amiable courtesans to accommodate the middle-aged Prince of Wales. Amongst the demi-mondaines of Paris the inimitable Goulou tickled his fancy and made him pay for it at the Moulin-Rouge; and *la reine d'ivoire*, diminutive Liane de Pougy, had her moments of triumph with le Prince des Galles, while *la belle Otero*, a Spanish dancer, made him wheeze himself into asthma.

Then there were the 'ladies'.

The Churchills had returned to favour after a long, long spell, and the Prince's barouche was frequently seen outside Lady Randolph's house at teatime when Lord Randolph himself was fulminating in the House of Commons. Lord Randolph had already caught the syphilis which was to kill him, and he no longer shared his wife's room.

There was also the fascinating Lady Dudley making herself as available as her quite fantastically rich and ancient husband would permit. A junoesque figure, she had a taste for banjo-playing, and passed on to as many friends as she could her mother's sage advice: 'Never EVER comment on a likeness'. Children, after the first two or three, often resembled family friends, and it was rumoured proudly that there were little Albert Edwards here and there in England, but it must never EVER be commented on.

Forced by the Tranby Croft scandal to give up 'baccy', the Prince now played an inferior game of bridge and few people cared to be his partner. As the evening lengthened and the losses mounted, his temper shortened. But the Tranby Croft scandal did not affect his choice of associates. People like his rich hosts at Tranby Croft, though not they themselves, continued to be his companions.

There were three sets in London at the time, the Queen's – that is the old-fashioned aristocracy and the Court, the Souls, who were well-bred and intellectual (or liked to think so), and the Marlborough House Set, which more and more included new-rich millionaires like W. W. Astor and Cecil Rhodes; Jewish financiers like Bischoffsheim and Baron Hirsch and his secretary Ernest Cassel; and foreigners like the American Jerome and Frewen and the Portuguese Minister to London, the Marquess de Soveral, nicknamed 'the Blue Monkey' by Albert Edward. To these were added the grocer Lipton and the furniture manufacturer Maple.

Everyone outside the Marlborough House Set waxed wrathfully against it while the Prince took little notice and went on trying to enjoy himself. It had to be a case of trying.

His cures at Marienbad did not appear to help a great deal. All they did was fray his temper. And even a superb dish or two, say *Escalopes de ris de veau à la florentine* followed by *Caille rôtie aux raisins*, were not worth the fact that he puffed so much on the

286

way upstairs. Or were they? He never could decide between being light of foot and heart and the mignardises, vignardises, friandises, diablotin and the exquisite frivolities which constituted such a strong temptation. He was smoking too much as well, and taking too little exercise, and getting took quickly blown, and far, far too concerned with family affairs. . . .

12

Always a serious man about his family, the Prince in late middle age took them, perhaps, too seriously to heart. That his Uncle Ernest should die was natural enough. He was an old roué who had worn himself out, and his time had come; but Bertie worried his nerves raw about Affie's inheritance, and what it would involve, and how Mama would take the death of her beloved Albert's brother. It occupied him, preoccupied him for days.

Then there was trouble with the Tecks about York Cottage. He was hurt by Mary Adelaide's ridiculing the place as an 'ornate hutch'. He was hurt too when Alix suddenly said the same. Between them the old Rumpenheimer friends got him to consent to have the place enlarged, and this time May was to manage the furnishings. Maple's man was not required.

After that he was virtually in charge of the marriage of Alice's son, now the Grand Duke of Hesse-Darmstadt, and Affie's daughter, Victoria. Mama was there of course, but he felt the responsibility greatly and he was far more flustered than she when Alicky, who had refused her cousin Eddy, accepted a proposal from Nicholas the Tsarevitch. So Alice's little daughter, who had refused to be Queen of England, would one day be Empress of all the Russias.

He lacked Mama's quiet acceptance of this momentous engagement. While he was commenting on it with wild excitement, the Queen was quietly arranging for Alicky to go with her to England – which, as much as anywhere, was her home, and arranging, too, for her to be reconciled to the Orthodox religion by the Bishop of Ripon, and instructed in it by a Father Yanisheff who was the

287

Tsar's own confessor. Between these events Alicky was to take the waters at Harrogate to expel, so to speak, the last of her Lutheran scruples with a chalybeate cure.

Needless to say, Willy regarded this proposed union as an encirclement of his Empire and this was a further worry. He was placated by the offer of the Colonelcy of the 1st Royals. Another uniform. Excellent. Willy was placated, although, fancying himself in the kilt, he had really wanted the Colonelcy of a Highland Regiment. Grandmama took the occasion to suggest in private that perhaps her grandson was too much on the gad in his gold, blue and cream train. Monarchs, she reminded him, ought to stay put on occasion. A Berlin newspaper was regretting that in the previous 365 days the Emperor had spent 199 of them in travelling. Willy, always gracious with Grandmama, took his displeasure out on his uncle. Bertie was irate.

Alix said (and without that warmth of tone which would have made it a joke) that her husband worried far more over May's first confinement than he had ever done about hers. To a degree this was true. Bertie had inherited his mother's dynastic ambitions; and he was enormously relieved when his daughter-in-law presented England with an Heir-but-Two. He was christened with a string of patriotic names, but always called David by his family.

Waiting for the birth had been a trying time. George had got thoroughly tired of his mother-in-law's unpunctuality and interference. May had found Motherdear's interest too vapid and sugary. Both had cause for complaint, but perhaps Mary Adelaide's failing was the more understandable. The Prince of Wales pointed out to his son that without May in the house, and with her husband getting pottier every moment, his huge mother-in-law was finding life extremely difficult. George accepted the point but was glad to escape to Cowes in August while his wife and mother-in-law went off to St Moritz to botanize. The Heir-but-Two was left with his nurse at White Lodge.

All this was very trying for Bertie. His normal routine was being broken into by family events, and though he had once loved novelty, routine had begun to matter to him.

The Season that year was infernally hot. In the middle of it, the French President was stabbed to death by a mad Italian, and at the end of it the Comte de Paris died. He had made a nuisance of himself in not allowing his daughter to change her religion, but he had been the Bourbon Pretender, and the Prince of Wales' formal mourning for the republican president was noticeably deepened. Then, within a month of the death of the Comte de Paris, his nephew Nicholas sent word from the Crimea that his father the Tsar was mortally ill, Alicky of Hesse was with the family at the Crimea, learning about Russian protocol, and it would be much appreciated if Aunt and Uncle Wales could go straight out to Livadia.

They set off immediately; Alix grieving for her sister Dagmar; Bertie wondering how the kindly gentle Tsarevitch would face up to his responsibilities.

Tsar Alexander III had been a giant of a man with a great capacity for work, an awesome presence, and great strength. He had once thoroughly frightened an Austrian Ambassador by twisting a large silver fork into a knot at table to show his scorn for three Austro–Hungarian divisions drawn up on the frontier. And having seen his own father blown into bloody gobbets by terrorists, he had kept an iron hand on Russia. How could his son, the small, fragile Nicholas, replace such a giant of strength and character. . . ?

Alix guessed Bertie's thoughts. There would be Dagmar, she reminded him. A Dowager Empress took precedence in Russia over everyone except the Tsar. And there would be Alicky to help Nicholas, a woman of decided viewpoints and most of them sensible.

Their train thundered along over the Central European tracks. Bertie was suddenly reminded of a time two or three years before when the Russian royal train had been derailed while the whole royal family were eating pudding, and the Tsar himself with his great strength had held up the the dining-car roof while the others escaped. Now he was dying.

When they reached Vienna they heard he was already dead.

The Prince of Wales once again acted as a family leaning post. From his nephew the new Tsar downwards everyone at Livadia depended on him. He was everyone's emotional standby.

It was he who heartily agreed with the Russian Grand Dukes that a Tsar must be embalmed and buried in St Petersburg, and thereby persuaded everybody else in the family.

It was he who agreed that, far from being unfeeling, it was practical and sensible for Nicholas and Alicky to marry

289

immediately after the funeral. The Tsar needed a Tsaritsa, and especially one of such character.

It was he who removed his niece's last remaining Lutheran scruples by insisting that it was her duty to be received at once into the Orthodox Church. This she did, in his presence; and afterwards Tsar Nicholas II issued his first Imperial Decree, that the former Princess Alix of Hesse-Darmstadt was in future to be addressed as 'the truly believing Grand Duchess Alexandra Feodorovna'.

Bertie sent for his son George hoping that Mama would permit him to represent her at both funeral and marriage, and generally made himself indispensable on the long and trying and, sometimes it appeared, ghoulish train-ride north, and in the following ceremonials. Like Willy he could not resist a uniform, and he was delighted to be allowed to accept from his nephew the Colonelcy of the 27th Dragoon Regiment of Kiev, though Charles Carrington who was in his suite, and the candid friend of former times, told him that a stout man could not possibly show to advantage in the shaggy regimental greatcoat. In fact, he more resembled a polar bear than a Prince of the Blood. The Prince took it well, but he felt bashful when presenting himself in his new uniform to Nicholas.

In the drawn-out funeral ceremonies which were 'endless and very smelly', the Prince was a model of patience. He was also a soother of outraged feelings, imagined or otherwise, making much of the unpopular King of Serbia whom everyone else seemed to ignore. He made several attempts to modify Nicholas' determination to rule autocratically as his father had done, but in this he failed. In all he was successful, being a great asset at the royal wedding which took place not long after the funeral.

The Prince showed avuncular concern for his dear Alice's daughter when, after the first night of their honeymoon, both Tsar and Tsaritsa looked completely normal and unaltered. Aware that from the age of nineteen his nephew had kept a young dancer from the Imperial Ballet in a two-storey house owned by Rimsky-Korsakov, it had never occurred to him that his poor orphaned niece might have gone to her marriage bed entirely ignorant as well as innocent.

'Nothing,' he declared to Carrington, 'has happened.'

But then his face lit up as he noticed Nicholas shyly give his bride an exquisite Fabergé flower with a massive diamond at its centre in a golden flower pot. It told him all he wanted to know. From now on he was certain that all would be well.

He was very happy to give Alix permission to stay on for a further two months and keep her widowed sister company. He and George returned to be thanked officially by Lord Rosebery for his excellent diplomatic work in Russia; to tell Mama every single detail he could remember for she would certainly want to know; to pull his brother Arthur's leg about 'falling' at last – for Daisy had let him know that the Duke of Connaught had lost his heart to Lady Randolph's sister Leonie, and probably wanted to lose more; to shoot innumerable partridges and pheasants out of the Sandringham skies; and to resign from The Traveller's because someone had had the impertinence to blackball his very special friend, the millionaire Cecil Rhodes.

13

1892 began with a great frost during which thousands of birds dropped like hailstones out of the skies and Mama's faithful Ponsonby had a seizure. It was a serious blow for such an old lady but providence kindly provided her with a young Ponsonby-trained secretary in Arthur Bigge, and Ponsonby's own son Fritz was employed to act as his assistant and keep the routine running smoothly.

After that Lord Randolph's syphilis sent him into a raving dementia and he died. Poor Jenny Churchill. The Prince of Wales wished to be especially kind to her and her children Winston and Jack, but he had a rule about fresh widows; and besides, Alix was in a great taking because, of all people, the Prime Minister wished to marry his youngest daughter, Victoria.

The Princess of Wales was now fifty, though she looked a good fifteen years younger, and her attitudes were hardening. Whereas once she had simply liked dogs they were now an obsession and she filled her homes with them. Likewise her strong maternal feelings had developed into a manic possessiveness. She would *not* let

Victoria go. Not if Victoria herself and Maud and George and May, and all her closest friends begged it. Not if her husband told her that the girls had to marry and to procrastinate was to be cruel. Not if the Queen commanded it . . .

Rosebery was a widower and older than Victoria, and an unusually honest statesman who had the premiership thrust upon him and only accepted it with reluctance. He was also a man of immense riches who knew how to use them. During his time as Prime Minister of one year and 121 days, he won the Derby twice, and in his beautiful homes at Mentmore, Dalmeny, Durdans and the Villa Rosebery at Posillipo, he was a happy marriage of squire and scholar and sportsman and invariably a perfect though quiet host. Often at Marlborough House he and the twenty-five-year-old Princess Victoria had found much in common between them. They liked the same sort of things and were obviously suited. Moreover Grandmama had the highest opinion of Lord Rosebery. Not only had he personally disliked Gladstone and made Liberalism respectable, but he was a very personable man. With dear Lord M and dear Dizzy, Rosebery was one of her very special First Ministers. Bertie too, liked him, and though he thought there would be political complications in Victoria marrying him, they were not insuperable.

But Alix would not have it.

Princess Victoria, the quickest and brightest of her daughters, was the most indispensable to her. She had to remain at home, and Rosebery, sensing her mother's hostility and being always a diffident man, ceased to press his suit.

Inadvertently Victoria's case was made worse when a little later the same year a definite offer came from the Danish Court that Prince Charles should marry her sister, Princess Maud. This time neither the Queen nor the Prince of Wales were to be put off, and Vicky added her voice by writing :

> It really is not wise to leave the future of these
> dear girls dans la vague for years longer.

With a painful display to everyone of what it would cost her, Alix said that because Prince Charles was her nephew and a Rumpenheimer and royal, and everyone was in such a blaze about it, she would consent to make the sacrifice. Maud was officially engaged and was happy to be so. But it absolutely fixed her sister's fate. Victoria was the last one, the only one left, sealed for life in the iron mask of her mother's egocentricity, to become a hypochondriac and a sad, sour woman called Princess Beck and Call at home because the Princess of Wales, looking absurdly youthful and helpless, surrounded by dogs and free doves and parrots, was for ever ringing a special bell to summon her daughter for something or other. Her son the Duke of York – and no one could have been more devoted to his mother than 'little George' – remarked to his wife that 'Motherdear is one of the most selfish people I know'.

Possibly had George of Cambridge not chosen just this time to be particularly difficult, Bertie might have made a vigorous attempt to defy Alix and free his daughter. But really he was almost powerless. Guilty about his own philandering and neglect of Alix, he felt he owed her complete liberty of action even when he knew in his heart that she was behaving wrongly and selfishly. And so Victoria was left a prisoner in her mother's cage while he turned his attention to the business of helping Mama persuade George of Cambridge to give up his post as Commander-in-Chief.

Stiffened by either Lady Geraldine – who continued to hover hawklike over his life, or, more likely, by the strengthening of his ageing prejudices against change, the Duke refused to accept any sort of reform or compromise or hint that he should resign his office. Eventually the Queen told him to resign, hating the necessity; and hating it still more when her son Arthur was not put in George's place as he ought to have been, but another non-royal, not even noble soldier, was given the appointment. Almost, but not quite, she refused to accept him. It was 'not quite' because Albert had trained her well in Queenship. Certainly, in private, she would have agreed with Lady Geraldine who, in a great taking about her Duke being supplanted, denigrated his successor with all her venom :

> *'Nasty brute of a fellow. And what a humbugging lying brute!'* ...

In public the Queen accepted the appointment, though with a marked lack of enthusiasm. Arthur was consoled by the promise of the Adjutant-generalship when it fell vacant, but Mama took it very hard, and told Bertie how sad it was that the post had slipped out of the family's control.

She was equally put out when Louise's father-in-law, the old Duke of Argyll announced that he was engaged to one of her younger Ladies. She discussed it with her eldest son. Was it not an extraordinary thing for an old man to do? Privately Bertie thought not, but he held his tongue.

When Rosebery fell from office Mama shed a tear or two until Bertie pointed out that no one could have welcomed a loss of power more genuinely than Rosebery, and his successor Lord Salisbury had served her adequately as First Minister twice before, and was no stranger. Salisbury was not in the run of modern politicians, being genial and cultivated and living partially in France and comparing the Irish to a lot of Hottentots. Moreover he had been a friend of Dizzy's, and therefore a friend of hers, for years.

Mother and son were closer than they had ever been and presented a formidable front to Willy when he came to Cowes determined to make mischief. He arrived in a huge yacht, built precisely to the specification of the Wales' yacht *Britannia,* though on a larger, Prussian scale, and he won all the races.

Mama was frosty with her grandson. She would have liked to be point blank rude because one of her ladies had overheard him referring to Bertie as 'fat old Wales', but Willy was an autocrat and an Emperor and political considerations put such candour out of the question.

Bertie abruptly sold *Britannia* outright and swore he would never race again. Willy had successfully spoiled his fun at Cowes by his unsportsmanlike determination to win at all costs, and by continuing the feud against his uncle. Very well, then, said the Prince of Wales, let him win.

Characteristically the German Emperor never appeared for the Cowes Regatta again.

Equally characteristically, when the situation between the English and Dutch settlers in the Cape was extremely delicate – Jameson having made an abortive raid into Dutch territory – Willy allowed himself to be hoodwinked into sending a congratulatory telegram to the Dutch on repulsing the English invaders.

The Queen was just getting over her shock that on 14 December, the Cypress Spray Anniversary, George's May had been delivered of a son. Poor, poor scrap. On *such* a day! She was mollified when told that he was to be named Albert, but the whole thing was more of a strain on her nerves than she could have believed possible and then she heard of Willy's impertinence in publicly congratulating England's enemies.

Her subjects were incensed. The Emperor's own regiment, the 1st Royal Dragoons, took his portrait off their mess wall and hacked it to pieces with dinner knives. The press was violently anti-German. Lord Salisbury waited with the cool detachment of the Cecils before making up his mind. . . .

Infuriated by the insult the Prince of Wales wanted to take strong diplomatic action. But the Queen disagreed. She told him that this was an occasion when she believed Willy needed to be told a home truth or two by his dearest Grandmama not by the Queen of England, and suggested that his odious conceit and impetuousness were best countered by calmness and firmness.

In her letter to her grandson she was very calm and very firm. The German Emperor was chastened. Salisbury continued being detached. The Prince of Wales cooled down. He respected Mama's advice and remembered it in all his subsequent dealings with his nephew. The Queen returned the compliment by asking her son's advice on an amorous affair which was threatening to destroy the peace of her own home. Louise's marriage with Lorne had unofficially collapsed. She had spent much of her time travelling in Europe, and until she found her master dead in his studio she had studied sculpture under Boehm at home. But neither travel nor monumental masonry had entirely satisfied her, and, out of sheer boredom, she had begun to cast eyes at Liko, Beatrice's good-looking husband. It was aggravating poor Beatrice to distraction, and she was already upset enough because Liko wanted to join Lenchen's boy on the Ashanti Expedition – an empire-building campaign to annexe the Land of the Golden Stool in Africa. Bertie strongly advised that Liko be allowed to go. His sisters would be less likely to quarrel and upset Mama if the object of their affections was out of sight for a time.

Later, when Liko caught a fever and died on the way home, and Bertie saw the agony it caused Beatrice and Mama he wished he had given any other advice in the world. But it was too late. Pickled in alcohol, Liko's body was brought home to be buried in a special sepulchre in Whippingham Churchyard not far from Osborne.

It was really almost unbearable to see Mama's grief. He had not realized how much she depended on her son-in-law. Distraught, and inclined to be off-handed, Beatrice took herself off to nurse her grief alone. Bertie warned Louise to keep out of everyone's way for a time. Trying to soothe Mama's grief was beyond him.

By an ironic quirk, that year, which was one of the saddest in the latter part of the Queen's life, happened to be one of the happiest ever experienced by her elder son.

With yachting now done with, he concentrated all his energies on the turf. He was personally at many of the meetings and his colours were often seen at the race tracks. It was one thing to win prizes with *Britannia,* another thing altogether to carry off the Derby. The difference, to his way of thinking, was almost that between being Deputy Lieutenant for Wigtownshire and being Lord Mayor of London, and on 3 June that year he achieved one of his greatest ambitions. His horse Persimmon won the Derby and there were roars to greet him as he led the victor into the enclosure. He capped this thrilling event by the Derby Dinner which he gave annually to members of the Jockey Club at Marlborough House, then on to Devonshire House where Louisa gave a Derby Ball, and, long after midnight, on to supper with the junoesque Lady Dudley. Both enjoyed the vulgar opulence of their place of assignation. Both enjoyed food. After a long, long day with enough excitement and food in it to give the average man a seizure, Albert Edward and his Georgiana, together with a good deal of very excellent champagne, much enjoyed themselves with plover's eggs, salmi of teal, and smoked breast of goose; an aspic of crayfish tails with chervil; poached mignon fillets of young cockerels stuck with roundels of truffle and ham and served on artichoke bottoms and mushrooms with a delicate suprême sauce; a sorbet or two; sylphides of squabs; asparagus; and canapés of curried haddock. So far as the Prince was concerned, not even the triumphant marriage of his daughter Maud on the last Saturday of the season could compare with the deliciousness of that Derby Day.

Then Mama and the Prime Minister showed their utmost confidence in him by proposing that he should undertake all the arrangements for Nicky and Alicky's visit to Balmoral that September. Both felt that only he, with his unrivalled knowledge of the protocol of other courts could arrange the event so that the All Highest could be received and take second place to his wife's ancient grandmother, and make sure, at the same time, that he was not assassinated. Nicholas and Alexandra brought with them their first child, the Grand Duchess Olga, and came officially as Tsar and Tsaritsa, but the Prime Minister was only to see them on the last day or two of a long family visit.

Worried a little by the smallness and dankness of his father's Gothick castle (for Bertie had seen the magnificence of the Russian Imperial palaces) he planned to brighten Balmoral, but Mama wanted nothing altered. Her oculist Professor Pagenstecher agreed with her that pastel shades and faded tartans were softer for her dimming eyes; and Nicky and Alicky were simple people, she said, they would not want fuss. Nor did they.

Bertie did his best. He went down to meet them at Leith, going aboard the Imperial yacht and welcoming them in his mother's name. Then, by train he took them north. After that, a royal cavalcade of open carriages drove them through teeming rain to Balmoral where Victoria awaited them under the portico. The rain had spoilt everything, drenching the guests, and dowsing flaming torches held by Highlanders which should have made a warm and romantic welcome; but Mama thought nothing of rain and so no one else did. Of all things she wanted to see the baby, though babies she had once disliked. And she wanted to gossip with her granddaughter Alicky – who, to her, was like a daughter.

The poor Tsar, less robust than his father, was subjected to the Balmoral routine of daily shooting, while day after day it rained.

> The weather, he reported to his mother, is awful, rain and wind every day and on top of it no luck at all – I haven't killed a stag yet.

But on one miraculously dry day Bertie made history by persuading Mama and her guests to subject themselves to the new-fangled cinematograph machine. For ever they were imprisoned in celluloid as moving people. Being new-fangled the machine

297

made them strut and stump like Willy, though in reality all were behaving as naturally as possible: George and May, standing shyly to one side, Alix severe, unruffled, looking younger than ever; Nicholas beribboned in a Russian uniform but absurdly like his cousin George of York because their height, shape of head and beards were identical, and Alicky in her invariable mauve superintending nurse and the Grand Duchess Olga; Mama, despite her hedgehog figure, moving with an extraordinary regal grace, and Albert Edward himself, walking with his chest thrown out almost as if he was breasting a wave.

The visit was a great family success, and afterwards without any appearance of enthusiasm Lord Salisbury reported that, while it had not been a conspicuous political success, it had not done any positive harm, and family unity was the thing to aim for as a preliminary. The Queen made sure that credit was given where credit was due. All this, she told Lord Salisbury, had been made possible by the care and attentiveness of the Prince of Wales.

14

The late Prince Consort's excellence as an organizer and committee man was clearly showing itself in his eldest son. Albert Edward's expertise was next in demand at the great event of the century: his mother's Diamond Jubilee.

Coming to the conclusion that the Queen ought not to be bothered with a single minor matter, the authorities decided to lay them all on the Prince of Wales. It was, in fact, surprising how the Queen did keep an eye on all that was done, but she was happy to let her son make most of the decisions.

His first decision was that the celebration should be a family and national and imperial event which excluded foreign rulers and therefore, happily, Willy.

He also recommended that the authorities learn by the mistakes made in Russia, when a stand had collapsed at Nicky's coronation and three thousand people had died in one way or another; and by the mistakes made in France where, recently, at a charity bazaar, two hundred people had been incinerated. Then he did his best to make sure that everyone of sufficient importance would receive appropriate accommodation. At the Golden Jubilee this had been muddled, as Willy had ungenerously pointed out; and accommodation had been so short that one of Beatrice's gentlemen-in-Waiting returning from dinner outside the Palace went to his room, put his hat on his bed, and found to his horror he had placed it on the stomach of a sleeping woman. Rooms had been reallocated during his short absence and he had not the least idea where to go. It was not as bad, of course, as Charlie Beresford crying cock-a-doodle-do at the Bishop of Chester and his terrified lady in the middle of the night — but bad all the same. It should not happen again.

The Prince took on himself all manner of duties from placating touchy officials, foreign envoys and native princes to dealing with members of the family. Mary Adelaide's sister Augusta, for example, wrote from Strelitz to say she was shocked to hear that because of the Queen's inability to climb the stairway to St Paul's there would be a brief Service of Thanksgiving outside the building

> *Has one ever heard of such a thing! after 60 years*
> *reign, to thank God in the Street ! ! !*

Patiently the Prince explained to his irate first cousin once removed that the intended Service would be simple and pious but absolutely magnificent and could not be mistaken for a Salvation Army rally. Moreover it would allow thousands more of Mama's subjects to see her at the height of the celebrations.

He had to endure other exasperations. One of the worst was the humiliation of seeing Alix's well-meant plan to give the poor of London a Jubilee feast they would never forget almost fall to the ground. With her refusal to take money in the least seriously the size of her own contribution was staggering, and made Sir Dighton Probyn tug his beard in horror, but very few followed her example. Bertie was not having his wife's scheme fail in the public eye and he persuaded his millionaire grocer friend to underwrite it. Lipton got a knighthood for it and was not dissatisfied.

299

Albert Edward was also a prime mover in establishing a hospital as a permanent memorial of the Jubilee, and he had a finger in the pie of a Victorian Era Exhibition in which the nursing section centred almost entirely upon Miss Nightingale; flowers being placed before her bust each day, and her bits and pieces from the Crimea venerated as relics. Clearly everyone supposed the great Flo was dead and the Prince was urged by his sisters Lenchen and Vicky to let the world know she was very much alive. In fact at that time the great Flo was deprecating the exhibition altogether in a series of viperish letters, annotating Shakespeare in her spare moments and busy trying to get more little girls christened Balaclava, 'one of the most beautiful names in the world'.

To all these duties the Prince also added hours of committee work, so much so that the Prime Minister – himself an unfussable and mildly lethargic man – was quite astonished. Some of the energies which Albert Edward had devoted almost exclusively to pleasure, turf, table and boudoir, were now being directed into other channels.

At one of his busiest times the Prince had to interrupt approving lists of acceptable jubilee presents, to visit his daughter-in-law at York House and see his newly born granddaughter, Mary. He found May herself laughing, half in tears because it had been kept from her that her mother had undergone a serious emergency operation at the time of her own confinement, and she had only just heard of it.

'I assure you, dear May, she is making an excellent recovery. And George and nurse tell me your baby is perfect and beautiful, so there is no need for tears.'

She explained, showing him a letter written in her mother's large sprawling hand and peppered with explosive punctuation. It described her rapid convalescence, and evidently her appetite was not in the least impaired for she was tucking into roast lamb and mint sauce, boiled mutton, roast chicken, asparagus and spinach, invalid turtle soup provided by a kind Lady Mayoress and every kind of jelly. Her last sentence in particular made the Prince smile.

My bed is placed in front of window overlooking beech tree, still pink-leaved! & I can watch the bicycles fly past!

The Prince took his daughter-in-law's hand – 'Like my Mama, yours will outlive us all. Now, come, May, show me please, my latest grandchild.'

Diamond Jubilee Day dawned with rainclouds chasing one another over London. Some people had been up all night but, apart from a few Scotsmen who, after a time, appeared to confuse the event with hogmanay, and what were described in the police reports as 'factory girls and paint-daubed youths dancing and playing pranks round Nelson's column', the gathering crowds were orderly. By the time the troops had formed up and contingents from all over the Empire began to march to St Paul's, the clouds had gone and the sun was up. It was to be Queen's weather as everyone had hoped.

The organisation was not precisely perfect. In such a huge enterprise it could not be. There were a series of muddled carriage placings, and stand tickets did not always get the holder to his rightful place. But very many of the Golden Jubilee mistakes had been scotched by the careful scrutiny of the Prince of Wales, and everything went well from the moment the Queen pressed a button in Buckingham Palace which signalled a message to be sent to all her millions of subjects at the beginning of her royal progress through the capital of the Empire.

Of the thousands who rode in that procession to give thanks at St Paul's for a reign of sixty years four received particular ovations. Inevitably Princess Mary Adelaide was one. With great stoicism she put up with the discomforts she felt because she was absolutely determined not to miss so great an occasion. She positively gave herself to the crowds, as a prima donna might give herself to an admiring audience. And the crowds responded with roars of love for their dear Fat Mary. Beside her sat the Grand Duchess Augusta, proud of her sister's immense verve and popularity, but still pursing her lips at the thought of thanking God in the street.

The Princess of Wales also drew an ovation of real affection from all the stands and windows as they passed. She sat beside Lenchen opposite to Mama and was dressed in lilac. She looked beautiful and young and appealing and caused a storm of loyal cheering. Because of her deafness she missed the compliments

301

shouted at her, and the noise was but a confused roaring. She had to guess at what the crowds might be saying and respond as royalty should, though at the forefront of her mind was not the splendour nor the uniqueness of the occasion but anxiety for her brother and his family who at that very moment were being harried by Turks and anti-monarchists in Greece. Her mind was far away, but the people were not to know and a nod or a smile from her was always a signal for a fresh outburst of cheering.

Alix's reaction was, in fact, as automatic as Mama's, who sat on a revolving stool which helped her to move from side to side with hand held up in greeting but whose failing eyesight prevented her from seeing very much. Mama could hear the shouts. Alix could see the smiles and fluttering handkerchiefs and raised hats.

Victoria who heard what the people cried wondered why Alix touched the English so. Was it simply her beauty, or her remoteness – made the more remote by her deafness and her foreign pronunciation? Or was she being cheered as a wronged wife? No, Mama decided, that could hardly be; for at the side of her carriage rode Bertie, and he was given a tremendous personal ovation. He was their Bertie, their own Prince of Wales.

How fortunate she was, thought the Queen, to have such a family. And how lucky to have such subjects. They shouted themselves hoarse in joy at seeing her, for the diminutive figure in the state coach in black and grey and steel and diamonds, carrying a parasol of black Chantilly lace against the sun, was at the heart of the whole Empire.

Bertie, bursting with pride at being her son, found himself often in tears.

Indomitable, inimitable Mama.

15

The Jubilee seemed to set a seal on the immortality of the Queen as though it were a ceremony not unlike the formal proceedings of canonization in Rome. Osborne and Balmoral were her personal shrines. Windsor, and less and less frequently Buckingham Palace, were the public temples where in short, breath-taking audiences, statemen from the world over saw the living legend, kissed her hand, heard her voice, and remembered it all their lives. Not in the least astonished at his mother being given quasi-divine status, the Prince of Wales urged his son George to forego philately and shooting and apply himself more studiously to learning about kingship. He knew that he and others were more mortal than Mama appeared to be and, having consistently used clichés ever since his tutor had forbidden them, he often spoke of 'the sear and yellow' and 'the fall of autumn leaves'.

The first to fall was May's mother. It was not hard to find a reason. Though devoted to her sons – even Frank who had turned out a regular Hanoverian scallywag – her life had turned on May for many years and, since May's marriage, and with the increasing eccentricities of the Duke of Teck, she had felt there was little to live for. Without the force to keep going, she slowly wound down. Her hectic welcome in the Jubilee procession was her last burst of public glory. Barely four months afterwards she took to her bed complaining of feeling generally unwell.

May happened to be staying at White Lodge as it was the customary time for them to sort out clothes and gifts for charities. It had been a life-long habit which had kept both mother and daughter busy every autumn. But this autumn the charity gifts had to be left: bundles of clothing, books, and tied-up parcels spilling over the tables in all the rooms and half-blocking the corridors. May sat with her mother all day. She used all her own considerable will power, and every ruse she could, to give her some zest for life.

She had always been a devoutly religious woman and May suggested asking the local clergyman to step by to read to her. Mary Adelaide shook her head from side to side. May tried something else. Should she and her Lady-in-Waiting play a duet or two, or perhaps a few valses at the piano below? 'No, dear' replied her mother, to whom music had meant almost as much as food.

Was there any special delicacy she would like prepared in the kitchen? or could some favourite dish be sent out for? The Duchess considered. She had a great liking for eggs and for years past she had proudly boasted to the family that the chef had no less than 126 receipts for egg dishes. She also had a passion for small game – snipe, woodcock, land-rails, and larks. But, no, she could not even interest herself in her favourite dish of all – an Ardennes thrush cooked in butter with juniper berries. She did not wish for anything special. 'A glass of milk, dear, perhaps, if you would be so kind.'

May brought the milk and made a further suggestion. Would Mama not care to dictate a few telegrams? . . . Mary Adelaide had always been a great telegrapher occasionally sitting at it from teatime until she had to dress for dinner, and there were few things she enjoyed more. But on this occasion, no – except perhaps to Alix at Sandringham. Would May kindly send a telegram to the Princess of Wales to say she wished to see her? The telegram was sent.

Then finally Princess Mary Adelaide at last admitted she felt exceedingly unwell. Perhaps the doctor could be sent for?

Her physician arrived, stepping over charity parcels and finding his way through the piles of clothes. And, to the family's alarm and terror, he instantly recommended a second emergency operation. It ought to be performed as soon as a surgeon could be found. A room was prepared. With great bravery Mary Adelaide told her distracted husband to keep his spirits up. He and May and Alge were to wait downstairs, she said, while the doctors did what they had to do. They might employ their time usefully in doing up parcels. May would check the lists.

The miserable trio did as they were told. The Duke's nerves would not let him sit still. Mary Adelaide had been his anchor. He realized that he would soon be adrift and miserable. May tried to calm his panic, but she, too, momentarily gave way to it when she realized that if her mother died, the responsibility for everything, for her father and her three irresponsible brothers must devolve on her. She was not by nature as religious a woman as her mother; or rather her religion was of a less buoyant, comforting kind; but she prayed hard now that the surgeon would succeed.

He did succeed; but that massive frame which had carried the most cheerful and passionate and merry Hanoverian of her generation, had worn out her heart, and two hours after the operation it failed.

Alexandra of Wales arrived to find White Lodge in a dreadful state. Mary Adelaide was dead upstairs. Alge was crying himself but trying to keep his demented father quiet. May and her husband George were dealing with the practical side of things; the latter arranging for the immediate removal of as many of the charity bundles and parcels as was possible, and for Grandmama to be asked if Mary Adelaide could be buried at Windsor. She had not wanted to lie at Kew with her parents, and had deplored the peculiarities of certain Princes of the Blood who had wished to be buried in Kensal Green cemetery. As in all things, she wished to go out in style.

Soon afterwards Princess Louise arrived. No one knew what to do with her. She was the artist of the family and it was conjectured that she might have come to make a death mask or sculpt the dead loved one's hands. May made discreet inquiries but learnt nothing beyond the fact that Louise had heard the news and, having loved Mary Adelaide – for who had not? – she had wanted to come to White Lodge. Then the Prince of Wales and the Duke of Cambridge arrived. Both had been summoned from the Newmarket races, and both were deeply moved by the sight of Mary Adelaide's huge corpse. Neither had been consistently kind to her, though she had never failed to be kind to them, and both felt it very much. George Cambridge leant on his cane and blew his nose and fluffed out his whiskers and looked utterly miserable until the Prince of Wales led him away.

Mary Adelaide had what she would have thoroughly enjoyed, ten days' national mourning and a gorgeous funeral, but, unhappily, she was only the first autumn leaf to fall. Her death seemed to set in train the deaths of many who were dear or close to the Prince of Wales.

One who had been exceedingly close but not at all dear was Frederick Weymouth Gibbs. His death at the beginning of 1898 brought back memories of days the Prince far preferred to forget. Birch had died years before and had been regretted, but Gibbs had lived on and on and on into a sour old age and he now obtruded once more into his pupil's life by willing him a picture of himself painted by G. F. Watts. Bertie still could not bear to look the man in the eye and he had the portrait consigned to a part of Marlborough House where he could never see it. A second bequest from Gibbs – a painting of a Roman landscape by Mama's old drawing master and the nonsense writer, Edward Lear – he passed on to May who showed great appreciation for it. As if this was not enough Gibbs left legacies to the Prince of Wales' children. It insinuated that in some way or other he belonged to the family. His

305

grim presence had made Bertie shiver as a boy. His grisly, Uriah Heep-like last will and testament made him shudder.

Then, later that same year, Gladstone died. Though the Queen detested him the Waleses had always been friends of the Gladstones. For Mrs Gladstone's sake they had been especially close in the past year as the old man showed increasing signs of senility. When he died on Ascension Day they were amongst the first to send their sympathy; and the Prince and his son acted as pallbearers in the state funeral which followed. Mrs Gladstone's loss, and the length and solemnity of the funeral, were almost too much for her. Afterwards she was led to a chair at the head of the open grave and the Prince characteristically went to her, took her hand and kissed it, and murmured a word or two of condolence. Prince George followed as did the remaining pall-bearers, the Duke of Rutland, the Marquess of Salisbury, and the Earls of Kimberley and Rosebery.

The Queen was not pleased. She telegraphed Bertie to ask who had advised him to be a pall-bearer and by what precedent he, the Prince of Wales, had acted as such for a commoner. He replied politely but firmly that he had not taken advice and that he knew of no precedent.

Bismarck died soon afterwards, planting trees to the last just as Gladstone had kept himself busy hacking them down. His end was more dramatic than the English statesman's: whistling 'La donna è mobile', and then, being offered strengthening broth from a spoon, he brushed it aside, grasped the whole brothpot, drank it off at a draught, cried 'Forward!', and died. In his time he had caused enormous damage to the Prince's family, but his death barely made any impression. Willy had already drawn his sting.

The pall-bearing affair had caused a temporary coolness between the Queen and the Prince of Wales, but this was instantly over when Bertie tumbled downstairs at Waddesdon Manor and fractured his knee cap. He was laid up for weeks. Victoria begged him to use the royal yacht *Osborne* as his own so that at least he could get about a little, and to his delight he was able to attend the Cowes Regatta. To everyone's relief Willy did not put in a personal appearance, but he sent his yacht *Meteor* to compete and she won every race in her class. Then he had the gall to telegraph his uncle as Commodore of the Royal Yatch Squadron YOUR

HANDICAPS ARE APPALLING. To his grandmother's displeasure Willy was still away from home and actually on a tour of the Near East arranged for him by Messrs Cook; though he strongly denied that a cultural tour was in any way a relaxation. He once told the Tsar: 'We poor rulers are not entitled to a holiday like other mortals.'

Albert Edward gritted his teeth, not only because of Willy's infuriating stupidity, nor because of the considerable pain he had to suffer, nor – just as bad – because of the inactivity forced on him, but because the autumn leaves continued falling.

Droning Louise fell desperately ill and Alix had to leave him and hurry to Denmark to nurse her mother. But it was too late. His mother-in-law died and he could not even get to her funeral. Then the eccentric Empress of the melancholy Franz-Josef of Austria was shot by an Italian anarchist. And much, much more serious for Albert Edward was the death of Affie's only son and heir to the Duchy of Coburg. It precipitated a crisis of succession which was only resolved after long discussion in which the Prince of Wales played a major part, and into which Willy, home from his cultural Cook's tour, stuck his imperial nose. He insisted on this, that and the other. Eventually it was arranged that Arthur of Connaught and George of Cambridge should sign renunciations of all claims to Coburg and, in the event of Affie's death, the duke-dom was to pass to Leopold's posthumous son, the little Duke of Albany.

By the end of the protracted negotiations Albert Edward was thoroughly exhausted and his nephew was still being offensive, this time about Lord Salisbury's part in the affair. The Prince was too tired to reply in the same vein, Lord Salisbury far too shrewd to do so. It was left to the Emperor's grandmother to deal with him. She did.

The tone in which you write about Lord Salisbury I can only attribute to a temporary irritation on your part, as I do not think you would otherwise have written in such a manner, and I doubt whether any Sovereign ever wrote in such terms to another Sovereign, and that Sovereign his own Grandmother, about their Prime Minister. . . .

So much for Willy, for the present anyway.

16

By a most curious coincidence in exactly the same month the Prince of Wales made two of the greatest friendships of his life.

His affair with Daisy was done with. She had fallen impossibly in love with an impossible man much younger than herself. The Prince, respecting her position, tried to help and he provided a broad shoulder to weep upon when the impossible young man, having made Daisy his mistress, married someone else. The Prince's relationship with Jeanne de Sagan, too, had moved on to a less tempestuous plane. *Fleur des Pois* continued to boast that his wife was and had been the only *Maîtresse en titre* of his friend Edouard. But the fact was that everyone's blood was flowing more sluggishly. Bertie believed that, apart from an occasional flirtation and a pinch or two – an unmannerly habit he had picked up in France – and supper parties with demi-mondaines in London or Paris, on the Riviera or at Marienbad, he was past all that sort of thing. More than most men he had had his share of passion and was grateful for it, but he was quite satisfied now to appreciate the wit and beauty of clever women without having the bother of falling in love with them. And then, suddenly, when he thought himself secure, he fell in love with two women simultaneously, and they could not have been more dissimilar.

It happened when he was feeling unwell and fractious. His cure at Marienbad in 1897 had served little except to chafe his temper. It had not even given him any feeling of virtue, and so he had been consoling himself ever since with a series of magnificent meals. Then his own favourite physician Gull gave him a grave warning about overeating. It was melancholy news for a man whose main passion now was for the table: but a copious nose-bleed after a banquet had saved him, Gull said, from apoplexy, and this was a serious thought.

In an attempt to improve his health and raise his spirits he took more exercise out in the open air, but this served chiefly to raise his appetite which had to be controlled. He was feeling very sorry for himself, very sorry for himself indeed, when on a duty inspection of the Norfolk Yeomanry he saw amongst the officers' wives one whom he instantly found startlingly attractive. He inquired discreetly from the old Earl of Leicester who she might be.

'George Keppel's wife, Sir. Albemarle's sister-in-law.'

The Prince said no more. He did not even ask to be introduced. His tastes had altered with age and he now preferred mature voluptuous women, but what he felt was no ordinary male desire. When he first saw George Keppel's wife he had experienced that rare and wonderful sentiment which a man knows seldom in his lifetime, in some cases only once.

He wanted to know all about the lady, but realized that he must be prudent. He could not hurry. Part of his curiosity was satisfied by inquiries made by Carrington about her family and Keppel's and their marriage. In Victorian peerages and directories the age of ladies was never printed, but by looking at their brothers' ages or their cousins' it could usually be worked out. Mrs Keppel, Carrington found out, was twenty-nine; three years younger than what Jeanne de Sagan termed *l'âge immortelle des femmes.* . . .

Not very long after the Yeomanry inspection the Prince was at a race meeting, and through his glasses he saw Mrs Keppel on someone else's arm. He stiffened. This, he told himself as he hurriedly adjusted the focus, was quite ridiculous. He was bald, grey whiskered, fat, not far short of sixty. When he saw that her companion was John Leslie he put the glasses down. Leslie was the husband of Leonie – the great friend of his brother Arthur and his wife, to that extent he was 'in the family'. But Leslie had something of a reputation. If Mrs Keppel was on his arm at a race meeting, and clinging to that arm at that, Mrs Keppel was available.

Without waiting an instant he waved his cane to attract Leslie's eye. Both came over, he to bow, she to curtsey. Leslie began to introduce his companion but he was cut short.

'We are already acquainted,' said the Prince, bowing. 'I am colonel of Mr Keppel's regiment.'

It was not precisely true and both knew it, but Mrs Keppel made not the slightest effort to correct the Prince. She too had felt something, the power of Edward's intense concentration. It seemed the most natural thing in the world for her to take his proffered arm. Leslie was acute. He knew exactly what had happened. Ruefully he excused himself, backed away, and went to the enclosure cursing his ill luck. He had lost his Alice.

Albert Edward's head was swimming that evening as it had seldom swum before. Though her manner and conversation had been entirely correct, in fact unexceptionable, Mrs Keppel had somehow conveyed an undoubted interest in him as a man. It remained to see how George Keppel would behave. Alix had accepted Lillie Langtry and Daisy as his official mistresses, presumably she would not object to a third. But not all men were as complaisant as the rather ridiculous Mr Langtry and Daisy's carefree husband who himself had always other fish to fry. What would the tall, debonair George Keppel do and say?

The Prince thought he could not bear to wait the necessary decent interval to find out. In the event he did not have to wait long.

In February 1898 he was invited to dine at the Keppels at a small exclusive dinner party, and, though once more nothing explicit was said, the Prince understood that Mrs Keppel regarded herself as seriously in love, and that as she already had two daughters, her elderly husband would not stand in the way of any arrangements she might care to make. Circumspection was required, of course; and a clear understanding that Alice was not to be treated like a cheap demi-mondaine.

Again without words Albert Edward was able to give this undertaking, and he and the demure, quiet, essentially discreet Alice began a passionate affair which astounded him – and caused Sir William Gull further anxiety.

Another great love of Bertie's life, and possibly the strangest, was introduced to him in the same month, but their friendship caused Sir William no sort of alarm, rather the reverse, because Miss Agnes Keyser was a tiny unmarried nurse. Her social background was not as grand as Alice Keppel's, her father being a member of the Stock Exchange, and as a single woman it ought to have been out of the question for her to have a close friendship with the Prince of Wales. But Agnes Keyser was a second Florence Nightingale. Both loved to dominate, both loved the sick, both bullied their undernurses and patients' visitors. The only notable difference was that while Miss Nightingale had no time for men,

Miss Keyser had no time for women. She liked men to heal, to scold, and to pamper; and almost from the first moment they met she adored Albert Edward. As for him, he had reached the age when, though still as restless as ever, his physical disabilities obliged him to seek quiet. Miss Keyser as Matron-in-chief of her own establishment and quite prepared to boss the Prince of Wales as well as the humblest porter, gave him just the sort of maternal love he had always required.

When the Boer War broke out Agnes Keyser came into her own. She and her sister had already tried to build up a nursing home at their private house in Grosvenor Crescent, but for lack of patients it had begun to fail. Now it was devoted exclusively to the service of officers wounded in Africa and shipped home for treatment. The Prince of Wales realized that although they had adequate private means the Keysers could not possibly run a hospital at their own expense. His sister Louise, far from rich, was already running into trouble and she was merely providing rooms and nursing for officers in a set of rooms in the Savoy. Bertie went to his friends, especially those who were deplored by the Queen's Set: Cassel who had replaced Hirsch as his financial adviser, the Sassoons, to the banker Hambro, to Iveagh and Burnham, and to his old Cambridge friend and fantastically rich Natty Rothschild. Between them they set up a fund, and Agnes' future as matron was secured. As a result Albert Edward's chances of actually succeeding his mother grew larger and larger. Agnes bossed and fussed him as neither Gull nor his valets would ever have dared to do. When he complained of his wheezing chest she told him he only had himself to blame and whenever he overate, which he still did with great regularity, she obliged him to eat bland milk puddings and gruel and nursery pap in her starchy uncomfortable rooms above the hospital in Grosvenor Crescent.

The contrast between Alice's voluptuousness and her love of going to places and the older, stay-at-home, handsome and somewhat formidable Agnes was striking. When Albert Edward confided in them Alice would soothe his anxieties, Agnes reason them away. Alice lived in Portman Square in a slim, high and pretty house, its narrow rooms spilling over with potted exotics, beautiful ornaments and paintings and elegant furniture. Agnes lived in Grosvenor Crescent on the top floor above her hospital, surrounded by photographs and family bits and pieces, loaded occasional

311

tables, Benares brasswork, and furniture upholstered in bullrush brown. Alice had a cloud of fair hair and a voice which caressed her hearers. Agnes' hair was tidily tucked away and her voice was trained to carry down long corridors. Alice adored bridge. Agnes preferred draughts. They were Cleopatra and Boadicea and Albert Edward dearly loved them both.

His family, too, accepted them. Whereas Alix had never tolerated Daisy Brook – and when Daisy wished to return to Court and Bertie naïvely tried to persuade Alix to help she merely ignored the request – she found Mrs Keppel charming and said so and she and her husband were quite often invited to Sandringham. She also liked and trusted Agnes or 'Sister Keyser' as she was always known in the royal family, aware that only she had the power to stop Bertie stuffing himself daily with a hunting breakfast, eight-course luncheon, heavy tea, sixteen-course dinner, topped with any amount of supper dishes. Like everyone else she was aware that her husband's friendship for the voluptuous Alice was anything but platonic, but she did wonder, sometimes, about Sister Agnes. Could the compulsory consumption of milk puddings reasonably be followed by the pleasures of the alcove?

17

On the night of the 8 October, 1899 the Prince and Princess of Wales dined alone.

This did not mean they were on their own. The Prince's Gentlemen in Waiting, the Princess' Ladies, and a quantity of servants were present; but there were no guests. It had not happened for a very long time and had a particular significance.

After the meal instead of the Ladies withdrawing, the Princess asked everyone to leave the room. She and her husband remained alone in chairs which Bertie placed closer to the wood fire. He asked Alix's permission to smoke. Then he told her what, until that moment she had had no idea of, that the Ministry was concerned about Mama. Bertie was also much concerned because a war between the Dutch republics in South Africa and the British

312

Uitlanders seemed to be inevitable. The Uitlanders, who lived in the Transvaal, were unfranchised and Kruger refused them the vote. There was bound to be a war. Did Alix think Mama would be able to withstand the strain?

Alix was not surprised to be asked. For some reason or other she was supposed to have a more intimate knowledge of Mama and a greater influence over her than anyone else in the family. Actually it was a myth. Beatrice, Vicky, even Bertie himself had far more – as Mama herself would have made abundantly clear had anyone troubled himself to ask. But the myth by now had cemented, and in anything concerning the Queen Alix's opinion was generally sought. It amused her that it should be so and fortunately her advice was generally sound. Although she was incapable of being objective about her children or closest friends, Mama was distant enough to be viewed with detachment. On this occasion, from Bertie's tone and from the way he had arranged this unusual method of asking for her advice, she realized the matter was of particular importance and so she considered for quite a time before she said anything.

It was true that Mama's energies were on the wane. At eighty and more it was only to be expected. Yet she still did far more than the majority of her elderly subjects. She had taken a very occasional Drawing-Room or Levée and had given some audiences – generally to foreigners or deputations which varied in interest from a petition signed by 336,000 women praying that convents should be brought under public control, to a deputation of 'Girls' Friendly Society' girls, not one of whom, she noted, had been under fifty years of age. And she kept in constant contact with the members of her widespread family, writing regularly to her children. No one's nose was sharper for detecting the least scent of scandal. It had been Mama who had smelt out that at Aunt Augusta's Court of Mecklenburg-Strelitz – a young and ignorant princess was with child by a footman. 'Drugged, of course!' exclaimed Mama. 'Poor girl.' She was equally sympathetic with the Snipe's sister who had left for Germany to marry a Prince of Anhalt and the marriage was going awry. Mama was determined to look after the girl herself should there ever be a separation.

All this, so far as Alix was concerned, pointed to a vigorous mind – working slower, perhaps, than formerly, but vigorous all the same. And added to her family interests Mama continued to

313

keep her finger on the pulse of national and international affairs through her Privy Purse and Private Secretaries. But her eyesight was failing, and this was a serious handicap because for really confidential work she was obliged to rely more and more on Beatrice who was acting as a supernumerary secretary and reading secret reports aloud.

'I think perhaps Mama depends too much on Beatrice,' murmured Alix.

Bertie drew slowly on his cigar and nodded. Beatrice, with growing children and constantly campaigning against her sister Louise, was understandably determined on living a life of her own. She loved sketching and recently she had taken to photography. As a result, urgent public business was frequently held up because the Queen's confidential reader could not be found as she was painting flowers in the conservatory or holding photographic plates to the sun.

'With an assistant, a thoroughly reliable Maid of Honour, to read in her place, the pace of business would be speeded up.'

Again Bertie agreed. It would make a difference. Alix noted with surprise that he helped himself to a second glass of brandy. Though he had a passion for food, drink did not interest him. He had had two glasses of champagne with dinner, and now was having a second brandy. Alix discovered why when he turned and said abruptly: 'Salisbury and his colleagues are of the opinion that Mama should abdicate.'

A sparkle which he had seldom seen before shone from his wife's eyes. He sat on the arm of her chair and put an arm round her shoulders. It was rare that such a demonstration passed between them. 'You would like to be Queen?' he asked.

She said no. There was only one queen and that was Mama. But he could read her thoughts because he shared them. They had waited so long. Abruptly he rose to his feet. 'Somehow,' he said, 'I don't believe I could face it now. The plunge would be too sudden. Knollys' précis are so dull. Reading them bores me. To be frank,' he added with a sudden smile. 'I'm not even sure of the ins and outs of this South African business, except that there's to be a war, and the war will make even greater demands on Mama.'

Alix had been so close to a consort's throne for thirty-seven years, and in that time there had been plenty of talk of abdica-

314

tions – from the press and radical members of Parliament, from the Queen herself in bursts of self-pity and rage. Several times Alix had caught herself restyling the royal apartments at Windsor and at Buckingham Palace in her imagination. Nevertheless it had never happened. And now that Bertie had expressed his doubts she found herself sharing them. Not on her own account. Though deaf and remote she was convinced she would make an adequate Queen Consort. But she shared Bertie's doubts about himself.

'I think, dear,' she said, choosing her words with the greatest care, 'that we may safely leave the question to Lord Salisbury and to Mama. Leave it entirely to them.'

War was declared the very next day, and though the British believed the rights of her nationals were sacrosanct, the rest of Europe saw it as a war of aggrandizement, a pro-imperial piece of piracy.

Far from wilting under the pressure of extra work the Queen appeared to find extra strength.

Far from shattering her the Boer War actually enlivened her, and when at last she heard that her ministers were discussing the advisability of her abdicating, she was instantly on the alert. She sent for Lord Salisbury and told him firmly that there was to be no further talk of abdication. It was bad for a country at war to change rulers. She could manage. The Prince of Wales had proposed she have an extra reader of confidential documents and she had found just the right young lady, the daughter of her old Privy Purse.

When he heard that Mama had solved his problem in a very characteristic way, Bertie heaved a sigh of relief. He would not have to face the thought of a crown after all. He bade his son George keep at his weak points, languages and history, and abandon all hope of being allowed to go off on active service. He was too close to the throne. George's special and unique contribution would be to study the art of ruling as a constitutional monarch like Grandmama, not like his cousin Willy. . . .

At that very moment nephew Willy was at Sandringham driving the family mad with his posturing and lack of tact. Had the visit not been arranged long before the outbreak of the war, and had

315

the Prince not thought it his duty to submit to his nephew's provocations like a patient in a dentist's chair in the hope of getting German opinion on to England's side, Willy would not have been tolerated there an instant. As it was he arrived with a huge suite including Bülow, his Foreign Minister, three valets, a hairdresser and an assistant hairdresser whose sole duty was to curl the imperial moustache. This was becoming famous because it swept up like the horns of a viking helmet and gave him a fierce, aggressive look.

Suppressing her dislike for the man, Alix coldly refused Willy's offer to give lectures after dinner on Norway, Corfu, ballistics, and the necessity of p.t. every day before breakfast; and Albert Edward was forced to suffer silently when Willy made his pro-Boer sympathies known before the servants, when he himself was teased for being a field-marshal who had never actually seen a day's active service, and when he was told off for putting up with that low-caste Munshi who had far, far too much influence over Grandmama. How he managed it, he never understood, but the Prince of Wales contrived to control his temper, and he talked sensibly of political matters. Bülow, aware of his master's impulsiveness, watched anxiously. He described their talks as 'a fat malicious tom-cat playing with a shrew mouse'.

'I believe,' said the Prince of Wales, not long after the Emperor's departure and in front of all his Household and upper servants, 'I believe that yapping voice will echo and re-echo round the house for weeks.'

It was a pardonable indiscretion.

Even after his return to Germany, or, rather to his perambulations about Europe, Willy continued to send long and unwelcome messages to his grandmother and uncle on how they should tighten up the British Army, use plenty of strategy, and get on with the war. Nevertheless he was pleased when George and May asked him to be godfather to their recently born son, Henry; and he showed geuine sympathy when, for the first time in his life, an attempt was made on the Prince of Wales.

The boulevards and boudoirs of France being at present out of the question, the Prince planned to accompany Alix for a three-week visit to Denmark and he was thoroughly depressed at the thought of what would almost certainly be a holiday of excruciating boredom. At Brussels they were steaming out of the Gare du

Nord when a Belgian of about fifteen jumped on to the running board of their carriage waving a pistol. Fortunately, although he belonged to an anarchist club, the boy was light in the head and a bad marksman. His pistol misfired, twice; then, when it did fire, a bullet went wide; but a second passed closely in front of the Prince and Princess, through Miss Charlotte Knollys' bun and ended in the compartment partition wall.

The Prince remained calm. He begged the bystanders not to harm the boy and himself extracted the bullet from the wall to keep for the souvenir room at Windsor.

The Princess, too, having helped Miss Knollys to adjust her bun, showed a bold and cool front, but later she expressed herself freely saying that only lynch-law would do for active anarchists.

Surprisingly, her daughter-in-law May agreed with her.

As for George, he declared indignantly:

hanging or shooting . . . much too good for . . . an Anarchist, they all ought to be exterminated like wasps.

Mary Adelaide's sister, the Grand Duchess Augusta, went even further. Had she the power, she declared, she would forbid all meetings and muzzle the press and imprison all declared anarchists male or female. This was not all. She would:

have them flogged daily, and if decided murderers, have them tortured then blown from a Gun! that is what I would decree!

Willy, hearing that the Belgian authorities had simply placed the boy called Sipido under police supervision until he came of age, exploded in a quaint letter to his uncle:

The behaviour of the Belgians in the Sipido affair is simply outrageous. . . . Either their laws are ridiculous, or the jury are a set of damned, bloody scoundrels; which is the case I am unable to decide. With best love to Aunty and Cousins.

317

18

For Albert Edward the year 1900 was a tormenting exercise in self-control. The war went badly and he did all he could to help by reviewing troops, distributing medals, visiting the wounded sent home, and badgering the Ministry to let Lord Roberts and Lord Kitchener have a free hand.

Mama, incredibly, was as active as he was.

She would allow no one to suggest a patched-up peace with the Boers. She even decided to go up to London to encourage people. War being the job of professional soldiers, it did not alter the tenor of life at home; but more men were wanted for the colours, trade which was always depressed in wartime needed to be stimulated, everyone required cheering up. To the family's astonishment Mama drove round the streets of London, showed herself again and again at the balcony in Buckingham Palace, and literally roused her people to an exhibition of loyalty to herself and trust in the empire which had not been seen since the time of her Diamond Jubilee. It was an extraordinary accomplishment for a blind old lady who already had far too much to do.

Then because the French were so pro-Boer she broke the established routine of years and decided to spend her spring holiday in Italy. It was a considerable sacrifice for a temperamental woman of fixed habits and it amazed her family and courtiers. They were even more amazed when she changed her mind a second time. She had been told that her Irish soldiers had been particularly courageous in South Africa and decided to visit Ireland instead. It was to be her first visit since she had gone there with the Prince Consort in the year he died, and the Irish understood that she was paying their country a very special compliment. She went even further, issuing an order that in future on St Patrick's Day all Irish troops should wear the shamrock in their hats, and she ordered the formation of a regiment of Irish Guards to add to the Brigade of Guards.

In the first few months of that year, considering all she had to do, the Queen was a marvel. Her reception in Ireland was not the unnerving mixture of hostility and loyalty which Bertie and Alix and Eddy had faced on the last royal visit to Ireland, but a warm and sincere demonstration of affection. The Irish admired Victoria exceedingly. She regretted now that she had not been there before. Perhaps it might have helped heal the constant running sore of rebellion in the island. But until that year she had been unable to bring herself to forgive them for their unpleasantness to Albert. Now because Irishmen had fought so gallantly in her army, she had changed her mind.

The Prince of Wales was relieved beyond measure that Salisbury's idea for abdication had been scotched and abandoned. He himself could never have managed to do so much; nor, he felt, could he have applied himself so wholeheartedly to the business of fighting the war against the Boers. While his mother devoted herself almost entirely to the war, he found himself more and more involved in family affairs.

In the main they were heartbreaking.

The only member of the family to die as a direct result of the War was Lenchen's elder son, Christle. He died, as so many soldiers did, of enteric fever, and Lenchen, already distressed that year because the unhappy marriage of her daughter Marie Louise to a Prince of Anhalt had been summarily annulled by German law, felt her loss very keenly. She flung herself and her daughters, and even her amiable husband, and all available members of the royal family into a frenzy of bandage-rolling and knitting khaki comforts.

Then May suffered a good deal when her father died early in the year. The Prince did his best to console her, but since Mary Adelaide's death poor Franz Teck had gone madder and madder and had ended living entirely alone at White Lodge with a doctor and four male nurses, and not even his children had been permitted to see him. It was this which somehow made her father's death seem worse to May. Everyone else saw it as a mercy. She could not.

After that, to Bertie's unspeakable horror, his brother Affie contracted cancer.

Like many fanciful men, Albert Edward dreaded the disease, and he was shocked at the speed and malignancy with which it destroyed his brother. In July, on the very same day as the King of

319

Italy was publicly assassinated, Affie died in his castle at Coburg. Bertie went there at once. He and Affie had not been close, but they were almost of an age and, to see a younger brother die from such a hideous cause unnerved Bertie absolutely. His sister Vicky, in trying to comfort him, increased the horror by admitting that she too had contracted the disease which he dreaded above all others. Two years before she had been riding in the Taunus woods and her horse had shied at a threshing machine, thrown her and dragged her for some distance by the stirrup. Since she had complained of pains in her back and though her physician had tried many remedies, they were already resigned to the fact that she had an incurable cancer of the spine.

Chilled by this terrible news Bertie embraced his sister. He promised that very soon he would be returning to Homburg for his annual cure and he would visit her at Kronberg as much as he could. When he did go he was dismayed to find his sister in such pain. Suppressing his distaste, the Prince saw his nephew and begged Willy that more morphia should be given to his mother. But Willy was discouraging. It was not German medical practice to soften their patients with too liberal doses of pain-killing drugs.

For Vicky's sake, Bertie kept a still tongue in his head but privately he consulted his own physician. Gull was not encouraging either. As long as the Empress Frederick was in Germany, medical convention bound her to accept the medical treatment. The Prince was appalled.

Although often in severe pain Vicky was as spirited as ever. On the whole the Prussians were pro-Boer, but she demonstrated that she was still the Princess Royal of Great Britain and Ireland, and publicly gave a bronze bell to the English church in Venice, dedicating it to the memory of the officers and men of the Army and Royal Navy who had fallen in South Africa. Her son was angry and pranced about. Her mother thought it a magnificent gesture and was proud of her.

Had it not been for Vicky's courage in the way she faced her cancer, and Mama's great courage and for the fact that in this year of all years, Bertie won all his racing ambitions, Bertie might very easily have given way completely to despair in the latter half of 1900.

His spectacular turf successes were a partial anodyne. Ordinarily they would have thrown him into sublime ecstasies for he had a series of resounding triumphs: his horses winning the Grand National, the Two Thousand Guineas, the Newmarket Stakes, the Derby, the Eclipse Stakes and the St Leger. No owner had ever done it before.

But even the exhilaration of these achievements, falling one after another to baste his year, as it were, with succeeding delights; even bridge and soothing suppers with Alice Keppel; even the less soothing but none the less beneficial evenings with Sister Keyser in her spartan apartment in Grosvenor Crescent; even the exacting business of financially propping up her hospital, even the whirling social round into which he threw himself with unaccustomed energy that year as though to shake off a malignant spirit – though they kept him from complete and utter despair, could not prevent him from falling into the blackest of depressions.

France was barred to him. His cure at Homburg had neither cured his general feeling of malaise nor eliminated the sluggishness which too much rich food invariably caused, and his dutiful visits to Vicky had upset his nerves. He was also hurt because some of his richer friends were strongly protesting against what they called his interference in politics. This had come about because, on opening a London County Council housing estate in Bethnal Green, he openly said to a working-class audience that the slum conditions of London were a disgrace to a Christian country, and he regretted that he could do nothing himself to rebuild because his property had been let in small lots years before on long leases. His mother was proud of him, hearing echoes of his beloved father in that frank and open speech; but he had dared to criticize the sanctity of private property, and this, said his friends, was too bad of him. It was a perplexing, muddling situation. The radicals whom he disliked agreed with him; the financiers with whom he got on so well, disagreed.

To avoid arguments, painful reflections, even thought itself, he rushed from place to place – to his daughter Louise of Fife, to his old cousin, the Duke of Cambridge, to Liko's brother who had married his sister Alice's daughter and lived in Hampshire, to the Arthur Sassoons at Tulchan Lodge in Scotland, to the Saviles at Rufford, to Lord Derby at Knowlesley, to Cassel at Moulton Paddocks, the Grevilles at Reigate Priory, to Iveagh the Guinness brewer in Suffolk, to the Vincents at Esher Place, to the Lawsons at Beaconsfield, and a new friend, Mrs Willy James, at West Dean

321

Park. Between times he was at Abergeldie, Sandringham, Marlborough House and Windsor.

Unconsciously perhaps he was refusing to face the fact that, like a fast spinning top, Mama was slowly running down. It was a slow process, and could be shouldered off, because the top had whirled so very rapidly at the beginning of 1900, most of the Queen's vitality being expended on her visits to London and Dublin – but the death of her second son in Coburg put a barely observable brake on the top. Thereafter her constant interest and anxiety about the war in South Africa slowed the pace down.

Lady Churchill would have told the Prince about it had she observed the process, but by now she was a very old lady herself who had almost died of a heart attack the previous Christmas, and she was not up to noticing things as she once had been. Randall Davidson, too, would have considered it his duty to inform the Prince, but he had long since ceased to be in close and daily contact with the Queen, having left the Windsor Deanery for the see of Rochester and thence to Winchester. Through her secretaries Davidson was the Queen's constant adviser in Church matters, and he saw her at infrequent intervals at Osborne or Windsor, but for most of the latter part of that year the Queen was at Balmoral when Bishop Davidson did not see her once. Beatrice said nothing either, perhaps because she was so close to Mama that she could not see the top running down, or perhaps because she was so taken up with her photography and etching and sketching and embroidery. Bertie himself saw Mama several times and thought he saw some little difference in her appearance, but her hardiness was by now proverbial. He refused to be alarmed by it.

Others were more percipient. Lord James, the Queen's physician, noted a radical alteration in the Queen between May and October. The Maids of Honour as they came into waiting noted to each other how often the Queen dropped off when being read to and how little she could sleep at night. They also remarked on her lack of appetite. She was forever pushing dishes aside. But no one in the Queen's Household considered it his special duty to inform the Prince of Wales of what was happening.

Finally he heard in an anxious letter from Vicky in Kronburg. Her correspondence with Mama had been vast and continuous for many years. A good many of Mama's letters were now dictated. Many dilated on her sleeplessness; on her anxiety about the war;

on her disappointment that, at the Commander-in-Chief's resignation, Arthur had not at last been given what he deserved but, under pressure from Lord Salisbury and Bertie himself, she had felt obliged to appoint the hero of the war, Lord Roberts; on her perpetual disgust for food; on her anxiety about 'poor Jane Churchill', who appeared to be breaking up. . . .

Bertie sent for Lord James. He went himself down to Windsor to see Mama, and found her pallid, apparently tinier than ever, living on next to nothing, but still hard at work. She was glad to see him. They secretly enjoyed the news that Willy was outraged at having been attacked by a mad woman brandishing an axe. There had been a black week of news from South Africa and she had just been snapping at Salisbury's nephew Balfour who had made some melancholy remark about the state of the troops. She had told him that no one was depressed in *her* houses, adding: 'We are not interested in the possibilities of defeat. They do not exist.'

'Quite right, Mama.' Bertie was proud of her; but all the same he sent for her Physician in Attendance.

'She eats nothing, Sir, nothing!' The doctor spread his arms wide in a signal of genuine distress.

After the talk he went to the Queen and suggested that perhaps instead of the regular meals, which interrupted her work and which she found such a bore, she should have an occasional glass of milk and whisky.

'An excellent notion,' she declared.

From that time it was her only diet.

Bertie and Bishop Davidson supervised the customary anniversary at the Mausoleum. The prayers were shorter than usual, the singing cut short too, but it all seemed very long to Mama, who leant on Alix and confided that everything was a great effort.

The New Year came in sadly. The fabric of Mama's domestic security had been shattered by the sudden death of Lady Churchill on Christmas Day. They had been close friends, barely ever separated for fifty years. She simply touched Bertie and Alix's Christmas present and made a conventional word of thanks, but she could not see it nor know that it had been selected with such care: two miniatures of her favourite pomeranians, executed under extremely difficult circumstances by the minaturist who, to keep the matter secret, had had no 'sittings' and been obliged to observe

323

the dogs at a distance through opera glasses. What use were they to a sightless, dying woman?

Bertie was able to accept the truth at last. The top was spinning so slowly that at any moment it might tumble. Reluctantly he sent his brother Arthur of Connaught to represent the family at the celebration of the bicentary of the foundation of the Prussian Monarchy. Miserably he went off with Alix to Chatsworth, hoping to find some sort of comfort in the company of his dear absent-minded friend Harty-Tarty and Louisa. But it was a great shooting party – far too large for the Prince's taste at that moment – and he dismayed everyone by showing no particular interest in his fellow guests, not even in Alice Keppel who was there as a matter of course, and Mrs Willy James, who was there by special invitation of Louisa Devonshire.

Like many others in the Liberal Party Harty-Tarty had been pushed into the Conservatives by Gladstone's obstinacy over Home Rule, and he now sat as Lord President of the Council in Salisbury's ministry. Quite by chance he happened to mention the possibility of an Anglo-German alliance. He was alone with the Prince in the library and mentioned the matter casually in the full belief that H.R.H. must know all about it. But the Prince knew nothing, not even that discussions were being held in London at that very moment.

Not often in recent years had the Prince betrayed his dislike of being left out of things. But now he did. His mother was dying. Soon perhaps he would be King and he did not even know that there was the slightest possibility of an alliance with Germany. How could he rule? How could he? Devonshire plucked at his beard. He was sorry to have let off such a firework. 'You'll manage, Sir,' he said reassuringly. 'They always do.'

The Prince was glad to get back to London, but he stayed a very short time. Restlessly he went backwards and forwards between Sandringham and Marlborough House. At last word came on 18 January. He was advised by the Queen's physicians to travel down to Osborne.

In his acute apprehension he actually turned to Agnes Keyser. He went straight to her rooms above the hospital and poured out his trouble. She fed him and mothered him, putting some muscle into his nerves so that when he caught a special train early the next morning for Portsmouth, he felt much more able to face things.

Osborne House lacked that urgent atmosphere which is sometimes felt in places where patients are critically ill. It had been so long now, the waiting, that no one caught his breath any more. In Bertie's eyes, Beatrice and Louise appeared callous. Their mother was semi-conscious and they were calmly at their needlework.

'What else,' asked the practical Louise, 'can we do?'

Beatrice said nothing. She slipped out of the sitting-room to her own apartments above where she could enjoy a calming cigarette.

Bertie could barely bear to look at his mother lying there, so frail and still tinier than ever. He kissed her and the prickle of his grey beard disturbed her. She looked up and smiled at him. He said something of no particular importance. Then his hand was touched from behind. It was Louise. She motioned to him to follow her out of the room. In the dark corridor outside was Fritz Ponsonby. He held an *en clair* telegram from Berlin. Willy had postponed the public celebration of the bicentenary of his dynasty. He and his Uncle Arthur were travelling as speedily as possible to the Isle of Wight.

'The yacht, Sir, has steam up at the pier,' said Ponsonby. 'And I have ordered your special train.'

The Prince cursed, loudly and roundly. He would have to go all the way back to London to greet his nephew correctly at London. He turned to go into the Queen's bedroom, but Louise said: 'I should go straight away. Mama will be all right for a time.'

'You are sure?'

She nodded.

He asked Ponsonby to telegraph Marlborough House that his uniform as Colonel of the Prussian First Dragoon Guards should be taken out and prepared.

Willy chattered on the way down to Portsmouth. Touched by his uncle's sensibility in greeting him in the uniform of one of his own regiments, he was doing his best not to offend in any way. He simply wished, he said, to be with Grandmama at the end, particularly as his own mother could not be there.

But he chattered, and the Prince of Wales and Arthur of Connaught dearly wished that he would simply sit still and be quiet.

Bertie took out a cigar and the way he lighted and smoked it showed some of his feelings. Deep down inside him there was a bud of panic. It was opening with the passing of each mile. It made the journey unbearable. Facing the death of a mother was one thing and dreadful enough in itself. But he had to face something else as well. He thought of his father and Stockmar painstakingly preparing him. They had bungled it, but their intentions had been good. He thought of old Palmerston, and Dizzy, and poor old Gladstone, and now Salisbury, all of them leading him as well as they could towards an inevitable destiny. To panic was to be unmanly. It was wasteful. It neither helped, nor could it be productive of anything but fear. . . . Quite suddenly he stubbed out his cigar.

When the moment came, Bertie scarcely realized it.

Willy had been good. That had to be said for him. Though Mama appeared not to recognize him and twice had mistaken him for his father, Willy had supported her with one good arm for hours, holding her in the most comfortable position possible, as she lay dying.

Davidson was there to pray with her, and the Rector of Whippingham. She received Communion. And she had asked for her favourite dog Turi to be placed on the bed close to her. Bertie had lifted Turi up and settled him. Then Mama had smiled at him and said quite distinctly 'Bertie'.

After that there was simply a flutter of the eyelids, long and deep breaths, and long periods of silence while she slept. A throbbing pulse in her tiny neck beat sometimes rapidly, sometimes steadily.

The silence was broken by the Bishop, who began the Prayers of Commendation. Behind him Bertie felt Alix slip her hand into his. George was crying, the tears coursing down his beard. May had that tight, restrained look he remembered her wearing when her father had died. As many as possible of the family were packed into that little room, and many of the Queen's most faithful servants and members of her Household. They were all as still as

326

marble, though sometimes a head would be turned, and shoulders would heave, and tears would be wiped away.

Then the Bishop looked up to the Prince. He felt Alix's hand slip out of his. She was moving, not to stand beside him but before him, and she curtseyed and kissed his hand. George, his beard wet with tears, did the same. Everyone curtseyed and bowed. Officials were saying things. . . .

Bertie took one last look at his mother, bent over and kissed her forehead. Then he took Turi in his arms and went to the door which was silently opened for him. Instinctively he turned right and opened the door into the Queen's sitting-room where there were still the twin, brass-edged writing tables of his parents; the one empty, the other, until so recently, heaped with state papers. Turi leapt to the floor and sat blinking into the fire.

He knew quite well that he could not do it. No one could take her place, least of all a sixty-year-old who was already worn out. Unaccountably he found that he had lighted a cigarette. Possibly there had never been tobacco smoke in that room before. He turned to throw the cigarette into the fire and stopped. He must rule in his own way, even if it had not been her way. But something made him change his mind and he threw the cigarette into the fire.

He walked dejectedly to the bow window. From there he heard something which, temporarily, enraged him. The death of Queen Victoria was a world-shaking event. It had been expected for days, and for days those old enemies he and Mama had shared, the representatives of the press, had been waiting below, tidily put away by a Gentleman of the Household in a suitable room. Now they had heard the news. It was half-past-six in the evening. The world must be told. One or two reporters were off in carriages. The others, eager to get to the nearest telephone down in Cowes, were pedalling away from Osborne House on that fast modern machine the bicycle. The lights of their carbide lamps showing brilliantly in the darkness. And as they pedalled they yelled to an expectant world: 'Queen dead! Queen dead! Queen dead! Queen dead!'

It was so unseemly, so brash, so utterly lacking in heart that Bertie could not bear it. The cry started the tears he had not yet been able to shed and it was through eyes which cried that he looked out to the Solent where the riding lights of the largest fleet in the world twinkled through the darkness.

He took out a pocket handkerchief and, with trembling hands, tried to dry his eyes.

For no reason at all he was reminded of something that had to be done. He went to Mama's desk, took a pen from the standish and a telegraph form and wrote a brief telegram to the Lord Mayor of London announcing the Queen's death. Then he pulled the bell stop marked *PAGE* beneath the desk and sat back in Mama's chair.

It was the first formal act of his reign.

R7

George IV

Frederick, Duke
of York and Albany, Bp. of
Osnaburg

1. George Noel
2. Ellen Jocelyn
   Cecile

William IV—m.—Adelaide of
Saxe-Meiningen

1. George   2. Henry
3. Frederick   4. Adolphus
5. Sophia   6. Mary
7. Elizabeth   8. Augusta
9. Amelia

Ernest
Duke of
and K
G.

1.

2.

3.

Francis Frederick
of Saxe-Saalfeld-Gotha

Edward, Duke —m.—(ii) Victoria (i)—m.—Emich
of Kent   Charles
                                       of Leiningen

Robert
Wood(and
others?)

children

VICTORIA —m.—ALBERT, the
              Prince Consort

Ernest I—m.—(i) Louise of Saxe-
               Coburg-Alten-
               burg
               (divorced)

            m.—(ii) Marie of
                Württemberg

Ernest II—m.—Alexandrina of
             Baden

Leopold, later—m.—(i) Princess
King of the   Charlotte of
Belgians   Wales

            m.—(ii) Louise of
                 Orleans

1. Leopold II
2. Charlotte —m.—Maximilian,
                 Emperor of
                 Mexico

. . . . and others

Beatrice—m.—Henry of
             Battenberg
             (Liko)

1. Alexander Albert
2. Victoria Eugénie
   (Ena)
3. Leopold
4. Maurice

Arthur, Duke —m.—Louise
of Connaught   Margaret of
                 Prussia

1. Margaret 2. Arthur 3. Victoria

Helena —m.—Christian of
(Lenchen)   Schleswig-
            Holstein

1. Christian Victor
2. Albert
3. Helena Victoria
   ('The Snipe')
4. Louise —m.—Aribert of
               Anhalt
               (marriage dissolved)

Alice —m.—Louis IV, Grand
           Duke of Hesse-
           Darmstadt

1. Victoria —m.—Louis of Batten-
                 berg

   1. Alice   2. Louise
   3. George   4. Louis

2. Elizabeth —m.—Sergius of Russia
3. Irène —m.—Henry of Prussia

   1. Waldemar 2. Sigismund

4. Ernest —m.—Victoria of
   Louis   Saxe-Coburg

            Elizabeth

5. Frederick William
6. Alix
   (Alicky) —m.—Nicholas II
                 of Russia
                 (Nicky)

   1. Olga 2. Tatiana 3. Marie

7. Mary Victoria

Victoria
Princess
(Vicky)

1. Willi
   (Willi

   1.
   3.
   5.
   7.

2. Char

3. Henr

   1.
4. Sigism
5. Victo
   (Mor
6. Wald

7. Soph

   1.

8. Marg
   (Mos

Leopold, Duke —m.—Helena of
of Albany   Waldeck-
                 Pyrmont

1. Alice 2. Charles Edward

Louise —m.—John, Marquess
            of Lorne

Alfred, Duke —m.—Marie of
of Edinburgh   Russia
and Saxe-Coburg

1. Alfred
2. Marie —m.—Frederick of
              Roumania

   1. Carol 2. Elizabeth 3. Marie

3. Victoria —m.—Ernest Louis,
   Melita   son of Princess Alice

            Elizabeth

4. Alexandra —m.—Ernest of
                 Hohenlohe-
                 Langenburg

   1. Godfrey 2. Marie

5. Beatrice